MICRORECORDING
Industrial and Library Applications

CHESTER M. LEWIS
Chief Librarian, New York Times

WILLIAM H. OFFENHAUSER, JR.
New Canaan, Connecticut

INTERSCIENCE PUBLISHERS, INC., NEW YORK

Interscience Publishers Ltd., London

TO OUR WIVES

Interscience Publishers, Inc.
250 Fifth Ave., New York 1, N. Y.

For Great Britain and Northern Ireland:

Interscience Publishers Ltd.
88/90 Chancery Lane, London W. C. 2

PRINTED IN THE UNITED STATES OF AMERICA

MICRORECORDING

Industrial and Library Applications

Within the last two decades microrecording has referred to something more than the mere materials and processes used to record images in miniature; it is now almost symbolic of the whole process of recording, reproducing and viewing, indexing and storing of all recorded data in such form that the data, ideally, are immediately accessible to the user in the form in which he wants them at a price he can afford and is willing to pay. Since new developments occur almost every day, the next decade will undoubtedly show more rapid expansion of microrecording than in the past several decades owing to the tremendous impact of accumulated research in its production of new ideas useful to our national economy and in its feedback to microrecording.

The rapidity with which the art is changing and the science is becoming established is so great that it is difficult for even the best informed and most competent specialists to keep abreast of current developments. With wide scattering of technical and other reports and with the sharply limited scope of the usual individual report, the layman user is at a further disadvantage; few who would use microrecording can obtain a complete and rounded picture of why the techniques presently used are employed. Few can afford the time necessary to unearth obscure facts; most find it necessary to rely upon the advice and suggestions, often fragmentary, that are furnished gratuitously and in good faith by the sales representatives of the suppliers of equipment, consumable supplies, and services. It is hoped that this book will fill the needs of non-technical and technical people alike with a common interest in the use of microrecording.

For such reasons this book sets forth in only broad outline the more important criteria of microrecording and of typical significant accomplishments made to meet them. The tabular data that describe equipment, while extensive for the more specialized forms, make no attempt to cover equipment used in common with other fields such as motion pictures. Understandably, such data are far from complete.

The objectives of the authors will have been met if a user, after reading this book, is able to determine and evaluate the primary considerations of his immediate problem. With suitable training in documentation procedures, the user will be in a position to know where additional data essential to the solution of his problem may be successfully sought.

Like other horizontal areas of intellectual endeavor, the literature of microrecording is widely scattered; the bulk is found in short papers dispersed in a wide variety of often unrelated publications media. A scientifically trained person with no prior knowledge would find these papers as small curiously shaped pieces of a large jig-saw puzzle for which there is no overall guide by which the pieces may be put together, or from which it would be possible to determine whether all the essential pieces are present. This book is the authors' attempt to provide the first such guide which sets forth essential criteria, not only of the nuts-and-bolts variety, but also beyond to the end use and the end user.

Technological bottlenecks are fast disappearing; improvements in the reproduction process have reached the point where at least one manufacturer is preparing to use silver film at a 1:60 reduction ratio with a promise of very little image quality degradation at even the sixth-generation copy. Such a process may be more adversely affected by airborne dust at the point of use than by the image degradation due to the finite limits of the detail-rendering ability of its lenses and light-sensitive materials. Many new methods anticipate rapid "dry processes" requiring no liquids whatever; copy images often depend upon electrostatic and electromagnetic phenomena that show surprising promise.

Despite these fast moving advances in apparatus and materials, we still have much to learn about how to encode data that we are to store in miniature in such fashion that it may be retrieved almost instantly by the man of goodwill who needs the data and is entitled to receive it. Apparatus for such encoding and retrieval must bear some reasonable relationship in cost and size to that used to store the data itself. In the ideal case this commonsense relationship must apply quite as much to the one-man business office or home as to the mammoth installation that might be required by one of our huge industrial organizations or even by the Federal Government itself. There are many unknowns ahead.

At this point we may again adopt our philosophy of a decade ago: "The difficult we do immediately. The impossible takes just a little longer." With this thought there is but one safe prediction for the future of America: The American public has many new and wondrous things in store—if the public wants them.

CHESTER M. LEWIS

WILLIAM H. OFFENHAUSER, JR.

March, 1956

CONTENTS

AIMS OF A RECORD
RETENTION PROGRAM

It has been said that the maturity of a cultural age can be judged quickly by the volume of recorded material purposefully preserved for a future time. This simple statement has far-reaching implications concerning the nature of the recording process in terms of what, why, when, where, and how—as it relates specifically to the persons under whose guidance the material is recorded and to the persons by whom the material will be used.

Recent technical advances in the field of human communications indicate that we are steadily moving forward at an increasingly rapid pace. We are producing larger and larger quantities of data daily; this is reflected by the steady increases in the total quantity of record medium materials consumed for recording purposes. In certain classes of such human communication, a large percentage of this recorded material is being preserved, not only because of the desire of librarians and archivists to preserve a copy of the material for the cultural benefit of mankind, but also in the interest of "the necessities of commerce."

The need for the retention of records is obvious. All of us as individuals cherish and save items of interest ranging from the purely personal to items of professional and business interest. Even for an individual it is mandatory that some items such as tax records be preserved for definite periods specified by law or statute. It is advisable to preserve numerous items for periods extending well beyond such mandatory periods.

Business, an activity involving the coordinated efforts of individuals, cannot be conducted satisfactorily without adequate records; and duplicate records may be required at several different points. Such points may be within a single business office or work area, or they may be in geographically separated areas located throughout the city, state, country, or throughout the world.

When an item has been documented, the document must be circulated to all interested parties or copies must be provided to them. Once such documents have been acted upon, they must either be stored for future reference if they are of long-term interest or destroyed after review. The decision depends upon the importance of the matter, the number of persons concerned, and the cost of informing them. The decision regarding the disposition of a particular document hinges upon the records retention program adopted; this program is an outline of policy indicating the types of records retained and the length of the period of retention.

A library, which is in reality a specialized form of centralized depository for large numbers of records of interest to many people, is judged by the user according to its ability to produce the desired records:

(1) adequate in content;

(2) in the most convenient form;

(3) in the shortest period of time;

(4) at the lowest cost.

These broad requirements are no different fundamentally for one class of document user than for another.

It would not be practical to attempt to preserve all classes of original records in their original form for indefinite periods of time. The cost of storage and preservation measured in dollars per item per year is even now too high for many classes of items and is almost certain to rise still higher. (See Chapter X.)

When an original document is preserved under the physical conditions * required to prevent deterioration, conditions which limit its deterioration with age to a minimum, the document has lost its most valuable asset, accessibility. Unless the data of the document are accessible to the person who needs them at the time he needs them, it fails in its primary purpose. The user may merely wish to look at or read the document and may care little how it is dis-

---

* In the case of a very valuable original document, such as the Constitution of the United States of America, these conditions might be:

(1) within a transparent vessel (glass bell jar or the like) that has been evacuated and filled with an inert nitrogen atmosphere;

(2) shielded from all ultraviolet light (illuminated by artificial light turned on only when the document is to be viewed);

(3) constant room temperature; and

(4) constant and low humidity within the vessel.

played or presented so long as it is reasonably clearly produced. He may merely want a readable fair-quality paper copy which he plans to employ as work material in the preparation of a new document. Or, he may wish to have a high-quality copy of the document suitable for reproduction in a book, magazine, or newspaper.

In summary, the form of presentation required depends upon how the user is to utilize the document and its data. He may wish:

(1) a visible display of all or part of the document; or

(2) a copy of all or part of the document—a paper copy or a transparency copy.

It is not uncommon for a user to want a copy for retention only *after* having inspected the document of interest; the copy may be of all or part of the document. Whether he orders all or part will often depend upon its availability, its cost, and its reproduction quality. A copy may be temporary or it may be (relatively) permanent; the user may need one kind or the other for his specific purpose. Readable copies may serve most users' needs, yet some uses may demand copies with excellent definition of the image, particularly if such copies are to be used in a new publication such as a book.

Any of these display forms may be presented at different ratios with respect to the size of the original. The copy may appear as:

(1) 1:1 representation;

(2) reduced representation;

(3) enlarged representation.

If the document appeared in color, it may be desirable to display it in color. Once again, however, cost affects the mode of presentation, as color reproduction* is appreciably more costly than black and white.

Since an original document, if it is to be adequately preserved, will be relatively inaccessible, a photographic copy of the document is made. As a matter of definition, we should distinguish between preservation of the original format and thought content as recorded on the original record medium, and the preservation of a facsimile of the original subject matter on a light-sensitive microrecord

---

* Unfortunately the color dyes used in multilayer color films are more or less fugitive. Multilayer color films are not used for the archival preservation of a colored image. Three-color separations on a black-and-white film are ordinarily made for this purpose; one such film yields the blue image, the second yields the green image, and the third film, the red image.

material such as microfilm and Microcards. In referring to the former we may imply the adjective "primary" wherever the word "preservation" is used unmodified. Where a facsimile of the original is preserved (as in the case of a photographic copy), the term "secondary" seems necessary and should be used explicitly. It is not unusual today for persons under whose guidance material is microcopied to discard the original document and preserve only the facsimile in microfilm form. The preservation of the original document might well be far too costly to justify keeping it, or its subject matter might make preserving the original entirely unnecessary. It may also happen that the original record medium was of a type that is subject to rather rapid decomposition. There are also cases where retention of the original document may be necessary because of poor quality of the available photographic reproduction methods, which might be due to poor photographic technique and handling and/or limitations of the equipment and of the reproduction process itself. In either event a photographic copy is indicated; the copy is made as a reduction to effect a saving in the storage space required and to effect a saving in the cost of the film used. "Reduction" is defined in American Standard ASA Z38.7.8-1947* as the ratio of a linear dimension of the object to the corresponding dimension of the image on the film. Common values for this ratio with today's materials range between 10 and 60 with 14 to 20 probably the most widely used values. The value selected in a particular case should be a compromise among the many quality, use, and process factors involved in the specific application.

In practice, microrecording makes possible a reduction in the number of cubic feet required for record and document storage by a factor between 10 and 100; such a factor may be called the space reduction factor. A "microphotograph" is defined in American Standard ASA Z38.7.8-1947 as a reduced-size photographic documentary reproduction (generally) too small to be read by the naked eye. Microphotographs are usually made for record purposes from documentary material such as texts or drawings, or from physical objects; they are most frequently photographed on microfilm.

Since the cost of active storage of documents is 3 to roughly 10 times the cost of inactive storage, it is not unreasonable for

---

* Reproduced in Appendix B, pages 369 and 370.

persons concerned with the costs of storage to seek the accessibility of active storage at the cost of inactive storage. If the documents under consideration can be microfilmed and, after microfilming, the originals can be destroyed, such an objective becomes possible if a space reduction factor of some value greater than 10 is used. Since reduction ratios as high as 60 and even more are feasible, and ratios of the order of 16 are very widely used, this economical objective can no doubt be approached, if not in fact actually reached. High space reduction factors are indeed the key to low costs; the use of microrecording where the space required is one-tenth or less of that required by the original documents deserves serious study and consideration. A study of the costs may well indicate that it is possible to maintain one or more active micro-recorded files and one or more microrecorded inactive files in all places required at a cost of but little more than maintaining only the original document in active storage. The great advantage of accessibility and active storage at the point of use combined with the low cost ordinarily associated solely with dead storage are the primary factors that encourage all who keep records to utilize microrecording on a very extensive scale.

In summary, microrecording aims to accomplish these objectives:

1. To make records so compact that the cost of storage of the microrecord is reduced markedly with respect to the cost of storage of the original document (values from 1% to 10% are common).

2. To make records (relatively) permanent, so that there is substantially no deterioration of the document with age (25 years or more is a common objective for ordinary storage).

3. To make records accessible and available:
   (a) when needed;
   (b) as needed;
   (c) where needed;
   (d) continuously over long periods of time;
   (e) to as many persons as need them, regardless of whether simultaneously or not;
   (f) in as many different locations as necessary, regardless of whether the needs are simultaneous or not;

(g) in the most convenient form for each use and each
     user, whether displayed visually or in the form of a
     copy—temporary or permanent;
(h) in quality adequate for each need;
(i) with an absolute minimum of skill required on the part
     of the user of the microrecords (simple foolproof de-
     vices are presumed);
(j) with a minimum of skill on the part of the technician
     or librarian making and preparing the copies for the
     user;
(k) in color, if there is need for color;
(l) at the lowest cost in terms of first cost of equipment and
     in terms of operating cost, including maintenance.

Microrecording, as of today, can go a long way toward meeting
these objectives if the attributes and the limitations of its apparatus
and its methods are fully understood when the compromise among
the many quality, use, and process factors is made.

BUSINESS AND LEGAL REQUIREMENTS FOR RECORD RETENTION

Since records are the means of recording the past, the present, and the future, the memory of an organization is only as good as its records.

In practice, records are processed* for future use. In libraries and in certain kinds of industry stored records are called upon frequently. In other situations, records may be called upon infrequently, and the rate at which they are acquired may increase quite rapidly. Under the latter circumstances, the costs of handling the records and the importance of small physical deterioration in storage become apparent. The rapid increase in the volume of material to be stored implies increased costs due to the need for increased storage space and for the additional insurance costs arising from the increased space requirements, as well as increasing problems in accessibility and day-to-day use.

Libraries have been concerned with the acquisition and archival preservation of knowledge in printed form; unfortunately there are few other fields where archival preservation has been an objective. Valuable data have been lost to potential users through carelessness, lack of knowledge, and the lack of a sound record retention program. Much that we have today remains because of the permanent nature of the materials of which the document of interest was made and the fortunate yet haphazard manner in which the document was stored rather than because of forethought and preparation on the part of the originator of the document.

A factor frequently overlooked is the need to retain records to provide data in the event of a law suit or to comply with government demands to provide records for tax and like purposes.

To solve the problems of preservation and use at a cost that the application can justify suggests that microrecording in one or a

---

* Processing is a series of acts in which documentary material is acquired and organized for use.

number of its various forms be utilized. One significant application is the reprinting of a rare work that has a restricted circulation, or, in the case of a first printing, a work with a very narrow field of interest. A typical example is a university thesis published as a routine requirement for an academic degree.

Other application aspects for microrecording are:

1. It reduces the amount of storage space required for *inactive* records, and therefore reduces the cost of such record storage. (A typical cost might be $2.00 per square foot per year.)

2. It reduces the amount of floor space required for *active* records and therefore reduces the cost of such record storage. (A typical cost might be $8.00 per square foot per year.)

3. It reduces the amount of insurance coverage required or lowers insurance rates, resulting in a lowered overall cost of insurance per document stored.

4. It permits the establishment of disaster or war damage controls.

5. It permits the duplication of records and their dispersal to geographically separated areas at a cost comparable with and possibly no greater than the cost of storing the original document. This duplication and dispersal effectively avoids irrevocable loss of the records.

6. It facilitates access to all, or given, points of desired information.

These points cannot be achieved without a thorough study of the records themselves and the laws pertaining to their retention. In turn, the retention of records may be dependent upon government requirements and the evidentiary value of such records in court. If they exist, some statutes admit certain types of microrecording and photocopies as primary evidence and others as secondary evidence. The laws may vary from state to state and from country to country.

RECORD RETENTION PROGRAMS AND SCHEDULES

Today the volume of stored recorded material is in direct proportion to the activity and interest of the user. Public libraries and college libraries can discard obsolete material with the knowledge that the discarded copy is not lost to posterity but is maintained in national or major libraries in some useful form should it be needed. On the other hand, special libraries of societies, organizations, and recording centers in the business and industrial world often find that they are the sole possessors of certain original recorded information.

The need for maintaining and preserving useful documents is an imperative one, but it is just as imperative to eliminate and discard useless material. Neither of these requirements can be accomplished without analysis of the material itself. The absence of such analysis leads to an annual waste of thousands of dollars in storage costs or unnecessary expenditures for microfilming on a nonselective basis.

The National Records Management Council Inc. of New York states the following about records in the average business:

(1) less than 10% need be kept permanently;

(2) some 20% must be kept in office space to meet current needs;

(3) 30% should be transferred to storage;

(4) the remainder should be destroyed or sold as waste paper. Big business and government have become increasingly aware of these recommendations. United States government agencies have saved nearly $5 million through a records management program. This has resulted in the recovery of office and storage space and the release of transfer cases and file cabinets for current records.

A January 1955 "Hoover Commission" report states the effectiveness of the progress made in the management of government records, surveys present objectives and operations, and makes additional recommendations for better control. In part the report* states:

Inasmuch as a survey of Government microfilming operations was conducted by the General Services Administration with the assistance of a consulting firm in 1953, the task force did not consider it necessary to conduct a detailed factfinding survey in this area. In lieu of that course of action, the task force has reviewed the findings, conclusions, and recommendations included in the report of the survey.

---

* Commission of Organization of the Executive Branch of the Government, Task force report on paperwork management, Part 1, January, 1955, p. 43.

During fiscal year 1953, almost 950 million documents were filmed at a cost of over $4,840,000. In addition, well over 25 million paper prints were made. The utilization of Government-owned equipment was small (approximately 18½ percent). Nonetheless, $250,000 was spent on rental of extra equipment, and new purchase proposals came to $660,000. Most Government agencies had microfilm equipment even though the typical installation was a small, part-time function.

The survey showed that of microfilm's many applications, 40 percent are used to save space. However, the low cost of records storage which resulted from the first Hoover Commission has made filming on most projects more expensive than the use of Federal record centers. Figures in the report show that microfilming costs on the average $20 per 1,000 records. Since record centers cost only about 30 cents per thousand records per year, the break-even point is not reached for more than 60 years. Of course, this 60-year figure does not hold true in all instances. For some projects the break-even point may be as low as 15 years. In this connection it is interesting to note that a recent British report * concluded that microphotography as a means of saving space is not normally economical and should not have a great part in the preservation of records.

The greatest potential of microfilming is undoubtedly as a labor-saving machine in day-to-day operations. The survey reported that about 28 percent of all microfilming was in this area.

An outstanding records management program went into effect September 18, 1953, in the State of New Jersey. It is known as the "Destruction of Public Records Act" (Chapter 410, Laws of 1953) and established a State Records Committee as the administrator. The program includes a records retention schedule for municipal and county officers and "standards and procedures for the photographing, microphotographing and microfilming of public records and for the preservation, examination and use of such records, including the indexing and arrangement thereof, for convenient reference purposes."

Westinghouse set up a records management program with the result that 120 carloads of valueless documents were destroyed and another 300 carloads were shifted to less costly storage space, saving the company some $250,000 annually. The National Records Management Council† has proved the effectiveness of its program to two state governments, three major cities, and more than

---

* Report of the Committee on Departmental Records (Her Majesty's Stationery Office, London, July 1954, p. 62).

† From "Money in the Waste Basket," by Perrin Stryker, *Fortune*, February 1953, p. 144.

forty corporations. The result has been the reduction of expenditures for filing equipment, elimination or reduction of microfilming programs, retrieving money through the sale of waste papers and by transfer of remaining records to low-cost storage areas.

Microfilming old records can save space, but *it may be cheaper to store the originals.* In some cases, owing to the rarity of the record, it may be desirable to seek some form of permanent preservation for the original and use microfilm copies for reference. No matter which course is taken, each is dependent upon a record retention program. Such a program can be established through the aid of specialist consultants assisted in their evaluation of the records in question by the business or organization involved. Before any material is discarded, competent legal advice should be sought regarding the Federal and state laws applicable to the retention of certain types of records for specified periods. Often it may become necessary to obtain specific advice regarding the types of records that may or may not be acceptable in microfilmed form. The December 1953 issue * of National Micro-News of the National Microfilm Association lists a communication from the United States Treasury Department stating which types of records should be retained in original form for Federal income tax purposes, and the types of supporting records that may be microfilmed.

Many data have been published regarding record programs. Some publications list types of materials that must be maintained to meet the requirements of Federal and state laws; others list common practice. Such data can be obtained from microfilming companies, record specialists, safe manufacturers, insurance companies, and fire protection associations. Since microrecording is in a stage of rapid growth and expansion, no single list can be completely comprehensive.

An individual analysis of record functions is essential in each case of potential application; two applications are rarely, if ever, identical in all details. One large advertising agency, for example, maintained a file of copyrighted radio scripts and commercials and some that were uncopyrighted. Proceedings were brought against one of the firm's clients regarding advertising slogans used in the commercials. It was necessary to trace record books for a fifteen-year period in order to establish that the agency's client

---

* National Microfilm Association, 19 Lafayette Ave., Hingham, Mass.

was the originator of the slogan. The case was dropped. This situation indicated that it might have been a wiser course to copyright all commercials. The danger would still remain that certain types of data, which it was not considered worth-while to copyright, might have been destroyed. Even if the data had not been destroyed, it is possible that they might have been lost or borrowed and never returned. Thus, instead of winning the case, the client might have lost it. If such records were kept in duplicate form, such as microfilm, it might have been possible to destroy the originals, saving storage cost yet assuring the agency that a complete record was more readily available when needed.

Lists of retention schedules may or may not recommend specifically that radio scripts and commercials be retained. Therefore, it is essential that record classifications be checked against such lists and, in particular, against classifications to be retained that are not mentioned on the list. Such a program can be accomplished only through joint consultation between a legal staff and the individuals intimately concerned with the records. This should be the average middle-of-the-road procedure. There are extremes where every record is kept and duplicated in some form or where very few records are maintained. One large business firm maintains a ruthless campaign of record destruction on the premise that the storage costs of the destroyed records exceeds the cost of the loss of an occasional law suit.

To begin an evaluation of records, it is necessary to study recommendations for record retention. One of the most useful lists of suggestions is that of Diebold, Inc., of Canton, Ohio, entitled "Business Records Classification and Retention Recommendations." This material appears in tabular form in Appendix A, pages 341 to 345.

LIMITATIONS FOR CIVIL ACTIONS

Consideration should also be given to limitations for civil actions in regard to contracts, judgments, promissory notes, and open accounts. The 1956 edition of the *Credit Manual for Commercial Laws*, published by the National Association of Credit Men, tabulates these limitations by states in chart form. See Appendix A, pages 363 to 365, for details.

FEDERAL REQUIREMENTS REGARDING RECORDS

A revised regulation, of the former Office of Contract Settlement, which is now administered by the General Services Administration of the United States, authorizes war contractors under certain conditions to destroy contract records. It appeared in pages 1318-1319 of *Federal Register* of March 7, 1953. In effect, this revision outlines the measures for reducing the retention period from 5 to 3 years for contract records. Aside from the reduction of the retention period, the regulation is precise in regard to standards and indexing. The specificity of these standards makes them a valuable guide for the retention of other types of material in the same form. For this reason the complete regulation is reprinted in Appendix A, pages 345 to 350.

Another useful pamphlet, entitled "Retention and Preservation of Records with Destruction Schedules," is published in a revised edition * by Record Controls, Inc. (formerly Chicago Bureau of Films & Indexing). It contains summaries of the major government regulations affecting business records such as labor, income tax, social security. There is also a survey in tabular form of the length of time a number of firms retained specific types of records; it gives the minimum, maximum, and average number of years for retention.

EVIDENTIARY VALUE OF MICRORECORDS

After an appraisal has been made of original records to determine which are to be retained and which are to be destroyed, it is feasible to determine which records may be kept in a duplicate form that will be admissible as evidence in court. Such determination should not be made without the advice of counsel. Certain types of photographic or photostatic copies are admissible as evidence. In fact, an additional basis for determining whether or not certain records may be microrecorded revolves around their evidentiary value. Most of the microfilming companies have lists of statutes and laws citing the admissibility of microfilm as primary or secondary evidence. One of the most concise studies regarding this point was compiled by the Special Committee on Protection of Business Records of the Commerce and Industry Association

---

* See Bibliography at end of chapter.

of New York, Inc. The report, entitled "Supplemental Data, Protection of Business Records," is reprinted in Appendix A, pages 350 to 362.

In 1951 a public law was enacted by the United States Congress which permits photographic reproduction of business records in *various* forms, assuring their acceptability as evidence in court. The text of the law is given in Appendix A, page 366. Report No. 536 of the House of Representatives of the 82d Congress, 1st Session, gives the historical background of the necessity for such a bill.

Information regarding European laws pertaining to microrecords, obtained directly from official sources of the countries listed, is given in Appendix A, pages 367 and 368. In general, at present there are no European laws in effect comparable to Public Law 129 of the United States. This may be due to the broader acceptance and use of microrecording in American government and industry. As such use increases everywhere, the probability is that many records accepted as secondary evidence will be accepted as primary evidence and, where needed, laws concerning the admissibility of records as evidence in this form will come rapidly into existence as soon as their effectiveness is realized both in this country and abroad.

DISASTER AND WAR DAMAGE CONTROLS

The destruction of valuable records and a complete or partial cessation of operations can occur at any time in industry as the result of fire, flood, explosion, theft, and sabotage. Normally the first four factors could also affect library operations. In both fields war is an additional hazard. Distance in itself is no longer a form of protection, and destruction by bombing, atomic or other, of large densely populated industrial areas is a possibility. Under these circumstances, protection of records is necessary if daily operation is to be continued. The extent and type of disaster may or may not permit some salvage, but initial planning for the protection of records from disaster or war should be made on the premise of total destruction of some geographical areas including an area where original records might be stored.

Protection, duplication, and dispersal of records are effective means of expediting reconstruction of operation. The extent to which these factors achieve protection varies with the needs of the individual industry or library.

Protection of records against disaster such as fire, flood, and theft can be achieved with limited duplication and dispersal of records in storage in fire and flood-resistive record vaults. However, the danger of bomb explosion necessitates additional cost and a more extensive dispersal and protection plan. For example, a library would need to place its original rare works in a well-constructed vault, perhaps on the premises of operations but preferably elsewhere. Its primary need would be to duplicate its card catalog in some form. This would be the basic starting point for resumption of its operations. The speed with which it could resume some form of service would depend upon the type of library.

A general reference library could restore portions of its collection through purchases, gifts, and second-hand book dealers. Such a program would permit limited service until the collection could be restored through new printings.

A highly specialized or technical library, on the other hand, would present a different problem. It would need to duplicate its card catalog and, working from it, could purchase any technical data available. In many cases such technical data might be the result of research or surveys within a specific organization and not available elsewhere. The need for the services of such a library, particularly if it belonged to a vital industry for defense, would be much greater than that of a general reference library. In addition to duplication of the card catalog, it would be necessary to duplicate one-of-a-kind records and surveys and engineering blue prints and drawings. The form in which these are duplicated would depend upon their relative importance to the industry served by the special library.

Libraries whose collections consist principally or solely of rare works could duplicate these works by some form of microrecording and store the originals and microrecorded copies in different protected or isolated areas.

Records in other types of industry, necessary for the operation of that industry, would have to be evaluated on the basis of what is essential for daily operation in the event of total loss. Here, too, the time element for resuming operation may vary. Records which are normally kept in original form may have to be

duplicated to meet such a contingency, for example, records of
clients, customers, and accounts.

When records are microfilmed solely for protection and the
maintenance of business ("on the same scale but not to increase it")
in the event of bombing, investigation should be made to determine
whether such expense is deductible as a tax expense. The United
States District Court of California recently awarded a refund of
disallowed tax deductions for this specific purpose to the Los
Angeles (Calif.) Times Mirror Co. This case is fully reported in
1954 Standard Federal Tax Reports published by Commerce Clearing House, Inc., Court Decisions—Cited 54-2 USTC, paragraph
9688.

Forms of Duplication

The evaluation of the use of a record will determine the specific kind of duplication necessary. Duplicates that have a limited
life and are economical to produce may be adequate in some cases.
The size of the original record may determine the type of duplicate
made. Duplicates with archival value may be necessary for certain
types of records.

Photostating may be selected if the necessary equipment is
owned and operated by a user, but the method is slow and such
records require more storage space than other types of duplication. Multigraphing, mimeographing, and Ozalid duplicates may
be used when there is need for numerous record copies, but the
processes themselves are time consuming and the cost of using
such processes, although not normally warranted for single copies,
might be extremely useful for organizations with numerous subsidiaries that require identical duplicate records.

Once original records have been reproduced in a duplicate
form, it might be advisable to make an additional set of the records
in similar form and place it in storage. Certain micro-opaques such
as Microcards and Readex Microprint can be readily duplicated
from microfilm or plates, respectively.

Microfilm duplicates used for visible display in a reader are
the most widely used form of microrecording at present. The flexibility of the variety of forms and applications of microfilm now
available is adequate for normal usage: 16mm microfilm may be
used for small documents up to a maximum of about 16 inches in

width, 35mm microfilm will accommodate documents and drawings up to about 35 inches in width, and 70mm microfilm is used for documents up to approximately 70 inches in width. These various sizes of microfilm may be used in the form of a reel, strip, or sheet. Many firms owning their own equipment undertake their own processing because of the economy of the operation. Off-premises processing (processing by outside suppliers of these services) may be indicated where there is not sufficient daily volume to warrant owning such equipment. When processing is undertaken off the premises, consideration must be given to the vulnerability of the processor in the event of war. In many instances processors have purposely selected non-vulnerable sites or have adequate subsidiaries that would permit continued protection.

Record Equipment

Consideration must also be given to the protection of record equipment. Equipment used for processing, duplicating, or projecting records may also have to be given additional storage protection, or identical equipment may be purchased and kept off the premises ready for use in the event of any emergency. If record duplication is performed off the premises by an outside processor in a non-vulnerable site, no additional precautions need be taken. When duplicates must be enlarged to be read, it is advisable to have additional viewing equipment available.

Utilization of Duplicate Records

Indexes of the location of duplicate records should be made and dispersed. Instructions for the reconstruction and use of records should be developed. Such instructions should also be duplicated and dispersed and should be understandable to a person not familiar with an operation. Personnel may not be available for reconstruction. Instructions should include legal authorization and the assignment of responsibility for the utilization by your own personnel, or others if necessary, for the complete program including salvage. In many instances economies can be effected through the reconstruction of records from other sources such as accountants, auditors, customers, and suppliers.

RECORD STORAGE

Evaluation of the utilization of records determines the retention period for original records and the question of whether or not duplication is undertaken. Such an evaluation will also determine the desired life of a record duplicate, which in turn determines the type of storage necessary. Some records and record duplicates such as microrecords may require archival storage for undetermined periods up to 100 years or longer; or they may require only short-term storage up to about 25 years or intermediate storage for periods ranging from 25 to 50 years. Processing and housing requirements may vary according to the storage terms desired. Economic considerations may prohibit or limit off-premises storage. For this reason many firms provide only fire-resistant rooms or vaults on their premises. Cash, securities, and similar assets may have to be retained on the premises in order to continue normal operation. When economically feasible, vital records and those necessary for the resumption of service in the event of disaster should be duplicated and kept in non-vulnerable storage areas.

The effects of the atomic bombing at Hiroshima indicated that well-constructed bank vaults could survive an atomic blast and retain their contents in good condition, even though the building containing such vaults was destroyed. European companies found that their vaults withstood bombing during World War II but that water from broken mains or water used in quenching fires often entered vaults through ventilators. This led to some destruction of records; the damage was especially evident when vaults were underground. The companies also found that the contents of vaults would burst into flames if they were subjected to intense heat for prolonged periods. This was believed to be due to spontaneous combustion; and the problem was solved by allowing prolonged cooling off periods of a week or longer. Heat and steam were found to affect microrecords contained in some vaults. Very few vaults are so constructed as to be completely waterproof, steamproof and heat-resistant for prolonged periods.

Radioactivity from an atomic explosion may make a storage area inaccessible. For this reason different techniques are used in the selection of off-premise storage. Some companies have selected storage facilities in isolated areas, yet conveniently accessible to their main operation. Storage sites have been chosen because they were not near military and industrial installations, rivers, harbors, and railroad centers. In certain instances access to the depository is only by car or bus. Vaults have been built within atomic-bomb-resistant buildings camouflaged to look like a residential dwelling or farmhouse. Some preference has been shown for the individual depository rather than a commercial depository because it was felt that a commercial depository, containing large collections of valuable material, might in itself become an enemy objective. Economically, it is not always feasible to construct an individual depository to meet the requirements of a particular operation; for this reason commercial depositories are used. However, in the opinion of some, commercial depositories and their contents do not in themselves become worthwhile as a military objective. Depositories of both types are springing into existence.

Commercial Depositories and Protection

An excellent example of a commercial depository is the Iron Mountain Atomic Storage Corporation which is located near Germantown, New York, some 125 miles from New York City. This depository was constructed shortly after 1950 in an abandoned iron mine in a 700-foot knoll that has been renamed Iron Mountain. The magnetite ore body assaying 60% iron is 70 to 80 feet thick in shale of indeterminate thickness. Natural protection is afforded both in site location of the depository and in the location of vaults within the mountain. At the present time there are approximately 117 vaults ranging in size from 275 to over 10,000 cubic feet. Provision can be made for additional custom-built vaults or space in a general storage vault.

Initial access to the vaults is through an administration building constructed of reinforced concrete. Access to the vault area is gained through a guarded grilled entrance to a vault door weighing 28 tons. Once entrance to this is obtained, the way is clear to private or general vault storage rooms. Each individual vault is equipped with a steel vault door, and corridors are built in the same structural pattern as the vaults. The mine itself is dry, all levels being above the lowest opening which permits the drainage of any minor seepage which might occur. Air conditioning extends throughout the storage area, and temperature and humidity controls are provided. The area has its own water supply and standby power facilities should the need arise. It has excellent security arrangements, both physical and with regard to personnel; there is a twenty-four-hour guard service. Its facilities are satisfactory for storing classified matter on a high security level. On the premises there is equipment for reading and reproducing microfilm. Heat-sealing of records and valuables in metal containers is also available. The canisters used are so constructed that, once sealed, they can not be opened without destroying the container. This commercial depository has taken into account every reasonable requisite for the protection of substantially all types of records.

Individual Depositories and Protection

Individual or private depositories should not be constructed without expert opinion about the selection of site and design of the vault and the protection methods for the records to be contained herein. A study of vaults and fire-resistive file rooms has been published by the National Fire Protection Association in their report entitled "Protection of Records," * in which specifications for fire-resistive vaults and file rooms are listed. This bulletin also contains information on the intensity, duration, and control of exposure to fire.

Photographic and microrecord storage often imposes tighter requirements upon storage facilities as reflected in terms of cost than those for paper storage. Theoretically, best storage is accomplished when the temperature and the relative humidity of the storage area are kept constant at the ideal values for the material being stored. It should be recognized that all air conditioning control systems function because some change in temperature or in relative humidity, however small, has occurred. The difference that causes the system to correct the change is called the differential. The difference in temperature that causes the system to act to correct the change in temperature to occur is called the temperature differential. Similarly, the relative humidity difference that causes the system to act to correct the change in relative humidity is called the relative humidity differential. Generally speaking, the smaller these differentials, the more costly the installation.

---

* See Bibliography at end of chapter.

Microfilm that is kept in air-conditioned offices ordinarily does not require either additional humidification or dehumidification within the file cabinet. Present-day film materials are approximately in balance with the atmosphere of a conventional air-conditioned office; this presumes a room temperature of about 68°F and a relative humidity of 40 to 50%. Ordinarily the temperature and humidity settings and the differential settings of good commercial air conditioning installations is approximately correct for the short term (25 years) storage of commercial microfilm materials that have been correctly processed.

Large differentials of either temperature or relative humidity are to be studiously avoided; these are indications of a poor air conditioning installation. There is no reason why a properly engineered air conditioning installation cannot maintain temperature within a conventional office or library storage area within 2°F and within a few percent of relative humidity. Relative humidity levels above 50% are to be especially avoided. When the humidity reaches the upper 90's, as it does in humid locations in humid weather, condensation frequently occurs within the file cabinet in which the microfilm is stored. Humidity cycling and its accompanying condensation, which result from changes in temperature when the relative humidity is in the 85-100% region, result in an almost ideal environment for the growth of fungus and mold on the emulsion (image-bearing) portion of the film; such mold grows luxuriantly and rapidly, destroying the microfilm image. (The mold feeds on the gelatin.)

In its study the National Fire Protection Association makes the following recommendations for the protection of microfilm against damage by fire:

> While cellulose acetate film does not burn any more readily than paper records, it may be otherwise affected by some of the ordinary storage conditions or fire conditions which would not affect paper records; for example, paper is not affected by the temperatures or humidities encountered under ordinary storage conditions, but high climatic humidity at ordinary room temperature may affect the base or the emulsion of microfilm. These effects are considerably aggravated when humidity is coupled with high temperature as for example, when the temperature is above 200° to 250°F or when paper is exposed to steam.
>
> When safes or other insulated record containers or record vaults are exposed to fire, the interior does not reach a temperature which is damaging to papers

within the period for which the safe or vault is rated, or during the subsequent cooling period. The interior temperature may, however, exceed 200° to 250°F and the interior may contain steam produced from the heating of the insulation or the vault walls. While these conditions would not be damaging to paper records on the interior of the safe or vault, tests made by Underwriters' Laboratories, Inc., by film producers and by safe manufacturers indicate that such conditions can affect the base or the emulsion of microfilm, either due to the high temperature or due to the steam.

Tests show that when microfilm is exposed for a long period of time to a temperature of 225° to 275°F in the presence of steam, or to a dry temperature at 300°F for a shorter period of time, the film warps or shrinks so that it cannot readily be run through a projector, although the individual frames of the film are legible and reprints of them can readily be made. The tests have not determined the point at which temperature alone, or temperature coupled with steam will avoid such damage. Experiments are being made to determine these critical points for film stored in various types of containers.

The tests which have been conducted to date indicate that for maximum protection against steam, microfilm stored in safes or vaults should be in friction-lid tin cans, rather than stored loose, or in cartons, or even in tin containers with telescoping lid.

Obviously in an uninsulated record container, microfilm will burn as readily as paper, because when exposed to fire the interior of the uninsulated record container is almost instantly at a temperature which will char either microfilm or paper.

In an informal communication the National Bureau of Standards, Washington, D. C., makes the following recommendations for storing microfilm:

For safety, even under normal circumstances, microfilm records should not be kept in the vicinity of the original records. During a national emergency, important records should be moved to an area not likely to be involved in hostilities. If this is not practical, an underground storage vault (not a part of a building) seems desirable. Underground vaults are usually damp and if this is the case, the film should be sealed in metal cans. Before sealing in cans, the film should be conditioned to about 30% relative humidity to allow for an increase in relative humidity in the cans due to lowering of the temperature to that in the vault. If the vault is heated to usual room temperature (65° to 75°F), the film need not be sealed in cans. The use of drying salts in the can with the film is not recommended though such salts could be used in the vault if properly replenished as needed. Cans need not be used if drying salts are used in the vault. Underground storage should protect the film records from damage by intense radioactivity but not necessarily from the explosive force of a direct hit.

Our recommendations for film storage under normal conditions are as follows:

Where film is stored in air-conditioned offices, no humidification of storage cabinets is necessary. However, microfilm storage cabinets equipped with trays for salt solution in the bottoms of the cabinets for humidification purposes are desirable.* We recommend saturated sodium dichromate solution with an excess of sodium dichromate (undissolved crystals in solution) for humidification purposes. This salt will maintain 52% to 53% relative humidity in air-tight cabinets at room temperature. If the cabinets are not reasonably air-tight, the relative humidity mentioned above will not be maintained.

Where humidified cabinets are to be used, it is extremely important that they have intelligent servicing. In dry weather, as in heated rooms in the winter time, the salt solution will evaporate and water should be replenished from time to time. In the summer time during periods of high humidity, the salt solution will take up water and some should be removed from the trays. It is very important to see that an excess of the salt is present at all times. If the solution becomes less than saturated, it will no longer act as a de-humidifying agent and in extreme cases may give up sufficient moisture to cause the film to become damp and promote the growth of fungus on the film. The optimum relative humidity condition for the storage of microfilm is 40% to 50%.

Diebold, Inc., in its Technical Manual 851 entitled "Approved Plan for Record Survival," makes the following recommendations:

Vaults should be on the ground, at the ground level or not too far below, because vaults in fire-proof steel frame or reinforced concrete buildings which are supported from the building structure of the lower floors may not preserve their contents unless the building is well braced and the vault substantially supported.

While vaults located below ground level are less vulnerable to an actual explosive bomb than those on the ground level or above, consideration must be given to the possibility of these basements being flooded from broken water mains by the explosion.

There is another reason for choosing vault and storage space in rural or distant areas which are far from the company's site of records and that is that all records in a vault may be contaminated by radioactive dust being driven through cracks in the vault walls by the force of the atomic explosion. Very few vaults are completely waterproof and equipped with gas-proof steel linings and vault doors, although these are now advisable in all vault construction that from here on is considered vulnerable to atomic bomb attack.

To sum up, in selecting vault and storage space it should be remembered that the best area for storage is a rural area far from an intended target, that the vault or storage space should be on the ground, or if below ground not near water mains which may be broken by an explosion, that no microfilm

---

* As a precaution against wide variations in humidity that may occur during breakdowns or during seasons of the year when air conditioning may not be used.

ever should be stored in a safe, no vault should be occupied by duplicate vital records on the company's premises, no bank vault should be used which is three or four floors below ground level where water and falling debris may damage the contents.

Note the reference to gas-proof steel linings and vault doors. Deterioration of the film base or paper or gradual loss of quality of the photographic image may be caused by chemical fumes, particularly in coal-mining and coal-burning regions. Proper storage should eliminate such fumes by washing or filtering the air circulated in vaults in storage areas. The entire storage area should be so controlled.

Storage conditions for Microcards and other photographic duplicates should be similar to that of microfilm. Storage of sheet film follows that of photographic duplicates and microfilm except that additional attention must be given to the manner of packing. To avoid injury to the photographic image, the adhesive and the paper in the envelope should meet the requirements of the American Standards Association specification for Photographic Filing Envelopes for Storing Processed Photographic Films, Plates, and Papers (Z38.8.21-1950)* Eastman Kodak Company has made available on the market slip-on transparent "Kodapak"† sheaths for sheet film, and sheets of Kodapak for photographic prints that protect photographic duplicates.

Processing requirements for archival and other types of storage are stated in the Eastman Kodak booklet entitled "Microfilming."

In practice, the stringent requirements for air cleanliness in terms of an inert atmosphere, and for small differentials of temperature and of relative humidity may be relaxed somewhat for Readex Microprint if the paper stock used has a high percentage of alpha cellulose and the other materials are non-nutrient for bacteria and fungi. In substance, Readex Microprint is a printing process and not a photographic one; for this reason the more elaborate precautions required for photosensitive emulsions utilizing gelatin as an ingredient (usual film emulsions) and for base materials in which a nutrient plasticizer has been used in manu-

---

* Reproduced in Appendix G, pages 427 and 428.

† A Kodak trade name for the plastic material used for protective sheaths and protective sheetings.

facture are not required for Readex Microprint due to the absence of such bacterial and fungal nutrients.

COPYRIGHTING OF MICRORECORDS

Works issued initially in the form of a microrecording may be protected by registration of a claim to a copyright in the same manner that any printed work is copyrighted. The decision to print in the form of a microrecording may be made because of the space and cost economies that this form of record offers for works of limited circulation such as theses and dissertations. Any work that is copyrighted in printed form and is identically reproduced in a microrecorded form such as Microcard, Readex Microprint or microfilm is covered under the terms of the original copyright. The Copyright Office of the Library of Congress* has this to say:

> Copyright relates to the "writings" of an author and secures to him or his assign the exclusive right to reproduce the work. It goes therefore to the form of expression rather than the format, medium or method of reproduction.
>
> There can be but one copyright in a given work and the setting up by registration of a second claim for a new copyright based upon a reprint in a different medium would be inconsistent with the original copyright, besides being an apparent attempt to claim a longer term of protection (based upon a later date of publication) than the law allows. It seems clear, therefore, that if the contents in the new form are identical to the old, the original copyright would cover the reprint in the new form.
>
> Where substantial additions have been made to a work the Statute affords ground for a new registration and this might possibly apply to a transparency of, say, a copyrighted painting, print or other graphic work where the transparency might, upon its own merits, be deemed a reproduction of a work of art copyrightable under subsection (h) of Section 5 of the Statute.
>
> Photographs are "writings" within the meaning of the Statute and where artistic skill and intellectual labor have gone into the creation of a pictorial transparency, the result may be a new work and come within Section 7 of the Statute subject, of course, to its limitations. But where the matter to be reproduced is text and the contents in the new form are identical to the old, the new form to all intents and purposes would seem to be merely a reprint of the old.

SUMMARY

The starting point for any program of this nature is a sound evaluation of records and the establishment of a record retention

---

* Communication of April 24, 1953.

program. Government requirements and the evidentiary value of microrecords in turn have a bearing upon a record retention program.

When the destruction of records has been decided upon, certificates of destruction of such records should be properly authorized and signed by the custodian or officer in charge of such records. Aside from maintaining these original certificates of destruction in safe storage areas, microrecorded duplicates should be made and kept in similar storage. Such certificates of destruction may be made for material no longer in existence and not duplicated in any form, or certificates of destruction may be made for material that exists only in duplicate or microrecorded form. In the latter case, the certificate of destruction should appear at the beginning and end of each microrecorded duplicate of the original record to which it applies. Such certificates should give a complete description of the documents destroyed and made only by the persons authorized to destroy such records. For legal reasons certain types of destroyed documents may also have to be certified by others than those authorized to destroy such documents.

Disaster or war damage controls are additional reasons for microrecorded programs. The form of duplication or microrecord may be dependent upon the size of the original or the life desired of the duplicate. Equipment for using or reproducing microrecords should also be dispersed to non-vulnerable areas along with microrecorded duplicates. Generally, storage for records and microrecords should be undertaken with expert advice. For the most part commercial depositories affording such storage have already resolved the technical and expense problems which the individual library or concern would have to undertake to resolve if it chose to establish a private depository.

Bibliography

Eugene B. Power. ''Microfilm for Periodicals.'' *Library Journal,* Sept. 1, 1952, p. 1379.

''The Problem of Periodical Storage in Libraries.'' University Microfilms, Ann Arbor, Mich., 1952.

Eugene B. Power. ''Microfilm as a Substitute for Binding.'' *Amer. Documentation,* Vol. 2, No. 1 (1951).

''Microfilming.'' Eastman Kodak Co., Rochester 4, N. Y., 1952. 50c.

"How to Plan a Successful Record Retention and Destruction Program."
Diebold Inc., Canton 2, Ohio, 1952.

"Business Records Classification and Retention Recommendations." Diebold
Inc., Canton 2, Ohio.

"A Basic Plan for Record Retention and Destruction." Remington Rand,
Inc., 315 Fourth Avenue, New York 10, N. Y.

"Safeguarding Vital Records with Burroughs Microfilming." Burroughs
Adding Machine Co., Detroit 32, Mich.

"How Long Should Business Records Be Kept?" Herring-Hall-Marvin Safe
Co., Hamilton, Ohio, 1949.

"Disposition of Inactive Records." Policyholders Service Bureau, Metro-
politan Life Insurance Co., 1 Madison Ave., New York 10, N. Y.

Perrin Stryker. "Money in the Waste Basket." *Fortune*, Feb. 1953, p. 144.

"Retention and Preservation of Records with Destruction Schedules." Record
Controls, Inc., 209 South La Salle St., Chicago 4, Ill., 1956. $4.00.

Robert A. Shiff. "Bank Records Management." *Auditgram*, Aug. 1950
(publication of the National Association of Bank Auditors and Controllers).

Dorothea M. Singer. "The Insurance of Libraries." American Library Association, 50 E. Huron St., Chicago, Ill., 1946.

Albert S. Davis, Jr. "The Legal Aspects of Machine Documentation."
Special Libraries Bulletin, Vol. 44, No. 1, p. 5 (Jan. 1953).

"Supplemental Data, Protection of Business Records." Commerce and Industry Association of New York, Inc., 99 Church Street, New York, N. Y.

"Evidentiary Value of Microfilm Records." House of Representatives, 82d
Congress, 1st Session, Report No. 536. Superintendent of Documents,
Washington, D. C.

"Protecting Records in War Times." *Studies in Business Policy*, No. 51.
National Industrial Conference Board, Inc., 247 Park Avenue, New
York 17, N. Y.

"Approved Plan for Record Survival." *Technical Manual* 851, Diebold Inc.,
Canton 2, Ohio, 1951. $1.00.

"Suggestions for Planning a Program for Protection of Business Records."
Commerce and Industry Association of New York, Inc., 99 Church Street,
New York, N. Y. 10c.

"Protection of Records." National Fire Protection Association International,
60 Batterymarch Street, Boston 10, Mass. $1.00.

Edward N. Jenks. "Micro-Editions of Newspapers: A Survey of Developments." *Journalism Quarterly*, Fall 1950.

Don Wharton. "The Safest Place in the World." *The Saturday Evening
Post*, March 22, 1952. (Iron Mountain Atomic Storage Corp.)

William H. Offenhauser, Jr. "Preservation by Microfilm," *Special Libraries*,
Dec. 1951, p. 369.

Chester Lewis. "National Microfilm Association." *Library Journal*, July
1952, p. 1178.

"Annex Regarding Repositories for Microfilm Reproduction." UNESCO
Document No. CL/443.

Albert Woodruff Gray. ''Microfilming Is Ruled a Deductible Expense.''
    Editor & Publisher, Jan. 1, 1955, p. 36.
''Records Management Program Rules and Regulations,'' December 4, 1953.
    State of New Jersey Dept. of Education Division of the State Library,
    Archives and History, State House Annex, Trenton 7, N. J.
''Index to Federal Record Keeping Requirements.'' National Records Man-
    agement Council Inc., 555 Fifth Avenue, New York 17, N. Y., 1955. $2.00.
Robert A. Shiff and Arthur Baracan. ''The New Science of Records Manage-
    ment.'' *Harvard Business Review*, Sept.-Oct. 1954, pp. 54-62.
Carl Spielvogel. ''Overhead Less Below Ground.'' The New York *Times*,
    Jan. 8, 1956, Sect. 3. pp. 1, 7.
''Credit Manual of Commercial Laws 1956.'' National Association of Credit
    Men, 229 Fourth Avenue, New York 3, N. Y. $10.00.
Charles Bishop. ''The Microcard Production of Single Journal Articles.''
    Amer. Documentation, Vol. 7, No. 1, pp. 33-35 (Jan. 1956).

SELECTION OF A
MICRORECORDING PROGRAM

CAPABILITIES AND LIMITATIONS OF THE
MICRORECORDING PROCESS

Reduction Ratios in Theory and in Practice

Since microphotographs which appear on microrecords are reduced in size to the point at which they are too small to read with the naked eye, the microrecording process must provide, at the point of use, for enlargement of the microphotograph to something approximating normal size. In practice there is rarely a need to retain a precise 1:1 relationship in size* between the original document and the display of its image to the user; it is often advantageous for the user to view the image in reproduction in somewhat enlarged size. One example of such enlargement is the display of newsprint in a newspaper column image, where the original type size is a little too small for best reading comfort; an increase of some 50% seems a desirable value. Since only a small cost difference occurs in a microfilm reader when the image size is so increased in reproduction compared with its 1:1 size, there is ordinarily little reason to overlook this opportunity to provide an image more convenient for the user.

If there were no practical limiting factors, reductions far greater than 1:60 would be desirable in the original microrecord. The use of greater reductions would make possible greater savings in the amount and therefore the cost of storage space required for the microrecorded documents. There are, however, practical limits to the amount of reduction that can be used in practice and to the amount of consequent enlargement that a particular equipment array and process will tolerate.

---

* The outstanding exceptions are engineering drawings and the like, which are made to scale.

The major limitations are:

1. The first is the quality of the original image itself. News-print for example, can often "stand" less enlargement without becoming fuzzy than some varieties of the highest quality of printing. There are significant variations in quality among newspapers; many newspapers are very well printed, some are good, others fair, and a few are poor.

2. A second limitation is the original microrecord medium itself, and in its exposure and processing. Even though microfilm and microrecord materials are the finest, in terms of detail rendition, that the sensitized film industry is capable of manufacturing, they are capable of recording only a finite amount of image detail. The limit is frequently reached in the neighborhood of the 1:60 reduction range; if reduction could be pushed farther readily without compromise or sacrifice of performance, there would be little reason for hesitation. Here again the quality factor enters: the quality of the film used for the original microrecord; the quality of the lens and of the camera used to make the exposure; the accuracy with which the exposure was made (as to the quantity, quality, and uniformity of light used, accuracy of focus, and the steadiness of the image relative to the camera); the quality of the processing for the original microrecord, including the quality of the methods, the processing machines, and the chemicals used, as well as the quality of supervision and know how.

3. A third limitation, one frequently overlooked, is the number of copying generations and their respective qualities between the original microrecord and the end-use copy derived from it. There is a loss in detail in every copying step between the original microrecord and the end-use copy; the least loss in detail occurs when the end-use copy is made directly from the original microrecord. Since a loss of about 30% in potential detail-rendering ability occurs in each added copying generation, and commercial operations frequently show much larger losses, there will be many cases where an end-use copy derived from intermediate copies printed from an original microfilm negative will not be adequate in quality. The best quality in end-use copies is

obtained when the number of generations between the original microfilm and the end-use copy is a minimum. In practice this usually limits the number of generations to only two, the original microfilm and the end-use copy, when large reductions of the order of 30 or more are used.

Generally speaking, the greater the reduction at which the original is photographed, the less is the likelihood that more than a single copy generation can be tolerated between the original microrecord and the end-use copy. Assuming usual operating practices with the usual vagaries of quality in processing (these include vagaries from organization to organization, from individual to individual, from material to material, and from time to time), second-generation end-use copy from a microfilm original should be adequate in quality whether this original was made with a reduction of 10 or of 40. It is quite probable that the print made from the negative photographed at a reduction of 10 would pass the quality test by a wide margin, while the print made from the negative photographed at a reduction of 40 would pass by only a small margin. With good commercial processing, a fourth-generation end-use copy from a microfilm negative photographed with a reduction of 10 should be adequate; with poor processing, such an end-use copy would probably be inadequate.

In recent designs of microfilm readers, there appears to be a trend toward greater microfilm reader enlargement from a low value of $19\times$ to as great as $36\times$; recently one has been announced at $60\times$. Since newspapers are usually microfilmed with a reduction of 1:16 (1:19 and 1:17 are also used), the effective enlargement of the newsprint* image displayed by a typical reader displaying typical newspaper microfilm is $1/16 \times 24$, or approximately $1.5\times$, roughly 50% larger than normal.

---

* The usual reason given for the use of 1:19 or, more recently, 1:17 reduction is the reduction in cost. With these ratios the image is usually placed crosswise to the length of the film. In a large number of cases, particularly with the smaller type sizes used for stock quotations, for example, the saving in space storage cost is not worth the readability sacrificed or the inconvenience caused by the constant readjustment of the reader required to present the top or bottom of the projected image clearly. Although more expensive readers can be designed to overcome such problems, such difficulties would occur with other microfilmed material photographed in conventional manner and shown on these readers.

PRESERVATION AND ITS RELATION TO
MICRORECORDING

If an original document is stored in an ordinary file cabinet
for future use, no special precautions are ordinarily taken with
regard to physical preservation to prevent deterioration in storage
if the time interval of storage is short compared with the normal
document life under such conditions. Thus, if an original letter
written on a good grade of paper with good ink and stored in an
air-conditioned office can be expected to meet readily the commonly
realized objective of storage for 25 years, it is almost certain to meet
the common statutory requirement of 7 years if that is all that is
required of it. If the paper used for the letter has a very high
percentage of alpha cellulose and meets other chemical criteria,
this original can be expected to last for 100 years or more under
such storage conditions; under almost ideal conditions such as are
used to preserve the original document of the Constitution of the
United States of America, it might be expected to last much longer.

It has been said that the contents of the average file cabinet
in a business office is two-thirds carbon copies. If the document
of interest were a carbon copy of a letter made on a very poor
grade of yellow second-sheet paper it might not last the full 7-year
period even under the excellent conditions of storage described,
that of an air-conditioned office. If the file cabinet and its contents
were stored under unfavorable conditions, as in a damp basement
where book bindings mold quickly, such poor grade second sheet
yellow paper could disintegrate in as little as a year or two. In such
a file, where most of the documents contain paper of only the poor
kind, frequent inspection of the files would be necessary to check
the condition of the documents. If the same kind of poor grade
second sheet paper were used for making replacement copies of the
documents that had disintegrated, three copies or more per document stored would be required during the 7-year storage period.
The cost of maintaining such a file would be prohibitive.

If the carbon copy made upon a very poor grade of yellow
second sheet paper were kept under the unfavorable conditions
mentioned, it would be necessary to inspect the file about once every
year to determine what documents should be replaced and what
documents could be retained until the next inspection would occur
a year later. If, however, the file contained carbon copies on a very

good grade of paper with a very high percentage of alpha cellulose, regular but far less frequent inspection of the documents would be required to check their condition, and the copying of deteriorated documents would be infrequent, if indeed it would be needed at all. Thus with poor paper, inspection of the whole file once each year would be indicated; the average carbon copy in the file would need to be copied about three times in 7 years just to maintain the file. With good paper, inspection of the file at the end of 3 years and at the end of the 7-year period would be more than adequate, and a replacement rate of approximately 1 document in 1000 stored might be a conservative estimate.

As mentioned previously, since the photographic facsimile of a document may be considered for preservation in the same way as the document itself, it seems prudent to distinguish between them when discussing their preservation. The term "secondary preservation" will be applied to the preservation of a facsimile regardless of the reduction at which the copy is made; the term "preservation" will imply the adjective "primary" when reference is made to the document itself.

In principle, the difference in storage requirements for the two, the original document and the photographic facsimile, depends upon the difference in the chemistry of the materials of the respective record materials. In practice, the differences are often small enough to be ignored as the chemical composition of film base for microfilm is similar to that of acetate sheeting used for laminating documents; the open question relates to the film emulsion which, fortunately, shows its longest life under storage conditions similar to those which are best for the film base.

If, in addition to storing an original microfilm facsimile record in such a manner that copies may be made from it or of selected portions of it as required, it is also necessary to store an original microfilm facsimile record for archival and similar secondary preservation purposes, it is not possible to have a single piece of film in storage under almost ideal conditions, where it is relatively inaccessible, and at the same time to use that *same* piece of film almost daily to provide end-use copies. The problem is solved by making two original facsimiles, one for secondary preservation in archival storage and the second for use as a pre-print material from which end-use copies are to be made. In this manner no compromise with principle is required to accomplish both archival storage and simultaneous availability of a preprint material from which end-use copies may be made as required. The film used as preprint material will become marred and physically damaged with each use, and the effects of such use are cumulative.

RECORD DISPERSAL

A record dispersal program may require duplicate records in several different places. Such record duplication may be accomplished by photographing the original document as many times as required, making as many microfilm facsimile originals as there are locations to be served. Alternatively, the various locations may be served by means of prints—photographic copies made on a copying machine (printer) from a single original or from a small number of microfilm originals. To a considerable extent the method chosen in a specific case depends upon how the dispersed records are to be used and upon how much records made by the different methods cost. The primary considerations as in all other applications of microrecords are:

(1) the accessibility of the record,
(2) its quality in end-use reproduction, and
(3) the cost of providing it.

Accessibility in the broad sense includes convenience to the user of the form in which the document is presented to him. His customary basis of comparison is the original document itself. In this sense accessibility includes:

(1) the size of the available document facsimile, normal or microrecord;
(2) its reproduced size, the size as seen by the user;
(3) its form, whether optical image (as in a microfilm reader) or transparency or paper print if in the form of a copy.

COST OF A MICRORECORDING PROGRAM

To accomplish all the required objectives at a minimum of cost in a specific microrecording program requires detailed consideration of many factors, some explicit, some implicit, all intimately related to the scope of the program and to how each portion is to be accomplished. If the program is for a business office, for example, the applicable record retention schedules should indicate whether an original document shall be destroyed or stored after it has been satisfactorily microrecorded. If stored, the period, the physical storage conditions, and the accessibility must be specified precisely because each aspect of a specific decision reflects a different cost. Where multiple copies of documents are ordinarily needed, many factors must be considered in determining whether to distribute original material in normal size or to reproduce it in some form of microtext; distribution of multiple copies in original size may be more costly.

After a specific program outline has been selected, decisions must be made about the portions of the program to be accomplished "in the house" (by the user himself), and whether with rental or purchased equipment, and what portions of the program (film processing and duplicating might be an example) are to be accomplished by outside contractors entirely. Before the choice is narrowed to particular sizes and forms of record, sufficient information must be obtained about all pertinent sizes and forms so that the user will know that his choice is based upon adequate information, not only about the forms and sizes actually chosen but also about all others that are "near" choices. Accessibility may be of primary importance in the end-use record because the individual document may be referred to frequently and must be located by the search methods in use almost instantly. The end-use of the microrecord may be such that frequent requests are made for the material or multiple simultaneous demands are made for identical material. These may be controlling factors in choosing a type of microrecord that lends itself most readily to servicing such requests. Multiple copies of microtext may be less expensive in opaque than in microfilm form in a specific case. Yet microfilm may be the medium chosen because of its higher definition or because microfilm reader distribution will make it available to more users.

Readers or viewers are usually purchased outright; arrangements can often be made for rental or leasing. Rental or purchase cost should be calculated on an amortized basis in all microrecording programs. "According to the United States Internal Revenue Department, microfilming equipment can be depreciated on a 16-year basis for income tax purposes. Therefore, you can normally expect your equipment to have a useful life of *at least* 16 years.*

Some of the uses and applications of microrecords are: economies in production, storage, collating, binding, handling, and transporting; preservation and disaster controls; primary publication in microtext form of historical or scholarly material that would be too costly to reproduce in other form for limited markets; microrecording business and other records that are acceptable as evidence in courts; microforms of research material such as periodicals, newspapers, abstracts, theses, maps, charts, engineering drawings, and other scientific data; microrecords used for interlibrary loans, card catalogues, charging, and projection for educational library lectures.

Although cost is usually the impelling factor in selecting a particular form of microtext for a microrecording program, there are instances when cost is not the primary consideration because of the end-use of the microtext. The pressing questions are "What will it do?" and "What will it cost?" A study must be made to determine the accessibility, storage, use, and filing costs of originals versus facsimiles in microrecord form; the retention and deterioration of the originals in storage; the point at which it is cheaper to microrecord than to retain originals; and whether in the final analysis it is more satisfactory to retain the original record than to utilize its content in the form of microtext. After these factors have been determined, selection may depend on whether multiple or single copies of the original are desired. If only a single copy, some form of microfilm is indicated. If multiple copies are desired, then the number required may dictate whether microfilm, Readex Microprint, or Microcards should be the chosen medium.

In general, but not necessarily in the given order, a user or purchaser of a microrecording program would prefer:

1. Microtext that can be read easily for prolonged periods if necessary.
2. Microtext that is self-indexing (thus eliminating extensive search).
3. Microtext that consumes the smallest amount of storage space and may be stored in existing equipment or require a minimum amount of new equipment.

---

* "30 Questions and Answers on Burroughs Microfilming," Burroughs Co., Detroit 32, Mich.

4. Microtext with archival properties of such nature that the manner of storage creates a minimum problem.
5. Low-cost readers or viewing apparatus that accommodates all or most types of microtext and gives excellent projection, without damage to the microrecord.

MICROFILM

It is usually better business wisdom to contract with a commercial or service microfilming company for all the services needed when a program is first put into effect. In microfilming there are many technical nuances, both photographic and management, that are essential to a smooth-running efficient operation which functions consistently at low cost. Some of the elements of this knowhow are quite elusive, especially for people who are not technically trained; seeing the work done by competent professionals answers many questions that might otherwise remain unsolved mysteries.

For this reason it is wise to present your microfilming problem to at least two or three competitive companies; from among these you may choose the successful one. Each will view your problem in a slightly different light; all will have something useful and constructive to contribute to the chosen solution and to your understanding of the microfilming process and the relation of your problem to it. Each reputable microfilming company can appraise your problem and recommend a suitable procedure for photographing and for processing; their prices will, of course, include their labor costs. Such costs, being competitive, usually fall within a relatively narrow price range; on the other hand, the prices of equipment needed to do the work vary over a very wide range, largely because of quality differences and performance differences among the various pieces of equipment and because of the wide variety available on the market.

One of the most important factors in determining the end-use form of the microrecord is the probable frequency of use of the record in micro form. Frequently the manner in which a microrecord is to be filed, indexed, and stored dictates the form chosen for the end-use record. A number of factors enter into the choice:

(1) the number of documents to be microrecorded per unit time;

(2) the character of the documents;

(3) the term of storage of the documents, whether destined to meet a legal requirement of statutory kind or for archival storage;

(4) the number and kind of end-use copies required;

(5) when the end-use copies will be required, whether simultaneously or not.

To a considerable extent, if the probable need for end-use copies can be predicted with some accuracy—in terms of the number of times per year that end-use copies will be required, and the form of copy best suited to each use (or if only a master file is required), the number and character of the items to be consulted—the most desirable form for the material to be stored becomes implicit. Other forms that are important but do not justify detailed description are mentioned in Chapter IX.

The microfilming service company cannot determine this use factor as accurately as can the record owner. If the required information is not available, a study should be made by the record owner to assist in determining it. After the required information is obtained, the service company can make the necessary recommendations as to the desirable forms of microrecords and the processes by which they are to be made.

Infrequent use of the microrecord usually implies that microfilm is best in reel form. Long reels may be desirable when reference is based upon chronological use of the documents photographed. In certain few cases negative images may be adequate for reference; when this is the case, the cost of the positive copy is eliminated. Ordinarily one or more master original protection negatives should always be kept in storage for protection purposes regardless of whether a negative or a positive is used for reference purposes. Such master original protection negatives are preferably photographed directly from the original document when the reference original negative is photographed.

When frequent use is made of the material in microfilm form, consideration should be given to one of the newer microfilm methods of using one or more frames of microfilm in protective cards or jackets. Using Filmsort cards, for example, it is possible to group multiple frames of microfilm on one subject on a single card. Subsequent material microfilmed at a later date can be added to cards containing the same subject. Using this technique, it is possible to group various film sizes on one card. For example, descriptive material regarding a subject may be microfilmed in 16mm size; blue prints, drawing, or photographs of the same subject may be filmed in 35mm or 70mm and correlated with the descriptive material on the same card. The additional costs of utilizing microfilm in card or jacket form may be offset by the reduction in search time and cost. This is particularly true when search is mechanized. Single or multiple frames of microfilm on a given subject can be mounted on a card that is punched or coded. Almost any type of commercial punched card can be utilized for this purpose.

Sheet film or 70mm film may sometimes be preferred for reference use. Paper positives or the so-called "Microtape" or "Microstrip" may be more economical yet satisfactory for other applications. The end use of the microrecord must be given very careful consideration when a choice is being made from the wide variety of microfilm forms available. It might also be helpful when multiple copies of microrecords are desired to compare the applications and costs of opaques such as Microcards, Readex Microprint, and those of transparency records in microfilm form. The final decision should be arrived at only after a study has been made of all forms of microrecords, their uses and respective costs.

Costs of microfilming should become lower per unit quantity as the volume of records to be processed becomes larger. In all cases it is the quality of the work done that is of primary importance. When competitive bids are obtained from service companies, a lower bid should not assure the order to the lower bidder unless the record owner can be assured that the quality of the work to be done is at least the equal to that required by the application and equal also in quality to the work of the higher bidders. Since the end result is so important, it is better to pay a slightly higher price and obtain microfilming of high photographic quality than to pay a somewhat lower price and obtain results that defeat the objectives of the microfilming program. Generally speaking, a large company or one that has been in business a long time has more know-how than the newcomer. Despite this generalization, new companies come into being from time to time because of the market demand for better quality at a lower price, and such new firms show a grasp of the technical and business aspects that make it possible for them to deliver a superior quality product at very little more than the general market price.

All too often the preparation of material for microfilming as well as its subsequent handling in process is left entirely in the hands of the microfilming company without any examination by the user of the methods, technical or bibliographic, or even of the facsimile original microrecord itself or of any of its end products. Since microfilming is a service operation, it should be clearly understood between the two parties just what services are to be performed. In the final analysis, the responsibility for correct bibliographic and technical practices should be jointly shared by the microfilming company and the owner. Knowing that the purpose of microfilming is to provide, at the point and time of use, a clear and distinct photographic image that is substantially free of deterioration, the user should take from the original, after it is developed, short samples in the form of test clippings from the ends of finished films; such clippings should provide special exposures for process check by means of such tests. The clippings should be tested for all required attributes by a competent testing organization. Since the average library or business does not ordinarily have competent engineers, physicists, chemists, and like specialists available for this work, the tests should be made by competent independent commercial testing laboratories; these, too, offer their services on a contract basis. A routine check of the dimensional, chemical, physical, and other standards including the standard tests such as those described in this book will be found very valuable and economically worthwhile when conducted as a routine matter in checking all products. Such testing can be budgeted on a percentage-of-the-total basis; such budgeting when worked out with the commercial testing laboratory will provide a maximum of service at the minimum cost when intelligently applied.

In doing this work for you, the commercial testing laboratory will apply the principles of statistical quality control. Such inspection must be expected to turn up defects; all that inspection can do is to reject that which is bad; it cannot improve a product already made. In the beginning it will be necessary to do considerable testing; it is reasonable to believe that the purchaser shall be more concerned about accepting something that is defective than he is about rejecting something that is good. A clipping sample should be taken from every roll, or at least for every day's output. A clipping sample should also be taken from all copies made, or all intermediate copies required to produce the desired end-use copies. If a sample from each stage in the process is available for each day, it becomes possible to locate the source of trouble and to specify how to correct it should an unsatisfactory product be produced. Generally speaking, when the product is "in good control," that is, when under test it consistently shows that all requirements are being met, the need for testing becomes a small percentage of the production cost; when determined in accordance with the American Standards Association statistical quality control methods Z1.1, Z1.2, and Z1.3, it becomes possible to meet the goal of statistical control—that of providing the maximum amount of *certainty*, of product satisfaction at the minimum of cost. The percentage of product to be tested depends upon the quality level of the product; when the quality level is consistent and high, the amount of testing required to assure that the quality level is what it is supposed to be becomes small. The collection of test data is necessary to determine just what the quality level is; if the quality level proves to be high, the amount of testing required can be reduced as dictated by the mathematical criteria. The commercial testing laboratory, in working out a testing contract with you, will be glad to tell you what they consider important and how they determine the order of importance. This knowledge has been gathered by specialists; it is decidedly to your advantage to make use of this most valuable know-how.

Inspection of the product by the commercial testing laboratory constitutes insurance that nothing serious will arise to interfere with accomplishment of the objectives of the microfilming program; if some deviation is noted, it can be determined accurately and corrected promptly. As described in "Are Your Microfilms Deteriorating Acceptably?" * 7 processors who supplied 42.6% of film in a certain microfilming program had the following amounts of film rejected because of excess hypo content, for example:

---

* See "Clapp, Henshaw, and Holmes" in Bibliography at end of this chapter.

Processor	% rejects	% of total supplied
A	8.9	17.4
B	6.6	1.5
C	5.5	1.8
D	0.5	19.1
E	55.0	0.9
F	6.6	1.5
G	0.5	20.0

When notified, Processor G requested the return of 42 reels for recheck which were returned in good order. Such deviations, if they occur, will be reported by the commercial testing laboratory; and it is probable that your supplier will correct the difficulty in the same way.

With the know-how acquired by observing professionals doing your work over a period of time, you may approach the problem of running your own installation and making the necessary cost estimates when there is a large and steady volume of documents to be recorded daily. Generally speaking, the volume of film to be handled daily must be really sizable to justify the purchase of processing equipment; ordinarily only a small percentage of users of microfilm can justify it. It is usually good business practice to purchase non-specialized microfilming services, as these are quite competitive; it becomes desirable to lease equipment for photographing with an option to buy in the case of specialized services after sufficient know-how has been acquired. It is the record volume that usually determines whether material is to be photographed on or off site and processed on or off site of the original record. In some cases security requirements or the fragility of the records may make it mandatory for the work to be conducted on the site. It is somewhat rare that the security requirements as established by governmental agencies will require that the documents must be photographed and processed on site by the contractor's own personnel; many contract firms have the special security clearances required for the various degress of security required. In such special cases the contract companies have modified their normal procedures to meet the security and other operational needs.

Microfilming is now at a stage of very rapid growth. A characteristic of rapid growth is rapid change of materials and methods for the purpose of improving the final product. Despite the fact that the U. S. Bureau of Internal Revenue has established 16 years as the depreciation term for microfilm equipment, there is no assurance that the equipment that you are buying will not become obsolete some time before the 16-year term has expired. Unless the savings resulting from owning and operating one's own micro-filming facility are large enough to show a saving even with ac-celerated depreciation, the purchase of camera and like equipment is difficult to justify.

Many manufacturers lease equipment with an option to buy; the sums paid under the lease are partially credited toward the purchase price in many such cases. Eastman Kodak, for example, quotes prices under lease and for outright sale on much of their equipment; the ratios between yearly lease costs and purchase prices for their equipment will be found comparable to the similar figures quoted by others. Such ratios are especially useful in making cost estimates for projected programs.

Generally speaking, the larger manufacturers, being strongly financed, are in the best position to offer a prospective user of microfilming the option of lease or purchase. Smaller manufac-turers often make at least equally satisfactory equipment, and sometimes make specialized equipment that is better suited to a specific need; such equipment may not be offered on lease but may only be sold outright. The products of such firms are not neces-sarily any better or any worse merely because of the way the firm is financed or its products marketed; it is the performance of the equipment that really counts. The performance is rarely described in the catch phrases advertising it; it is described in the day-to-day workings of specialized equipment that produces the desired docu-ment copies when, where and as needed with the desired quality at the lowest cost.

16mm Microfilm

Documents that are approximately 8½ by 11 inches, or not more than 16 inches in width, such as letters, books, bank checks, are usually recorded on 16mm microfilm. Diebold, Inc., has made

STORAGE FILES

Estimated costs of PHYSICALLY STORING records

	Transferring one active file and storing it for one year
1. Acquisition of file, $6.20 per drawer estimated landing cost including freight. Amortized over 10-year period	$ .62
2. Floor space @ 5½ sq. ft. per drawer to provide for adequate aisle room. Space cost per file @ $2 per sq. ft., stacking files 6 high	1.84
3. Supplies, on basis that it is more economical to transfer file folders etc. than to salvage	4.75
4. Transfer costs (labor) including transportation to file room, labeling of drawers, preparation of new file folders, eventual destruction of contents of drawers	3.50
5. File room maintenance and supervision, on basis of file clerk @ $2,000 salary can supervise 5,000 storage files	.40
TOTAL COST of Transferring One Active File and Its Storage for One Year	$11.11
RECURRING ANNUAL COSTS to be added each year the file is retained (computed by adding Items 1, 2 and 5 as shown above)	$ 2.86

The figures above show the basis used in arriving at the $11.11 first year cost and the $2.86 annually recurring costs involved in storing transferred records. These two figures are the basis on which the following table has been built, as indicated by the 1-file, 1-year figure of $11.11 and the 1-file, 2-year figure of $13.97 ($11.11 plus $2.86).

The costs contributing to the figures used in this study will vary widely. Costs are presented in sufficient detail to permit item-by-item adjustments to correct the figures to your own local costs.

A few known items of cost have been omitted entirely — for example, the cost of labor involved in referring to stored records; it varies so greatly that any attempt to use a figure in this analysis would be more misleading than helpful.

Retention Period in Years	No. of File Drawers To Be Transferred										
	1	10	20	30	40	50	60	70	80	90	100
1	$11 11	$111 10	$222 20	$ 333 30	$ 444 40	$ 555 50	$ 666 60	$ 777 70	$ 888 80	$ 999 90	$1111 00
2	13 97	139 70	279 40	419 10	558 80	698 50	838 20	977 90	1117 60	1257 30	1397 00
3	16 83	168 30	336 60	504 90	673 20	841 50	1009 80	1178 10	1346 40	1514 70	1683 00
4	19 69	196 90	393 80	590 70	787 60	984 50	1181 40	1378 30	1575 20	1772 10	1969 00
5	22 55	225 50	451 00	676 50	902 00	1127 50	1353 00	1578 50	1804 00	2029 50	2255 00
6	25 41	254 10	508 20	762 30	1016 40	1270 50	1524 60	1778 70	2032 80	2286 90	2541 00
7	28 27	282 70	565 40	848 10	1130 80	1413 50	1696 20	1978 90	2261 60	2544 30	2827 00
8	31 13	311 30	622 60	933 90	1245 20	1556 50	1867 80	2179 10	2490 40	2801 70	3113 00
9	33 99	339 90	679 80	1019 70	1359 60	1699 50	2039 40	2379 30	2719 20	3059 10	3399 00
10	36 85	368 50	737 00	1105 50	1474 00	1842 50	2211 00	2579 50	2948 00	3316 50	3685 00

How to Use

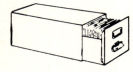

The following charts automatically extend all figures for a period of ten years, which is the normal amortization period, and compute actual annual costs depending upon the number of file drawers to be transferred annually.

If your normal annual transfer is 50 file drawers and if the retention period involved is five years in storage, you would use the 50 file drawer column and add the figures from one through five which would complete your five year retention cycle. In this five year period, each of the figures indicated would have been spent.

To make the comparison against Microfilming in this same period, it is necessary to find out what equipment amortization would be, which is indicated in the very first column at the 5 year mark, namely $885.70, and again move over to the 50 files to be transferred annually and add those five sets of figures.

FIG. 1. A method of comparing record

MICROFILM

Estimated costs of MICROFILMING records

Microfilming one active
file and storing film for
one year

1. Camera cost, $750 (Diebold Portable Camera) amortized over 10-year period $75.00

2. Reader cost, $245 amortized over 10-year period 24.50

3. Maintenance and inspection of camera and reader on an annual contract basis 75.00

4. Film storage (on basis of 10 film file drawers amortized over 10-year period plus 5½ feet of floor space at $4 per sq. ft., assuming film will be stored in general offices at a higher floor space rate than a file room) .14

> The above figures are annually recurring costs. The figures that follow are one-time charges and represent the estimated costs of filming a single file drawer at the time of transfer.

5. Film cost (magazine load, film, reduction ratio of 24 to 1) based on 3,000 individual documents per drawer. Two film magazines @ $2.50 .... 5.00

6. Copy preparation (labor @ $1.50 per hr.) 3.00

7. Filming time (labor @ $1.50 per hr.) 1.50

8. Editing, including inspection of film, making corrections, splicing, storing in boxes, indexing boxes etc. (labor at $1.50 per hr.) 3.00

TOTAL COST of Microfilming One Active File and Storage of the Film for One Year $187.14

RECURRING ANNUAL COSTS to be added each year the file is retained (computed by adding Items 1, 2, 3 and 4 above). $174.64

Variations in labor costs, condition of copy to be microfilmed and varying inspection requirements can alter the total costs considerably.

The labor costs indicated here are an average computed from our own technical laboratories and the experience of several large firms having extensive security programs involving millions of documents.

No. of File Drawers To Be Microfilmed

Retention Period in Years	1	10	20	30	40	50	60	70	80	90	100
1	$ 187.14	$113.76	$240.16	$366.56	$492.96	$619.36	$745.76	$872.16	$ 998.56	$1124.96	$1251.36
2	361.78	115.16	242.96	370.76	498.56	626.36	754.16	881.96	1009.76	1137.56	1265.36
3	536.42	116.56	245.76	374.96	504.16	633.36	762.56	891.76	1020.96	1150.16	1279.36
4	711.06	117.96	248.56	379.16	509.76	640.36	770.96	901.56	1032.16	1162.76	1293.36
5	885.70	119.36	251.36	383.36	515.36	647.36	779.36	911.36	1043.36	1175.36	1307.36
6	1060.34	120.76	254.16	387.56	520.96	654.36	787.76	921.16	1054.56	1187.96	1321.36
7	1234.98	122.16	256.96	391.76	526.56	661.36	796.16	930.96	1065.76	1200.56	1335.36
8	1409.62	123.56	259.76	395.96	532.16	668.36	804.56	940.76	1076.96	1213.16	1349.36
9	1584.26	124.96	262.56	400.16	537.76	675.36	812.96	950.56	1088.16	1225.76	1363.36
10	1758.90	126.36	265.36	404.36	543.36	682.36	821.36	960.36	1099.36	1238.36	1377.36

The Charts

A rapid calculation indicates that the actual physical transfer of the paper into steel storage files involves a cost over this period of time of $4,207.50.

Microfilming on the Diebold Portable Camera during this same period and the same quantity of records would involve an expenditure of $4,054.50.

Therefore the aforementioned transfer program would actually be more economical under a microfilm procedure than the physical handling of the files themselves.

For your ready reference the red line indicates the break-even point at which either files or microfilm are similar from a cost standpoint. Floor space variables will affect these figures somewhat. Convenience to or inaccessibility of the file storage room will also affect these figures.

retention costs. (Courtesy of Diebold, Inc.)

a management study of record retention costs based on records that can be recorded on 16mm film. The study compares the estimated costs of physically storing records and of microfilming records. Involved is the purchase of a portable camera and reader. These costs are usually amortized over a 10-year period. An estimate should also be obtained from the service company of the cost of the service alone without purchase of the camera. Although the Diebold study cannot apply precisely to every 16mm application, it does provide a good starting point. The charts indicate the break-even point at which either files or microfilm are equivalent from a cost standpoint. Because it is feasible to insert your own figures in the formula outlined, the study is included here for guidance (see Figure 1).

It is customary for microfilming cameras to record identification data of the document being photographed at the same time; such data include the document number, the date, etc. Where large numbers of items of a single size are handled such as bank checks, for example, automatic feeding mechanisms are customary which require an operator to do little more than keep the hopper filled. Such machines often combine other operations; check microfilming machines, for example, often are designed to endorse the checks they photograph. After all operations are completed upon a check, such machines stack the finished documents neatly in another hopper from which they may be removed. Generally speaking, machines that perform multiple operations are quite costly; their purchase can only be justified when the number of documents to be handled each day is quite large.

Costs for 16mm microfilm used in card or jacket form will vary according to the application. A typical example is that of a newspaper using 16mm microfilm in Filmsort jackets at a 1:17 reduction ratio for its collection of clippings. The preparation, photographing, and insertion of the film is undertaken by the service company. Using jackets 6 by $3\frac{1}{2}$ inches, approximately 50 to 90 clippings, depending on their size, can be inserted in microfilm form. In this form 1750 clippings per inch can be filed in 25 jackets as compared to an average of 80 clippings per filing inch in their original form. This is based on an 8-inch length to the average clip. The microfilm cost per clip is approximately $1\frac{1}{2}$ cents. The cost per each completed card, which holds 16mm strips, date, and classification, is

55 cents. This includes the cost of the jacket card, which is about 9 cents. Jacket card prices on the average vary from 2½ to 20 cents each or higher. Prices of aperture and jacket cards depend upon quantity and type.

35mm Microfilm

Newspapers, maps, charts, and drawings are typical of the records that are commonly filmed in 35mm microfilm. Any record that exceeds 16 inches in width but does not exceed 35 inches can be filmed on 35mm microfilm. Usually only a single image such as a newspaper page appears on a standard 35mm frame. The cost for a negative of a newspaper page photographed at a reduction of 16½ is approximately 2 cents per exposure or 16½ cents per foot, on the basis of 8 frames to a foot. This may vary slightly with the method of photographing, the number of frames to the foot, the reduction used, and the quantity photographed. The cost for a positive of the foregoing is approximately $0.0352 when the pages are photographed in large quantities or $0.06 per foot for short runs of 100 to 200 feet.

35mm film can be used in jackets when this method of self-indexing material warrants the increased cost because of the reduction of search time. The jackets can be obtained for one or more frames of 35mm microfilm. The costs of 35mm microfilm are proportionately higher than those of 16mm microfilm, but the same ratio applies to filing and storage costs of the originals before filming.

Typical Government Costs. Owing to the marked differences in accounting methods as they affect such factors as overhead, obsolescence, amortization, etc., it is not practicable to compare directly Government costs and those of private business on a dollar-for-dollar basis. Excellent specific data on how much costs are calculated in the Department of the Army are given in Army Regulations 345-218, 23 August, 1955. The labor costs of a small installation based upon Civil Service rates and classifications for 1954 are:

1	GS-5 supervisor	$1.64 per hour
1	GS-4 senior microphotographer	$1.53 per hour
4	GS-3 junior microphotographers	$1.42 per hour
2	GS-2 clerks	$1.32 per hour

"Experience in the Army Establishment in microfiling records indicates that on the average project a camera operator can photograph 1.5 [file] drawers or 27 linear inches of records per day. For each day of camera operation, an additional one-half man-day will be required for inspection and indexing of the film. Unless the file is in unusually good condition and free of wire staples, which must be removed before the papers are introduced into the camera, the services of an additional person will probably be required to prepare the papers for the camera. Total personnel requirements would there-fore amount to 2.5 persons per camera per day. At this rate 2.66 days will be required to complete the contents of one four-drawer file cabinet. These costs may be summarized as follows:

Equipment rental, 2.66 days at $1.20 per day	$3.19
Film, 6 reels at $3.125 each	18.75
Labor, records preparation, 2.66 days at $10.56 per day	28.09
Labor, camera operation, 2.66 days at $10.56 per day	28.09
Labor, film inspection, indexing, labeling, etc., 1.33 days at $10.56 per day	14.04
	$92.16

The above data presume a rotary camera. Direct costs vary widely in practice; flat-bed camera costs usually run appreciably higher because of the greater costs of hand document feeding. Costs may range from as little as $30.00 to $480.00 or more per cabinet. With a flat-bed camera, microfilming assorted sizes, labor costs range from $42.37 for 1:17 reduction to $65.88 for 1:30 reduction; materials costs range from $16.10 for 1:17 reduction to $17.44 for 1:30 reduction. These costs assume 35mm film at $6.00 per roll and equipment rental at $2.25 per work day.

Table I shows the principal items affecting costs of microfilming opera-tions. (This table and the preceding data are abstracted from Army Regula-tions 345-218, 23 August, 1955.)

Microstrip and Microtape (Opaque Microprints Produced Photographically)

Microstrip is the trade name for micro-opaque paper positive prints of 16mm and 35mm microfilm produced by Hall & McChes-ney Inc., of Syracuse, New York. The positive is produced by photographic printing from a supplied developed negative; it is sent in a convenient dispensing box ready for immediate use. The price of Microstrip is $9.50 per 100 feet of 16mm, and $12.00 per 100 feet of 35mm both net f.o.b. Syracuse, New York.

The back of the positive is treated with a plastic-type adhesive formulated for permanence and ease of use. The adhesive is not water-soluble, and the bond has extreme strength and gives flexi-bility with minimum curl. The positive is applied to card stock of

TABLE I. Principal Items Affecting Costs of Microfilming Operations

Operation	Least costly	More costly	Most costly	Typical example*
Preparation of documents	a. Checking order of containers and order of filing guides if any	a. Checking and refiling as necessary by an established system b. Checking mixed files for identification of documents to be filmed on reverse side c. Removing specified folders for immediate disposal d. Removing staples, paper clips, fasteners, and other devices	a. Collecting essential documents in sequence to an established system b. Removing specified units of material within folders for immediate disposal c. Segregating administrative and program records by predetermined categories d. Searching and transcribing data to documents prior to filming e. Repairing mutilated documents and arranging pasted attachments	Cost per M images per lin ft) using factors in "more costly" column Filing sequence checked and fasteners removed (1½ drawers—4500 images—per man-days)—$2.35
Messenger — labor service	a. Flat-bed camera (1 man per 8 cameras)	a. Rotary hand feed camera (1 man per 6 cameras)	a. Automatic feed camera (1 man per 4 cameras)	Rotary hand feed camera—21 cents

TABLE I (*Continued*)

Operation	Least costly	More costly	Most costly	Typical example*
Camera activities	a. Automatic feed camera b. Card size and uniform color	a. Rotary hand feed camera b. Letter to legal size c. Average color variations	a. Flat-bed camera b. Oversized documents c. Faded ink and variable colors d. Extracting technical requirements	Cost per M images rotary hand feed camera, letter size, average color variations, and mixture of paper stock. (4500 images per man-day)—$2.52
Inspection of developed film	a. Light box, average density test	a. Spot check of frames	a. Frame by frame	Extensive spot check (12,000) images per man-day—$1
Retakes, splicing, and mounting	a. Uniform documents b. Minimum legibility criteria c. Retakes spliced to front of film only	a. Mixed documents b. Average legibility criteria c. Average color variations d. Retakes spliced in place throughout film	a. Difficult color and ink problems b. Exacting legibility and definition criteria c. Film cut for envelope or "film-sort" assembly	Average of one retake per M @ 50 cents (withdrawal and preparation of additional documents; preparation of retake targets; refilming, reinspection, splicing, refilling of documents)
Indexing, boxing, and labeling	a. Numerical file	a. Alphabetical file	a. Subject file. b. Geographic file	Simple alphabetical file—4 cents

TABLE I (Continued)

Operation	Least costly	More costly	Most costly	Typical example*
Supervision (one supervisor per five cameras)	a. Automatic feed rotary camera	a. Hand feed rotary camera	a. Flat-bed camera / Personnel cost for example	Hand feed rotary camera—58 cents / $7.20
Film (processing included in cost of film)	a. Permanent film 16mm / b. Reduction ratios 36:1 to 24:1	a. Permanent film 16mm / b. Reduction ratios 24:1 to 17:1	a. Permanent film, 35mm / b. Reduction ratios 17:1 or less	Permanent, 16mm film at 24:1 reduction—$1.04
Equipment	a. Automatic feed and rotary camera	a. Rotary hand feed camera	a. Flat-bed feed camera	Rotary hand feed camera—24 cents
Contingencies at 5% of operating costs			Film and equipment cost for example	$1.28
				42 cents
			Total cost for example per 1000 images	$8.90

* Large number of drawers of mixed letter sized documents, presenting a microfilming problem of moderate difficulty. Cost estimates are based on 1954 levels.

any size by moistening the adhesive. The cards containing the positives can be typed or indexed before or after the Microstrip is applied. The positives come in strip form of the same width and length as the negative supplied.

The Microstrip images can be read in most readers designed for viewing opaque images. Hall & McChesney furnish a modified reader that enlarges at 16× for 35mm filmed at reductions lower than 1:20.

Microtape, the trade name of a product of the Microcard Corp. of La Crosse, Wisconsin, is similar to Microstrip in cost and in use. The chief difference between the two products is in the adhesive used. The Microtape adhesive is a pressure-sensitive tape laminated to the reverse side of the tape. The Microtape dispenser automatically removes a protective layer from the tape and cuts the strips to the desired length. When cut, the strips are merely pressed into position on the file card desired; no moistening is required.

70mm Microfilm

70mm is a recent newcomer compared to the other two sizes. Its format has not yet been standardized through the American Standards Association; in many respects it has followed the practices of the other sizes except that it is usually stored and filed as individual frames rather than in the customary 100-foot roll. ASA Standard Z38.1.3-1948* specifies the dimensions of the film proper.

The emulsions used for coating 70mm film are the same as those used for the smaller sizes. Since 70mm is twice the width of the next size, 35mm, it will accommodate drawings as large as twice the size accommodated by 35mm film. In one typical equipment there is a standard aperture which is twice as wide as the maximum image width on 35mm film; it is 2⅝ by 3½ inches and is equidistant from both edges of the film. Since the width of unperforated 70mm film is but a few thousandths of an inch greater than 2¾ inches, about 1/16 inch is allowed on each side of the film beyond the limits of the photographed image. A spacing of ⅛ inch between successive images is used. 70mm film, after developing, is frequently cut into individual frames for filing, or

---

* Reproduced in Appendix B, page 385.

it may be stored in roll form. Most 70mm cameras use an aperture of fixed height, $3\frac{1}{2}$ inches; manufacturers who follow this practice include Microtronics Division of Photostat Corp., Varifile of Photographic Products, and Microfilm Corp. When 70mm film is cut into individual frames, it is of uniform size and may be inserted in file cards or in film jackets. This operating practice differs from that in the 35mm and 16mm sizes where the height of the aperture is usually altered to meet the needs of the document being photographed; the individual frames are not of constant size, owing to their variation in height from one frame to another.

In practice, 70mm film is photographed with reductions ranging commercially from a minimum of about 4 to a maximum of about 14. For engineering drawings it is customary to use a magnification in the reader which matches very closely the reduction of the camera so that drawings so displayed are reproduced to scale. In such cases it is customary to photograph a scale on the drawing so that the scale may be checked when the microfilm positive is displayed, or when a paper enlargement is made. At present it is necessary for a user of 70mm equipment to be quite specific with regard to the tolerances in magnification that are implied by his needs.

Because of the convenience in filing individual frames, 70mm is now being more widely used than previously. Aside from the filing convenience, the New York *Times* selected 70mm because it presents an area 4 times as large as the largest 35mm frame. This makes it possible to photograph a large area of material at a low reduction; it was used for filming clipping files on a selective subject matter basis. In many cases the entire contents of a file on one individual or subject are contained on a single 70mm frame. This permits the researcher to view a large number of clippings within the single frame without adjusting the reader for scanning. The reduction used was 10, the enlargement $14\times$. Thus the projected image is approximately 40% larger than the original.

With a relatively large number of selected clippings available within a single frame as a single photographic image projected with excellent image quality with good image brightness and easy to read with a minimum of eye strain because of the excellence of the image, the increase in cost due to the use of 70mm compared with smaller sizes is almost negligible when the added convenience to the user is taken into account. In general, 70mm can be quickly justified by a marked increase in end-use convenience to the ultimate users. This is the result of the considerable preparation required for the suitable layout of the items located within the photographed frame.

This procedure of recording clipping files on 70mm film is technically practical but not inexpensive. A New England librarian who was concerned about the comparative costs of microfilm clipping files found that there was not so great a difference in cost as might be expected for the results achieved.

The costs are:

1. The reader $2200 (full frame projection). Smaller readers that project only a portion of the 70mm image range in price from approximately $360 to $470.

2. Each 70mm negative, 13½ cents; each positive, approximately 5 cents additional.

3. Labor: this factor varies with the wage scale and locality. The maximum labor cost for mounting clippings at The New York *Times* is $3224 annually. This is done by a file clerk; selection is made by supervisors.

4. Additional incidental costs; the acetate tape used in mounting, the mounting paper, and transportation charges for shipping the material to the microfilming company.

What are the results? The time required to lay out a sheet of clippings is approximately 30 minutes, depending upon the fragility or condition of the clippings. Thus an average of approximately 14 layouts can be made in one day, or a total of 70 a week, or a maximum of 3500 annually. The annual cost for negative and positive prints is $647.50. Thus approximately 98,000 columns of New York *Times* clippings can be placed on 70mm film on an annual basis at a cost of slightly over $4000. This expenditure more than pays for the cost (on an amortized basis) of maintaining the original material. Storage space is sharply reduced, filing costs are lowered, search time is lessened, reference material is always in correct order and can not be lost, and the deterioration of newspaper pulp clippings is no longer a problem.

Many other interesting uses of 70mm film are being found almost daily; one of particular interest is x-rays. Substantially all the detail of a full size x-ray plate of 14 by 17 inches can be found in a 70mm. film frame exposed by the newer x-ray cameras.* Also available is copying equipment to reduce from the large x-ray plates to 70mm and to 35mm microfilm. When it is recognized that some 3 or 4 x-rays may be added to each patient's file each year in connection with his annual health checkup alone, the importance of saving storage space by using microrecords for x-rays and other health records can hardly be overemphasized.

Engineering drawings, maps, charts, charts and clipping files are some of the current applications for 70mm film. Other applications will come into use as the flexibility and the advantages of 70mm film become more widely recognized.

105mm Microfilm and Larger Sizes

For engineering drawings and the like of large size such as are found frequently in drawings of large aircraft, ships and the like, 70mm film is often too small for convenience and a larger size, 105mm, is coming into use. It is too early as yet to present details of 105mm equipment and its operation; present indications are that it will follow the trends of the 70mm size. Reports indicate that the Microtronics Division of the Photostat Corporation will probably be one of the first to market such equipment commercially.

One interesting use of the larger sizes of microfilm that is important industrially and will become more important as time passes is the enlargement of such images directly on a sensitized coating applied to sheet aluminum and the like that is to be fabricated into an aircraft skin, for example, which developed image is used as the marking template for the performing of the mechanical operations such as drilling and forming, to be subsequently performed on the sheet metal. In this application as in engineering drawings made to scale, the dimensional accuracy of the enlargement is very important in the manufacturing process, and special pains are taken to assure that the photographic reproduction process does not introduce scale errors or dimensional inaccuracies that might adversely affect the finished product. This process is especially valuable where the number of items to be manufactured is relatively small and where the amount of tooling that is justified is likewise small. It is particularly valuable when mock-ups or per-

---

* One such camera is manufactured by Fairchild Camera and Instrument Corp., Roberts Lane, Syosset, New York.

formance samples are to be made, as it makes possible a marked reduction in manufacturing time and cost.

To some extent film in roll form wider than 70mm which is subsequently cut into individual frames has been marketed in Paris for a number of years as a form of microfiche but has not had wide use. Present indications are that the American attempt to exploit the 105mm size will be successful, as there is a real need for this size now and it is not entirely unexpected that a need will develop for still wider films as each new large width begins to acquire commercial acceptance. It should not be entirely unexpected to find that sizes up to the standard widths of aerial mapping films will be used in the future; much apparatus that is already available for aerial mapping purposes may be adapted to industrial microfilm uses.

Film Strips

Film strips of 35mm width are approximately 210mm (8¼ in.) in length; this is the common length used in Europe. Such a strip contains 10 pages as microframes with accession numbers or other type of micro-index. The cost of negatives and positives should be approximately the same as for other 35mm film. It will vary according to the quantity filmed and the reduction. Additional costs for the pockets or containers that hold from 10 to 100 strips range from 70 to approximately 360 francs.* Such film strips customarily use 35mm film with perforations.

Sheet Films (Microfiches)

Sheet film has been used principally in Europe. In the United States the Standard Register Company and The Griscombe Company are among those developing sheet film equipment.

A typical example of costs for sheet film or microfiches are those of Les Appareils Controleurs, Paris, France. In the 75 by 125mm (3 by 5 inch) size, it is possible to mount 2 to 8 horizontal lines of microphotos or views of 3 to 16 views per line, which represents a minimum of 6 views and a maximum of 128 views per microfiche. Through a combination of this number of pictures, it is possible to produce 98 different formats of microphotos. The

---

* The present exchange rate is 350 francs (F) per $1 U.S.

title of the microfiche is produced photographically.

The sheet film negative in this size is approximately 175 francs per view. Therefore, the picture of one proof comprising 30 views will cost approximately 245 francs. Reprints on positive transparent microfiche or on opaque microfiche cost 92 francs each for 1 to 4 proofs, 75 francs each for 5 to 25 proofs, and 60 francs each for more than 25 proofs.

The positive or negative microfiche can be read on American Microcard or microprint readers by backing the transparent film with white opaque paper. Special readers are available for sheet film; they are not generally available in the United States.

Microcards (Opaque Microprints Produced Photographically)

Microcards are often selected for a microrecording program when a minimum of 15 copies is required. According to the "Manual on Document Reproduction and Selection" of the International Federation for Documentation, Boni, founder of the Readex Microprint Corp., divides publishing projects of microfilm, Microcards, and Readex Microprint "into three groups determined by the size of the editions that are to be marketed as follows:

(1) from 1 to 14 copies;

(2) 15 to 49 copies;

(3) 50 copies or over.

This distinction is made because Microcard offers its product for minimum editions of 15 copies. Therefore, for editions of from 1 to 14 copies, there is only one choice; microfilm has no competitor. Where editions of from 14 to 49 copies are desired, one must weigh the relative merits and costs of Microcard and microfilm. Readex Microprint enters into the third field, where 50 or more copies will be called for. Here one must consider all three processes."

Fremont Rider, the promoter of the Microcard, sums up its advantages as follows:*

And Microcards, as they developed in my mind, were simply an attempt to devise a better form of microtext than microfilm had been, to change it

---

* "The Challenge of Microphotography," Fremont Rider, Florida State University Studies, Number 12, *Challenges to Librarianship*, pp. 63-64, Florida State University, Tallahassee, 1953.

in ways that seemed to make it more directly responsive to the practical needs of the Library.

How ''more responsive''?

Well, first of all, Microcards are a microtext printed on paper, and sensitized photographic paper is much cheaper than sensitized photographic film. As for binding, Microcards, like microfilm, eliminate it entirely as a cost. And on storage they save from 92% to 96%, where microfilm saves from 75% to 90%. Finally, because Microcards are provided with a complete, and completely standardized, catalog entry, they save their purchasers from 80% to 100% on cataloging cost.

But Microcards are also "more responsive" than microfilm in their physical form. Being flat and tough they withstand handling abuse better than reels of film do; being of standard library catalog card size, they are more quickly taken in and out of storage, and more easily inserted in, and taken out of, reading machines. Also they are more easily carried in the pocket and sent through the mails.

But this comparison by no means implies that I believe that microfilm is entirely out-moded or that I think that Microcards should, or will, wholly take its place. Quite the contrary. As a matter of fact, for the last two years most of my speaking and writing has been devoted to furthering the idea that a correlation of all of the various forms of microtext into one integrated whole is both possible, and from a library standpoint extremely desirable.

A typical application of microcards is found in the Color Control Department of the Eastman Kodak Company at Rochester, New York. They found that such cards provided the most practical means of making the greatest amount of information available to the greatest number of individuals within the department who need it. "The complexities of manufacture and the control of quality of color photographic materials make it a prime necessity that a staff man have immediately available all the information that is useful for his particular work."* When source data are available in only a single copy in its original size, someone else may be using the copy, and the item may arrive weeks and even months later at a particular user's desk because others are also interested in the document. When a valuable reference is actually in hand, there is the problem of how to retain the data it contains. Much more can be done than merely having volumes of valuable information on library shelves and in files; to be of maximum value the information must be readily accessible to all who need it, whenever they need it, and at a cost that is realistic for its end use. Most of the

* "Microcards and Microfilm for a Central Reference File," by J. W. Kuipers, Ind. Eng. Chem, Vol. 42, pp. 463-467 (August 1950).

data referred to are in the form of technical papers of such size that a complete paper may be accommodated on a single card.

When data are to be circulated among a number of persons, as in a large group like the Color Control Department of the Eastman Kodak Company, a price of some 15 cents per card can be realized; 250 pages on 5 microcards can be duplicated in an edition of 100 copies for about $60 by commercial microcard makers. For the person who may need a small quantity of specific information from the microcards, an ordinary reading glass with somewhat higher magnification than usual (about 10×) makes it possible to read the portions of interest without leaving his desk. When a user must run through a quantity of reference material word by word, a microcard reader is a "must" to avoid undue eyestrain and fatigue.

The reduction ratio commonly used for microcards is about 1:20, and approximately 36 to 48 pages of copy (6 by 9 or 8½ by 11 inches) can be placed on a standard microcard. As many as 100 pages can be placed on one card, depending upon the size of the original copy. Thus it is feasible to place a book of average size on 8 microcards. If a 15-copy edition were processed, the microcards would cost about 20 cents each. In a 200-copy edition, the cost might be as little as 8 cents. An average of these two extremes would be approximately 14 cents per card. Thus the average cost of an average size 8-card book in its microcard form would be $1.15. Additional average cost to cover recataloguing and storage would give an over-all cost of $1.32 for a volume of average size in microcard form.

Minicards * (Transparency Microtext Produced Photographically)

The Kodak Minicard System represents a significant step forward in recording more data per square inch and in speeding up the "reading out" of the data so recorded. Its operating characteristics show the impact of recent developments in information theory relative to data compression and mechanical search toward

---

* Kodak Minicard System, Eastman Kodak Company, Rochester 4, N. Y. (Recently mutual agreements were signed by Magnavox and Eastman giving to each other world rights to manufacture, use, lease, or sell the Minicard System or units thereof.)

the end result of better utilization of the available media, which is explained in detail in Chapter IX.

The basic unit is the Minicard itself, "a piece of photographic film 32 by 16mm (1¼ by ⅝ inches). Near one end is a slot that permits the card to be handled by means of a metal "stick." A "stick" handles up to 2000 Minicards.

The Minicard carries digital information in the form of clear or opaque dots; in addition it may carry images of documents. The proportion of the card area devoted to digital information and to document images depends upon the specific application; the maximum number of image areas to be accommodated is 12 arranged in a 6 by 2 format with each recorded from a document of 8½ by 14 inches maximum size. When the card carries no graphic images, the maximum amount of digital information it can carry amounts to 70 columns of 42 bits each or a total of 2940 bits.

For making Minicards the camera performs two functions:
(1) it photographs the code pattern; and,
(2) it photographs the document images on photographic film.
After processing, the film is cut into separate Minicards.

The reduction ratio at which the Minicard system is operated is 1:60, a value appreciably higher than even the best of other commercial systems operated today with an equal number of copy generations. It is claimed that acceptable prints can be made from 6th generation Minicard duplicates. A much lower contrast is maintained than is usually the case for photographic copying purposes; this makes possible satisfactory reproduction of both line and continuous tone copy throughout. These objectives are accomplished by the nature of the processing and by the characteristics of the sensitized film used.

The standard Minicard magazine handles the full capacity of a Minicard stick—2000 Minicards. A 100 magazine file unit occupies a volume of about one cubic foot. Two million Minicards are roughly equivalent to 1000 file cabinets of documentary material. Ten million Minicards could be placed conveniently in a floor area of 10 by 10 feet; the volume required would be allocated to 5 cabinets of 15 by 30 by 50 inches each.

Since one of the important characteristics of the Minicard system is its capability of search, sorting information can be added during the process of duplicating a Minicard. When the original facsimile (Master) Minicard is first made, it will contain only initial coding information; the presence of the text on the Minicard will make it possible to determine additional coding information from time to time. Such additional coding information may be added during the duplication of a Minicard.

Many of the details of the Minicard system are still under study; this is true especially of the specialized sorting and classifying equipment associated with its coding aspects. The photographic aspects with regard to sensitized materials and to processing methods appear to be substantially complete. Although it is still too early to mention prices, the Minicard development is one that deserves careful watching from this point on. Other important details of the Minicard such as coding are given in Chapter IX.

Readex Microprint (Opaque Microtext Produced by Offset or Mechanical Means)

Microprint is selected when there is a basic demand for at least 50 copies of the original record. Cost per card then averages approximately 20 cents. The Readex Microprint Corp. states that the advantages of Readex Microprint* are:

First, it is economical in cost. Since it is printed and not merely another method of photographic reproduction, its cost is approximately one half that of microfilm, and from one-third to one-fifth that of other forms of micro-reproduction.

Second, since each 6 by 9 Microprint card contains 100 pages of the original text, a Microprint edition takes up about 3% of the space needed for the original work and there is therefore a tremendous saving of space on library shelves.

Third, it is permanent in use as well as in storage since the Microprint image is formed by ink on paper and is protected in use by a glass covered tray.

Fourth, since the cards are stiff enough to handle with ease, it is simple to locate any specific card in its container, slip it into the reader, and refile it when finished. Each card has a caption which can be read with the naked eye, identifying contents and specific pages thereon. The decimal arrangement of the pages makes it easy to bring rapidly any desired page onto the screen.

Fifth, since the individual cards are kept in cloth-covered cardboard boxes, individually and clearly labeled, in shape and size similar to royal octavo volume (6½ by 10 inches) these boxes may be filed as books and shelved with them.

---

* Readex Microprint is a proprietary product of the Readex Microprint Corp., New York, N. Y.

Microlex * (Opaque Microtext Produced by Photographic Means)

Microlex may be selected when the edition to be published runs from 100 to several thousand. A 400-page book is recorded on two faces of a single card 6½ by 8½ inches; a 100-volume set of books is shelved in the space needed for only four of the original volumes.

According to the Microlex Corp., the material to be reproduced is photographed, page by page by a step-and-repeat camera on negative sheet film of 6½ by 8½ inches; the horizontal dimension of the page runs the long way on the negative and card. From each such negative photographic prints are made in the number required. The prints are then laminated back to back, so that the final product is a series of 6½ by 8½ inch cards each containing 400 consecutive pages of the original material, 200 pages per card side, with the necessary identification such as volume numbers and page range printed in large readable type at the head of each card.

In May 1954 the Microlex Corp. announced that it had completed deliveries to a law publisher of a micro-opaque edition of over 400 volumes of legal reference works.

Uses of Opaque Microtext. Readex Microprint, Minicards, Microcards and Microlex are employed where multiple copies of the original are desired. However, this does not preclude employing them if only a single copy is desired. In certain instances one of the basic advantages of one of these forms of microrecording might be of such importance that it would warrant the additional cost of producing a single edition of the original record in the chosen forms. In certain instances size might be a factor and, in still others, permanency.

EVALUATION OF SAVINGS EFFECTED BY A MICRORECORDING PROGRAM

The savings in a microrecording program can be estimated on:

1. The reduction in storage space required for original materials that are microrecorded.
2. The feasibility of lowering insurance rates through the duplication of records.
3. The reduction of loss due to litigation by assuring that

---

* The Microlex Corp., 1 Graves St., Rochester 14, N. Y.

microfilmed copies or other types of microrecorded copies of all records are available in correct order for periods required by law.

4. The added protection to a firm or organization of having microrecorded records dispersed in safe storage in different geographical locations as a disaster control measure.

5. The low cost (as compared to the same originals) of reproducing multiple copies of documents in microrecorded form.

6. The facility with which microtext can be used.

* * *

In practice, a single copy of an original document, a letter, for example, is by no means equivalent to the simultaneous availability of multiple copies to all who need them. Such simultaneous distribution of information can be effected economically only in microrecorded form. It is a common occurrence that several persons require specific information from a particular source document.

It is impractical to attempt to "share" a single document or a limited number of document copies. Few large industrial organizations can afford a wasteful, inefficient, time-consuming, and ineffective data communication and distribution system. The system must be the servant of the user if it is to justify its existence.

Bibliography

Edgar L. Erickson. "Microprint: A Revolution in Printing," *Journal of Documentation*, Sept. 1951.

Edward N. Jenks. "Micro-Editions of Newspapers: A Survey of Developments." *Journalism Quarterly*, Fall 1950.

Albert Boni. "Microprint." *American Documentation*, Aug. 1951, p. 150.

Fremont Rider. "The Possible Correlation of All Forms of Microtext." *American Documentation*, Aug. 1951, p. 152.

Henry M. Silver. "The Publication of Original Research Materials." *American Documentation*, Jan. 1950, p. 13.

Fremont Rider. "Archival Material on Microrecords." *American Documentation*, Jan. 1950, p. 42.

Fremont Rider. "Microrecords vs. the Cost of Book Storage." *American Documentation*, Aug. 1950, p. 39.

Eugene B. Power. "The Use of High Reduction Microfilm for Libraries." *American Documentation*, Aug. 1950, p. 139.

R. W. Batchelder. "The Scope and Value of the Microcard." *Special Libraries*, May-June 1952, p. 157.

Fremont Rider. "Warehouse or Microcard." *Library J.*, Part 1, p. 832, May 15, 1950; Part 2, p. 927, June 1, 1950.

The Microcard Bulletin, No. 2, Sept. 1948. Issued by The Microcard Foundation, c/o University of Wisconsin Press, Madison 2, Wisc.

Manual on Document Reproduction and Selection. In 2 parts. International Federation for Documentation, The Hague, Netherlands, 1953. $7.10.

Thompson Webb, Jr. "Microcards and Their Uses in Scholarly Publishing." *Publishers Weekly*, Vol. 165, No. 1, Bibliography pp. 67-68, 70, 72 (Jan. 2, 1954).

Eugene B. Power. "The Use of Sheet Film for Newspaper Clippings." *Special Libraries*, Vol. 45, No. 3, pp. 111-114 (March 1954).

George Cameron. "Applications of 70mm. Film," paper delivered before National Microfilm Association, 1951.

Eugene B. Power. "Factors Influencing the Cost of Microfilm." Rapp. 17th Conf. F.I.D., Berne, 1947, Vol. 1, pp. 79-83.

Atherton Seidell. "The Cost of Microfilm Copying in Libraries." *J. Doc. Repr.*, Vol. 4, 1941, pp. 164-167.

Chester M. Lewis. "Libraries Find Microfilm Answer for Clipping Files." *Editor & Publisher*, May 1, 1954, pp. 11-53.

Charles A. Brown, III. "16mm. Jacket System Uses Portable Reader." *Editor & Publisher*, May 1, 1954, p. 52.

Clapp, Henshaw, and Holmes. "Are Your Microfilms Deteriorating Acceptably?" *Library J.*, pp. 589-595, March 15, 1955.

From *Proceedings of the National Microfilm Association*,* second annual Meeting, New York, March 19-20, 1953:
  Lewis Orgel. "A Program for Microfilming Municipal Records," pp. 7-13.
  R. H. Darling. "The Use of 70mm. Microfilm in Safeguarding Engineering Drawings," pp. 34-43.

From *Proceedings of the National Microfilm Association*,† third annual meeting, 1954:
  E. Scott Finley. "Industrial Microfilming Procedures," pp. 1-10.
  W. H. Bowerman. "Microprint Documents in Business and Industry," pp. 29-46.
  Earl P. Bassett. "Individualizing Microfilm," pp. 68-78.

Tyler, Myers, and Kuipers. "The Application of the Kodak Minicard System to Problems of Documentation." *Amer. Documentation*, Vol. 6, No. 1, pp. 18-30 (Jan. 1955).

David A. Rhydwen, Chief Librarian, Toronto *Globe & Mail*. "Microfilming of Newspaper Clippings." Address June 14, 1955.

---

* Available from National Microfilm Association, 19 Lafayette Ave., Hingham, Mass. Approx. $2.00 per copy.

† Available from National Microfilm Association. $3.00 per copy.

Don Wharton. ''Microfilm Holds the World's Records.'' *Reader's Digest*, Aug. 1955, pp. 175-178.

''Microfilming Requirements for Engineering Drawings and Associated Data.'' Military Specifications, MIL-M-4875 (USAF).

R. H. Carruthers. ''A Simple Method for Figuring Microfilm Footage on a Slide Rule.'' *Amer. Documentation*, Vol. 7, No. 1, pp. 44-45 (Jan. 1956).

THE MICRORECORDING PROCESS. THE FILM.
SPECIALIZED FORMS OF MICROCOPYING

HISTORY

It is usually surprising to persons active in present-day microfilming to learn that microfilm was used successfully during the Franco-Prussian War. René-Prudent-Patrice Dagron is credited with having used microfilm during the siege of Paris with something like 1000 telegrams recorded in such small form on a film 2 inches wide that the small roll could be carried from Tours or Bordeaux to Paris in a capsule attached to the leg of a carrier pigeon. An etching* of the time shows that the telegrams were projected upon a screen where their contents were read by the persons to whom they were addressed. The reports seem to indicate that the process used was considerably more reliable than the pigeons, even though the pigeons arrived at their destinations with even greater frequency than might be expected. By the end of that short war, the service organized by Dagron had reproduced some 2½ million official and private messages.

Numerous efforts were made after 1870 to develop the process; description of some of the more significant ones may be found by consulting the publications listed in the bibliography at the end of this chapter.

One of the more recent significant steps was the establishment of the *Journal of Documentary Reproduction*,† first issued by the American Library Association in 1938. By the time the Normandy

---

* "Multiple usages du microfilmage en France," by Jacques Boyer. **Technique** (Montreal), Sept. 1951, pp. 471-474.

† This ceased publication in 1942. The *Journal of Documentation*, published by ASLIB, 1945 to date; *American Documentation*, 1950 to date; and *National Micro-News*, of the National Microfilm Association, are also publications of interest.

beachhead was established during the latter part of World War II,
V-Mail, started as a war measure, was so well established that more
than 200 million V-Mail letters had been sent from England to the
United States. The use of V-Mail reduced the weight of mail to
be transported from 2700 to 31 tons. In V-Mail operations, the
original letter was microfilmed, and the microfilm shipped. Upon
arrival, the microfilm was enlarged to original size as a paper print.
The long part of the journey between sender and receiver of the
letter—over the ocean—was taken only by the microfilm.

GENERAL NATURE OF THE PROCESS

Photographing at a Reduction

The initial step in the microrecording process is photographing
the document at a reduction; this is done on microfilm or sheet
film. By definition in American Standard ASA Z38.7.8-1947,*
"Microfilm shall mean a transparent flexible material carrying
photographs for optical, but not cinematographic projection or
viewing."

Figure 1 shows typical microfilming equipment. Such equipment for photographing original facsimile records includes:

(1) a document support for holding the document to be
photographed in a suitable position with reference to the
camera;

(2) a stand for mechanically supporting the camera;

(3) lights to provide the illumination necessary for the exposure of the film;

(4) a photographing camera or cameras (some manufacturers
furnish two cameras so that duplicate films may be exposed
simultaneously);

(5) stand and camera adjustments to permit accurate alignment of the document with respect to the camera, and to
permit accurate adjustments for focus and exposure.
(Cameras are discussed in detail in Chapter V.)

Once the document has been photographed, the film is developed to provide a visible image from the latent image produced
by the exposure. The image on the original facsimile microfilm is
a negative similar in appearance to a Brownie negative.

---

* Reproduced in Appendix B, pages 369 and 370.

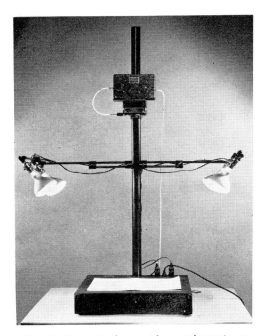

FIG. 1. Typical microcopying equipment, consisting of film magazine, camera, illuminating lamps, and document support. Adjustments required: height of camera from document; focus of lens; shutter time; intensity of illuminating lamps. (The aperture of lens diaphragm is fixed in some designs at the opening providing maximum resolving power.) Equipment is operated in the dark except for illuminating lamps. (Courtesy Graflex Corp.)

Equipment is needed to make copies of the document in the required form once the microfilm is available. Since the reduction at which the original is photographed is such that the image cannot be read with the unaided eye, enlargement of the image must occur. (See Chapter VII.)

Printing

In the simplest case, visible display of the document, a microfilm reader is required to view the enlargement of the image.

Although it is possible to place the original microfilm facsimile negative in the reader, the image will appear white against a black background rather than black against a white background, just as in a Brownie picture negative. A positive print is used in a reader; this is a photographic copy made from the microfilm negative by contact printing. In the print, the blacks of the original object appear as blacks in the print image; the tonal scale may be said to be "right side up" in a print.

Fig. 2. Contact printer (strip) (courtesy of Ilford). The negative bearing the image is placed over the illuminated aperture with the base of the negative facing the lamp (the emulsion up). The raw stock positive is placed directly over the negative, with its emulsion facing the lamp and in contact with the negative emulsion (with the base of the positive up). The raw stock is exposed with a suitable intensity for a suitable time interval. Adjustments required: rheostat for lamp brightness; timing switch.

Figure 2 shows a contact printer for printing a microfilm positive from a microfilm negative. A contact print is customarily made on print film of the same width as the microfilm negative; after positive raw film is so printed, it must be developed.

Readers

The optical arrangement of a microfilm reader is similar in principle to that of a slide projector. There is a light source, a lamp, which illuminates an aperture within which the micro-image being projected is located. A projection objective lens projects the image within the aperture to the screen where it is viewed by the observer. There are two types of screens: a reflective opaque screen viewed in the same manner as the reflective opaque screen used with a slide projector, or a translucent screen similar to a ground glass screen (the image is transmitted through the screen) used in a table slide viewer.

Figure 3 is a reader with a reflective opaque screen that presents the image of a transparency upon its screen. (See Chapter VIII for a detailed discussion of readers.) A reader with a transmissive screen would merely put a mirror in the light path just below the lens, projecting the image on a ground glass screen (or equivalent) that is viewed from the side opposite that on which the image is projeced.

Theoretically it is possible to place photosensitive print paper on top of the reflective opaque screen in Figure 3 with its emulsion facing the light source in the reader for the purpose of exposing that paper so that, after development, the paper will be an enlargement. Theoretically it is also possible to place photosensitive paper with the emulsion side face down on the translucent screen, as in Figure 2, to accomplish the same purpose. With good equipment, suitable exposure and processing of suitable paper, and careful handling there is little reason why the quality of such enlargements should not be satisfactory in practice for work copies, if not for copies of better quality. When conventional photographic paper is used, the microfilm negative is used in the reader; when direct positive paper is used, the microfilm print from the microfilm negative is used in the reader. ("Reversal" papers are also available.)

As mentioned above, a document may be displayed from an opaque print similar to a paper print copied from a "Brownie" negative. One widely used form of micro-opaque of this kind is the Microcard. On its photographically sensitive side such a card will accommodate up to 60 pages of documentary material 8½ by 11 inches in size at a reduction of about 1:20, and on its reverse side it contains the customary library and index identification informa-

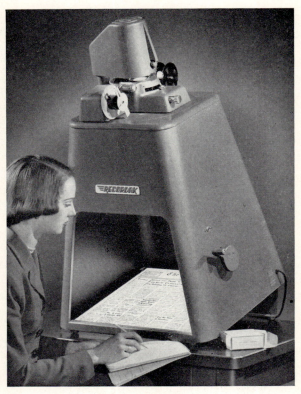

Fig. 3. A reader with a reflective opaque screen, consisting of lamp; condenser lens; rotating prism to rotate image as and if required; film spools; lens; housing to restrict the entry of ambient illumination from the room; projected image on reflective screen. (Kodagraph film reader, Recordak Model MPE, courtesy Eastman Kodak Co.)

tion—all on a card about 3 x 5 inches. Another form of micro-opaque is Readex Microprint; in this form 100 pages 6 by 9 inches in size are on each of two sides of a card roughly 6 by 9 inches in size. (See Chapters VI and IX.)

In principle the optical arrangement of a reader for micro-opaques is quite similar to that of conventional opaque projectors except that there is additional magnification because the image is small. Here again it is theoretically possible to utilize either a reflective screen or a translucent screen. In practice, the reflective screen has been used commercially almost to the exclusion of the translucent screen; the light efficiency of the latter has been poor. Recent advances indicate a significant shift in trend.

Enlargers

A generalized description of microrecording equipment would not be complete without mention of enlargers. Functionally enlargers are like readers. There are two kinds of enlarging equipment: those which make single exposure enlargements upon cut paper that is photosensitive or upon a roll of such paper, and those which operate as continuous flow enlargers making continuous flow enlargements upon a roll of steadily moving photosensitive paper. Within the latter group there are two sub-groups: equipment in which both the roll of microfilm negative and the large roll of photosensitive paper move steadily past the optical system of the enlarger, and equipment in which both the microfilm negative and the large roll of photosensitive paper move with intermittent motion past the optical system of the enlarger in a manner similar to that of a motion picture camera.

The photosensitive paper may have any conventional surface from glossy to dull matte, and it may have any contrast commercially available; it may be conventional or it may produce a direct positive. The choice of paper grade and sensitometric characteristics used (which affect the contrast of the final image), as well as the process used, depends upon the end use of the copy to be furnished. Enlargements may be furnished in any needed size; an enlargement of a birth certificate, for example, might be furnished at one-third original size so that it might be carried in a wallet, ordinary letters at normal size, and newspaper enlargements at as much as $1\frac{1}{2}$ times normal size to make the text easier to read.

If a transparency copy of the desired document is required, it too can be made with a suitable enlarger upon sheet film. Since this form is not called for frequently, the necessary raw film holders may not be available for the enlarger in use. Such a transparency may be desired so that multiple paper copies may be made from it by some process such as Ozalid and other direct positive materials and methods. (See Chapter VII for details of enlarging.)

THE ORIGINAL MICRORECORD

Film Sizes and Forms

The original microrecord is recorded upon microfilm or upon sheet film. Microfilm is currently manufactured in three common widths; 16mm (0.6 inch approximately), 35mm (1.3 inches approximately), and 70mm (2.8 inches approximately). (25.4 millimeters = 1 inch.) Films of larger widths are under consideration. The length of the original roll customarily depends upon how many documents are recorded at a particular time. Should the number be large, the customary maximum length of the film is 100 feet regardless of the film width. This roll length has been standardized nationally through the American Standards Association. Most commercially available microfilm storage cabinets have been designed specifically for this roll length.

Microfilm in any of the three standard sizes may be perforated along both edges or along only one edge, or it may have no perforations (sprocket holes). Unperforated film can not be used in equipment designed for perforated film; if run in such equipment, the film will be ruined by the sprockets of the equipment. Although perforated film may be threaded in equipment designed for unperforated film, a significantly large part of the photographed image will be lost because part of the image in the microfilm camera would appear at the perforations. Most American microfilm equipment in commercial service uses unperforated film, because, in all three sizes, the percentage of the useful area lost as a result of perforations is so great that perforated film is considered uneconomic in the United States. Unless there are very special reasons, films perforated along a single edge should be avoided entirely, as very little equipment is made for it; such film is not ordinarily available as a regular item of commerce except on special order. If the equipment available is designed for film perforated along both edges, only film perforated along both edges should be used. Orders for such film must be specific, because most microfilm is furnished without perforations unless otherwise specified.

Some of the earlier experimental and commercial microfilm equipment used motion picture film because it was widely available at the time; this occurred before film manufacturers made special emulsions for microfilm purposes. Special microfilm emulsions as furnished by film manufacturers began to appear commercially soon after fine-grain film was first introduced, in about 1935, for motion pictures. Motion picture film used for microfilm purposes, called "silent film," comes in the same widths as microfilm. The greatest percentage increase in useful film area due to use of the area otherwise assigned to sprocket holes occurs in the narrowest film, the 16mm.

Some still cameras and the like, such as 35mm miniature still cameras, have been adapted by their makers by minor changes in design for what is termed in commercial advertising "microfilm recording." Most of the changes are intended to reduce the cost of manufacture of the camera and therefore its selling price, eliminating expensive construction features essential for still camera use but not essential for microfilm use. To keep design changes to a minimum and to make as many parts as possible interchangeable with still cameras, such equipment usually retains the sprocket-driven film transport mechanism of the still camera and therefore requires perforated film. Despite all other advantages, such equipment suffers the following disadvantages:

1. The space reduction factor at which the equipment can be operated effectively is often less than 10, a value considered the minimum economic value practicable for average microfilming purposes.

2. Since most microfilm raw stock does not have perforations, the procurement of such microfilm raw stock is usually more difficult. (Perforated film for microfilming is often handled only as a special order.)

3. Since most microfilm is unperforated, copying costs whether for contact microfilm prints or for paper enlargements or other copies are often more costly than such copies made from conventional microfilm. (Unperforated film is preferred.)

Since microfilming has not become an important factor in the economy of Europe, European microfilm equipment is more likely to use sprocket-hole perforated film than not, especially when equipment is made in the same factories for motion picture and still camera markets.

The film width chosen for the original facsimile microfilm negative depends to a great extent upon the size and nature of the documents to be recorded. A number of cameras will accommodate film rolls considerably longer than 100 feet; the customary maximum is about 400 feet. Such cameras are usually furnished with some form of cutter as part of the camera assembly to permit cutting off the exposed portion of the film roll so that it may be developed without need to wait for the exposure of the remainder of the roll. In any event, the roll length is usually limited to a maximum of 100 feet.

Some microfilm cameras are made only for the 16mm film width. Others are made for the 35mm film width; by changing a few parts supplied by the manufacturer, some cameras may be converted to the 16mm size. Still others are made for the 70mm width; again, by changing a few parts, certain of these may be converted to the 35mm width. Where such parts substitutions can be made, they are ordinarily simple to accomplish and rarely require tools. Generally speaking, if a camera is convertible to another size, it is more costly than a camera of equal quality that is not convertible. In practice the convertible feature is not very advantageous; microfilm camera equipment is most economic in only a single specific size. The convertible feature may be advantageous where there is a wide variety of sizes among the documents to be microfilmed; but even in such a case there may well be a better solution to the microfilming problem than size convertibility.

Most microfilming camera equipment is equipped with counters to show how many exposures were made and how much film remains in the raw stock magazine. Many of these indicators, which are often Veeder counters or the equivalent, are capable of being reset automatically every time a new roll of raw film is placed in the feed magazine and/or a roll of film is removed from the takeup magazine holding the exposed film. Some microfilming equipment provides indexing and accessory recording wheels to record specific indexing and cataloging information; such indexes are usually photographed simultaneously with the document and conveniently along the edge of the film or under the image of interest. The features required depend upon the needs of the specific installation; a wide variety of equipment is manufactured that permits much freedom of choice among products of different manufacturers for an intended purpose.

Recording Formats and Sizes

In general, a reasonable rule-of-thumb states that the maximum practical width of a document measured in inches is about equal to the film width in millimeters. Thus a reasonable maximum document width for 16mm film is 16 inches; for 35mm film, 35 inches; and for 70mm film, 70 inches. This rule presumes a two-generation process (a microfilm facsimile original negative and an end-use copy made directly from it)* with negative and print made with good commercial equipment, materials, and techniques of operation and materials use as would be accomplished when *all* elements of the production operation are under good engineering supervision and control. Microfilming of ordinary commercial quality such as that provided by well-run average organizations might require up to twice that film width: 1 inch of document per 2 millimeters of film width. The extent to which actual microfilming approaches the rule-of-thumb limit may be considered a measure of the accuracy of the control of quality of the microfilming process with present-day materials, equipment, and methods. In general, it may be said that many microrecording operations fail to a significant extent, and occasionally to a major extent, to utilize the major portion of the quality potential of the best light-sensitive photographic materials currently available.

The American Standard Practice for Microfilms, ASA Z38.7.8-1947, specifies that microfilms shall be made only on safety (slow-burning) stock (regardless of width) as defined in ASA Z38.3.1-1943,† and that microfilms intended for permanent preservation should be made in accordance with ASA Z38.3.2-1945.† It further specifies that 35mm raw stock shall conform in width and perforations to ASA Z22.36-1947 ‡ and that 16mm raw stock shall conform to ASA Z22.12-1947 and ASA Z22.5-1947.‡ In the dimensions shown on the last three standards, an additional tolerance of 0.2 to 1.0 percent may be added at the time the film is first removed from its

---

* If four generations occurred between the original facsimile microfilm negative and the end-use copy, the upper limit might be 1 inch of document width per 2 millimeters of film width, or other suitably larger value, because of the additional image quality losses in the added stages of the copying process.

† Reproduced in Appendix B, pages 371 to 373 and 374 to 380.

‡ See Appendix B, pages 381 to 384, for revisions of these standards.

original container. In all cases the film thickness shall be within
the range 0.11 to 0.17mm (0.0045 to 0.0065 inch).

The width of the image shall not exceed the following values:

Kind of film	16mm	35mm
Perforated along both edges	10.4mm(0.410 in.)	24.0mm (0.945 in.)
Perforated along one edge	12.7mm(0.500 in.)	28.6mm (1.126 in.)
Unperforated film	15.0mm(0.590 in.)	31.75mm(1.250 in.)

The format for 70mm film has not been standardized as yet through
the American Standards Association; the dimensions of 70mm film
were standardized some time ago in ASA Z38.1.3-1948, "Dimensions for 70 Millimeter Perforated (and unperforated) Film." Like
other important standards, it will be found in Appendix B,
page 385.

The applications of 16mm, 35mm, 70mm and other sizes have
been given in Chapter III in connection with a discussion of their
costs.

Reels for Microfilm (Standards)

16mm and 35mm microfilms that are 25 feet (7.6 meters) long
or longer are wound on standard reels as specified in American
Standard for Reels for Processed Microfilm, ASA Z38.7.17-1946.*
The customary size is 100 feet for all three widths; a 50-foot reel
has also been standardized for 16mm film. The standard for 70mm
is implicit, as Section 4.2 states, "If reels of other capacities are
required, the dimensions of the first three sections of this standard
shall be met. In no case shall the outside diameter exceed that
specified for 100 foot reels."

Because of improvements in film base that have come about
recently, it is expected that the overall thickness of film for motion
picture purposes will be reduced from 6 to 4 one-thousandths inch.
It seems probable that thinner film base will be marketed for microfilm uses soon after it has been adopted for motion pictures. When
this has occurred, reels which now hold 100 feet of film will then
hold 135 feet; 50-foot reels will hold 68 feet.

How Microfilm Is Wound on Reels. Section 2.3 of American

---

* Reproduced in Appendix B, page 386.

Standard Practice for Microfilms, (ASA Z38.7.8-1947) states, "Processed microfilm prints are wound with the emulsion out for negatives and with emulsion in for positives. If the supply reel of processed film has a round spindle hole, the film should unwind downward from the right-hand side when the round hole is toward the observer." An illustration showing how this is determined is shown in Standard ASA Z38.7.8-1947.

THE FILM

Since microrecording is only as practical as the ability of the light-sensitive materials to record fine detail, all microrecording emulsions are fine-grain. Fine-grain emulsions are emulsions that have resolving power ratings of 90 lines per millimeter or greater. Resolving power is a measure of the ability of an emulsion to record fine detail distinguishably; additional data will be found later in this chapter.

Like motion picture film, microfilm consists of a mechanical support called the film base and a photosensitive gelatin-silver halide coating called the emulsion. All microfilm base materials are of the safety type in accordance with American Standard ASA Z38.3.1-1943 and are considered no more combustible than an equal volume of paper. Base materials used for microfilm must meet the requirements for permanent records specified in Section 2.1 of American Standard ASA Z38.3.2-1945: "Permanent record film is photographic material so composed and treated that the image and support shall have maximum keeping quality under ordinary room storage conditions."* Microfilm, like motion picture film, is usually 0.006 inch thick; the base thickness is 0.005 inch, and the emulsion 0.001 inch. American Standard ASA Z38.7.8-1947 permits the thickness of the film to range from 0.11 to 0.17mm (0.0045 to 0.0065 inch).

By definition in Section 3.2 of American Standard ASA Z38.3.2-

---

* This presumes commercial storage for periods of 25 years without special precautions. Since the keeping properties of such film depend importantly upon atmospheric conditions (temperature and humidity) of storage and upon the manner and the frequency with which the film is used, frequent inspection of such film is necessary to keep track of its deterioration rate. The period between inspections should be as short as 3 months in humid climates and may be as long as 2 years in temperate climates.

1945: "Gelatin-silver halide emulsions shall be used for permanent records that are suitable for development either as original negatives, as positive prints from negatives, or as direct positives by the reversal-development process. Photographic materials producing final images composed of dyes shall not be used for permanent record films." Dyes are specifically excluded because those currently available are fugitive; images produced by them fade. Such images as those in Kodachrome, Kodacolor, AnscoColor, GevaColor, and like multilayer substractive color films are therefore barred by this specification as non-permanent.

Film Characteristics

One outstanding difference between microfilm raw stock and raw stock for other purposes such as motion pictures is the ability of the microfilm to record fine detail. One characteristic of the ability to record fine detail is called resolving power; its measurement will be described later. The rated resolving power of Kodagraph Micro-File Film, the major Eastman microfilm negative material, is 180 lines per millimeter; Eastman Type 5240 Panatomic Safety X, a fine-grain high quality panchromatic negative for motion picture and miniature camera use, is rated at only 60 lines per millimeter. Microfilm, of all sensitized silver halide materials, is capable of recording the maximum of fine detail.

Since microfilm is but one of a variety of film materials manufactured for sale on the open market, it is usually manufactured with machinery used for the making of other sensitized materials. One reason is that film manufacture is a large quantity, continuous flow process; this class of manufacture makes possible the highest level of consistent high quality at the lowest cost to the user. An economic characteristic of such a process is that the first cost of the equipment required to produce the film is very high, and only a large market capable of consuming a large quantity of such material can justify the large investment required for film manufacture. As a result, relatively few firms offer competitive products for sale, and the quality of the products sold is high. Unfortunately the total consumption of sensitized materials by the microrecording industry is rather small compared with that of other sensitized products such as amateur films for still cameras and motion pictures.

Although silver-emulsion films have been in use for more than 50 years, very little has been published on many important phases of film manufacture and use. Emulsion making is one such phase; manufacturers have usually considered this to belong to the practice rather than the theory of photography. With the technical voids that this attitude has produced in the literature, it is difficult for a new student to obtain a balanced overall view that can be expanded as needed for specific specialized applications. As in any other field of technology, in microrecording an understanding of the raw material, the film, is required in order to understand the finished product.

Microfilm consists of two basic parts, a mechanical support called the base, and the photosensitive material called the emulsion. The emulsion is bonded to the base by a solvent-cement that may contain cellulose nitrates as an adhesive; the weight of nitrate, when used, is but a fraction of 1 percent of the total weight of the film. The performance of microfilm is truly remarkable in view of all the chemical and physical changes that are required between the initial exposure of the raw stock and the appearance of the final image after processing.

For base manufacture, a liquid mixture that is essentially cotton mixed into acetic and other acids and solvents is fed continuously into a narrow hopper several feet wide. The long narrow orifice through which the liquid flows by gravity provides mixture flow at a very uniform rate to the periphery of a slowly rotating drum, made of stainless steel, that is several feet in diameter and somewhat wider than the orifice. As the drum rotates, the solvents evaporate and a film of base material forms on the drum. After the material so formed rotates through a portion of a revolution on the drum, it is peeled off in a continuous sheet. The edges are trimmed, as they are not of uniform thickness. The sheet is then rolled up into suitable length for coating with the photosensitive emulsion. A typical sheet length is 2000 feet; a typical roll width is 8 feet. After being rolled, the base material is stored until needed for coating.

The composition of the mixture used for the base is not fixed; it differs in wide degree from one manufacturer to another for presumably equivalent products, and from one group of products of a particular manufacturer to another group of products of the same manufacturer. It may differ also to a lesser yet important degree from one batch of manufactured material to another made by the same manufacturer. The exact mixture used for a particular batch of base material is determined by the performance the film manufacturer desires and expects to obtain. Users should expect to find measurable and important differences in physical characteristics between, for example, Eastman Kodak's Kodagraph Micro-File Film (the negative used in the microfilm camera) and the DuPont Microfilm negative. It is not surprising to find such differences since they are inherent in any manufacturing process. What is especially important is that production runs of material should conform precisely to samples provided for test; good performance can then be maintained in the finished product as a routine matter. On the whole, American film manufacturers are very cooperative and helpful; they manufacture good products and are anxious that users obtain as large a part as possible of the quality potential of which those products are capable.

Since gelatin holds silver halides in suspension in the emulsion, the preparation of the gelatin is very important in the process. Among its chemical functions are:

1. It acts as a protective colloid to maintain dispersion of the silver halides and to protect them from reduction by a developer without exposure.
2. In solution it enables a stable suspension of silver halide particles to be formed.
3. In the jelly state it supports mechanically the microscopic particles of silver halide and silver and permits soluble materials to act upon them.
4. It affects the sensitivity of the silver halide.
5. It combines with, and thus removes, the halogen liberated by the action of light.

Among the physical functions are:

1. It acts to adhere to and cooperates mechanically with the base.
2. It shows minimum distortion when swelled as during developing, and when shrunk, as during drying and subsequent use. Not only must it suffer minimum distortion itself during such swelling and shrinking, but it must also cause the

halide crystals and their corresponding silver nuclei to suffer minimum distortion and shift in orientation.

Gelatin is usually made from selected clippings of calf hide and ears and cheek pieces and pates. For photographic purposes, all pieces must be free of bacterial infection. Two common processes are used in refining gelatin; they are known as the lime-acid process and the soda process. Both processes require soaking of the pieces for an extended period (several months); as the character of the gelatin has a marked effect upon the contrast characteristics of a finished emulsion, the process used to refine the gelatin depends upon the effects desired in the emulsion to be made.

There are three important stages of emulsion preparation:

(1) Emulsification and initial ripening.

(2) Removal of excess soluble salts.

(3) After-ripening and sensitizing.

In the first stage, solutions of 10 percent or more of soluble halides are mixed with silver nitrate solution. Silver bromide is one of the common halides in most emulsions of both the negative and the positive types; negative emulsion types also usually contain silver iodide. To prepare the emulsion, a small amount of relatively inactive gelatin is swelled in cold water and then heated to form a melted gelatin solution; this gelatin is but a small percentage of the total required for the emulsion. The halides are then added; an excess of potassium bromide is always used. Silver nitrate solution is then added while the gelatin solution is continuously stirred; an excess of bromide is necessary even locally where the nitrate solution is introduced. Halide precipitates are formed which are always microcrystalline; they are so fine that the solution appears deep red by transmitted light. When more nitrate is added some precipitate forms around crystals already present increasing their size, while the remainder forms new small crystals. The emulsion is then ripened by heating after all the nitrate solution has been added. In this process, the large crystals become larger and the small crystals smaller; this is called initial ripening, digestion, or Ostwald ripening of an emulsion. During heating, the gelatin partially decomposes, causing minute specks of silver sulfide, called sensitivity specks, that play a very important part in the formation of the latent image. The exact nature of the complex physiochemistry involved is not yet understood. Since microfilm emulsions are fine-grain, the nitrate solution is added slowly and ripening occurs at a lower temperature than with photographic negative films. At this early point in manufacture the grain distribution of the emulsion is established and continues substantially unchanged throughout the remainder of the manufacturing process and, to a considerable degree, during subsequent development after exposure. After this initial ripening, gelatin of the chemically active type is added to bring the gelatin content of the heated mixture to about 10 percent. This step is very important since the subsequent contrast properties to be obtained depend largely upon the properties of the gelatins so added. After this gelatin is thoroughly dissolved, the emulsion is set in a cool place for several hours; when cooled, it is a stiff, jelly-like mass. At this point it has low contrast and low sensitivity.

In the second stage the excess soluble salts are removed by washing to remove the excess potassium bromide and potassium nitrate; these would crystallize out during drying when the emulsion is coated on the base of the film if the salts were not washed, and their presence would interfere with proper second ripening. Water is used; to make washing easier, emulsions are often shredded into "noodles" by forcing the gelatinous mass through a wire screen or perforated die or plate. The halide crystals of the emulsion, being insoluble in water, are held in position mechanically by the gel structure and are unaffected.

In the third stage, after-ripening and sensitizing, the emulsion is drained and then melted. The remainder of the gelatin required for the final emulsion is then added. At this point the emulsion is chilled and stored until needed. When it is to be coated, the sensitizers and other ingredients are added.

The final ripening results in a very large increase in sensitivity without appreciable increase in grain size; this is especially true for photographically fast negative emulsions and less true of microfilm negatives. As in initial ripening, the increase in sensitivity is due in great measure to the sulfides produced from the partial decomposition of the gelatin. The temperature and the length of time heat is applied depend upon the type of gelatin used and the result desired. Over-ripening results in a serious increase in fog; under-ripening results in a slow continuation of the ripening process during subsequent storage, which continues even after the emulsion is coated on the base. Proper ripening is indicated by maximum sensitivity and minimum fog.

Without sensitizing dyes, the emulsion is "color blind"; it is responsive only to ultraviolet and to blue light in the region from 350 to 450 millimicrons. The materials used and the manner of application and treatment are closely guarded secrets of the manufacturers; very little has been published on this subject. The amounts of sensitizing materials required are minute; a concentration as small as 1 part in 100,000 parts of water or dilute alcohol equivalent will cause an emulsion to show color sensitivity for other colors. A dye must actually stain the silver halide crystals to be effective; of dyes that stain, only a comparatively few are sensitizers. Some sensitizers are unstable to light; others are quite stable. The exact nature of the sensitizing action is still obscure, although numerous theories have been advanced to explain many of its aspects. Some of the widely used sensitizers were originally off-shoots of the coal-tar diazo dye and explosives industry of I. G. Farben in Germany before World War I: one group of chemically related materials is used as the light-sensitive material in the Ansco Ozalid paper printing process used for making copies of tracings and like drawings.

After an extremely thin "subbing" coat is applied to the base to cause the emulsion to adhere, the mixture of liquid emulsion is coated upon that one side. The emulsion is warm when applied and is chilled as it passes over a chilled roll after coating; the emulsion is then dried. A typical coating might be 0.01 inch in depth; this dries to something like one-tenth its application depth. After coating, the film is slit to the appropriate width and, if required, it is perforated. The typical length is 100 feet regardless of the width of the microfilm; this is the size of the ASA standard container for microfilm rolls.

Despite the complexity of the manufacturing process, the uniformity of product from roll to roll of microfilm is remarkably high, and it is very rare indeed that any film with evidences of under-ripening or over-ripening or other abnormal sensitometric behavior is encountered. It has been the consistent practice of American film manufacturers to ship only film which has passed stringent test requirements; should a defective batch be manufactured by some manufacturing error (this is extremely rare), such a batch would not be shipped from the factory.

Since microfilm emulsions are fine-grain emulsions and since they are among the most stable sensitized products manufactured, a user will rarely encounter film that is fogged or of poor quality because it is old.

Synthetic carriers replacing the gelatin in film will progressively be introduced as soon as they can be manufactured in sufficient quantities at a sufficiently low cost with the required properties. DuPont has made considerable progress commercially in this direction, and it is only a matter of time before other manufacturers follow suit. The combination of such base materials as the duPont Cronar and the duPont carriers will provide an inherent resistance to bacterial and fungal attack that should make the probable life of microfilms using these materials exceed by a significant margin anything we have expected in the past.

The Sensitometric Characteristics of Film

For convenience in analysis, the relation between the blackness of the developed silver image of the film and the illumination used to provide the exposure is measured by means of the relationship of the common logarithm of the opacity of the image (known as the density) to the common logarithm of the exposure. The test exposures used are an arbitrary series providing an increased exposure for each succeeding step in the series; the instrument that provides these test exposures is called a sensitometer.* In the

---

* Commercial sensitometers are of two general types: (1) variable intensity, in which the exposure time remains constant for all exposures and the intensity is changed, and (2) variable time, in which the exposure intensity is kept constant and the exposure time is varied. Owing to what is called reciprocity law failure, if exposure time of a film is reduced, say, to one-tenth its former value, an increase in exposure intensity of more than 10 is required to produce the reference density under the reference developing conditions. Thus the preferred type of sensitometer, being that type which most closely approximates the actual exposure of the film in use, is the variable intensity type. A suitable sensitometer for making routine test exposures is the Eastman Kodak Type 1A sensitometer; a suitable densitometer for measuring the densities of the steps of the developed sensitometer strips is the Eastman Kodak Type 1A densitometer. These instruments cost roughly $100 each.

usual instrument, the exposure provided by a particular step is
1.414 times that of the prior step; a series of some 20 steps is
common. When the data are plotted on a logarithmic scale as a
curve in which density is the ordinate (vertical reference line) and
the relative log exposure is the abscissa (horizontal reference line),
the curve is known as an H & D curve (after Hurter and Driffeld,
the men who proposed its use). The lower portion of the curve is
known as the toe; this is concave and curved noticeably. The
middle portion is known as the straight line portion. The top portion is known as the shoulder; this is convex and tends to flatten
out at the end. If a tangent is drawn at the flattest part of the
straight line portion, the slope of the tangent is called the gamma
or gradient. The gamma indicates the rate of change of density
with change of exposure at the flattest part of the straight line
portion of the H & D curve. Figure 4 illustrates H & D curves

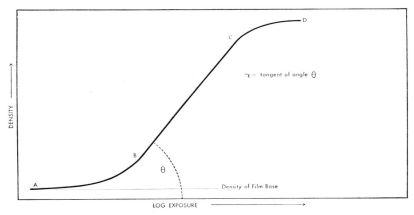

Fig. 4. The H & D or characteristic curve (for plotting the sensitometric
characteristics of photographic materials). (Courtesy Eastman Kodak Co.)

for Kodagraph Micro-File Film. The rated gamma for the curve
for a development time of 3 minutes is in the range from 2.5 to
3.5 with a common value of about 3.1.

TYPES OF FILM

Negative Film

Negative film is used for the first-generation original negative microrecord. Since images of different colors and shades are to be properly rendered in black and white on the original film, the film ordinarily used in a microfilm camera for this purpose is panchromatic negative. Kodagraph Micro-File Film, for example, exhibits a color sensitivity as shown in the published spectrogram data, from 365 to 630 millimicrons. The portion shorter than 400 millimicrons represents the response of the film in the near-ultraviolet range, the range from 400 to 500 millimicrons represents the blue, the 500 to 600 millimicrons range represents the green, and the range from 600 to the response limit at 630 millimicrons represents the red. By definition (ASA Z22.5-1947), "Negative film is the raw stock specifically designed for negative images." When negative microfilm raw stock has been properly exposed in a microfilm camera and is suitably processed in appropriate solutions by the conventional negative developing process, the light scale of blacks and whites of the original negative film appears inverted just as it does in a negative from an ordinary Brownie camera. Negative film and negative processing are most widely used for the original microfilm record. There are three major performance differences between Kodagraph Micro-File Film (negative) and a fine-grain panchromatic negative film used for miniature cameras such as Eastman Type 5240 Panatomic Safety X:

Property	Micro-File	Type 5240
Resolving power	180 lines per mm	60 lines per mm
Grain	Very fine	Fine
Recommended gamma for developing	2.5–3.5	0.65

Conventional photography uses faster and more grainy films for what it terms its finest grain films than microrecording does, mainly because the light levels required for such less grainy films as microfilm are difficult if not impossible to obtain and use.

Being a typical high quality negative microfilm material, Kodagraph Micro-File Film, when used as recommended, is excellent for reproducing printed text, line cuts, written matter, and the like where high image contrast is desirable in the document being photographed between the white of the page and the black of the ink, but it is less desirable for reproducing continuous scale photographs. Since it is characteristic of all very fine-grain materials that the maximum resolving power obtainable under the best conditions depends upon the contrast and is highest when the contrast is high, Kodagraph Micro-File Film is not so suitable for reproducing photographs and radiographs and the like as is Kodak Micro-File Film Type X, a low speed panchromatic negative material of appreciably lower gamma and likewise of somewhat lower resolving power.

Reversal Film

If the reversal process is used to develop a suitable original microfilm, the image obtained on the film after processing is "right side up" with regard to tonal scale. By definition (ASA Z22.56-1947), "Reversal film is a film which after exposure is processed to produce a positive image on the same film rather than the customary negative image." Reversal film is used rarely if at all for microrecordings; its most common use is for 16mm and 8mm motion picture films.

There is little doubt that some area of application can be found for the reversal process where its potential advantages can be realized in microrecording operations; possibly microfilm may follow the pattern of the motion picture and enlarge the potential use of microfilm by amateurs by the application of the reversal process just as 16mm motion pictures did in 1924. In reversal processing the large grains of the film (which are most affected by the exposure in the camera) are developed first and then bleached. The film then receives a fogging exposure in the developing machine which exposes all the remaining grains of the film not affected by the camera exposure; these grains are then developed by a second development. After the film has been fixed, washed, and dried, the image on the film is appreciably finer-grained than if the film were developed as a negative, and its tonal scale is "right side up." Reversal processing of a suitable film always results in an appreciable improvement in the graininess of the film image.

To realize the advantages of reversal processing would require an increase in the accuracy of exposure control and an increase in the accuracy of processing that would be unlikely of commercial

accomplishment at present outside of possibly a very few highly
specialized and technically qualified microfilming organizations.
As the basic technical concepts of microfilming operations become
more widely appreciated and understood than they are now,
microfilming copying operations may include reversal processing
and may ultimately follow the three-generation duplication procedure widely used for 16mm film; this procedure anticipates the
need for archival storage of the 16mm original film. Such a procedure* would anticipate a reversal film for the first generation
original, a duplicate negative for the second generation pre-print
material and a very fine-grain positive film for the release print
material. This is a matter for the future, as suitable film materials
are not available commercially for the purpose.

Positive Film

Positive film is used for copying from the original negative for
second-generation prints. Since the different colors and shades of
the original document are correctly rendered on the original negative film, it is merely necessary to retain the scale uniformity in
the copy that appeared in the original. For this purpose positive
film is used; since positive film is color-blind, it responds only to
light in the blue and near ultraviolet region (365 to 480 millimicrons). Since this is the case, it may be handled safely under a yellow safelight in the darkroom; this convenience of handling makes
it possible for a laboratory technician to see what he is doing. Negative microfilm, being panchromatic, is sensitive to light of all colors
and must be handled in complete darkness before it is developed.

Because positive microfilm such as Kodagraph Print Film has
not been sensitized for green and red light, it is photographically
less sensitive than microfilm negative. Its characteristics are best
indicated by comparison with Micro-File negative, shown in the
following table:

---

* For a statement of a parallel preservation and storage problem for
16mm motion pictures, and a suggested solution in terms of 16mm film, refer
to Chapter XI, "Preservation and Storage," of "16mm Sound Motion Pictures,
A Manual, pp. 355-363, by Wm. H. Offenhauser, Jr., published by Interscience
Publishers, Inc., New York-London, 1953.

Property	Kodak Micro-File Negative	Kodagraph Positive
Resolving power	180 lines per mm	145 lines per mm
Color sensitivity	panchromatic	blue-sensitive only
Recommended gamma for developing	2.5–3.5	2.2–3.0
Laboratory handling	complete darkness	yellow safelight
Subject contrast for optimum exposure	30:1	30:1

Generally speaking, microfilm positive film is used primarily for making copies from microfilm negatives; the size of the image on the copy is usually the same as the size of the image on the negative, since the copies are usually made on a contact printer. After development, the print is ready for use.

DETAIL RENDERING AND ITS MEASUREMENT

The term resolving power as used in the trade by film manufacturers, lens manufacturers, and other suppliers of equipment, materials, and services is rather loose. Test patterns consisting of parallel lines in which the width of a line is equal to the width of the space between lines are photographed in a regular series of spacing widths; the numerical value of resolving power assigned is the value expressed in lines per millimeter for the just-distinguishable lines of the series.

In the National Bureau of Standards Circular C428, "A Test of Lens Resolution for the Photographer" (1941, Government Printing Office, Washington, D. C.; available from the Superintendent of Documents at a price of about 40 cents postpaid), a set of high quality photoengraved charts is furnished by which the resolving power of lenses may be numerically measured to a definite scale of values, in lines per millimeter. A detailed description is given of the procedure and technique to be followed in order that comparable values may be obtained by different observers (eliminating personal error in the measurements). Since the basic method is applicable to films being tested as well as to lenses, a small part of the text of the circular has been paraphrased so that it applies to film in the text which follows:

The present prevalent practice of making enlargements of several diameters from the original negative has created a general demand for lenses (and films) giving sharper and better-defined images than were considered satisfactory some years ago. The simplified test can be made by means of a very good microfilm camera and can be conducted by one skilled in photographic technique to the extent that is required for the successful operation of a miniature camera. In testing the film it is necessary to be certain that the resolving power of the camera as used is preferably greater than that of the film being tested. (A very good microfilm camera equipped with a very good lens, such as the Kodak Micro-File Ektar, adjusted accurately for focus should be adequate for routine purposes.)

The test comprises a measure of a characteristic that determines the sharpness of the image and the degree to which it can be enlarged. If one attempts to photograph a pattern of parallel lines, it will be found that the lines, if too close together, will photograph as a gray patch and the individual lines cannot be distin-

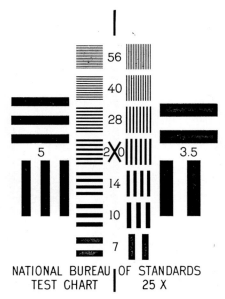

Fig. 5. National Bureau of Standards resolution test chart. (From Circular C-428.)

guished. If, however, the lines in the object are so far apart that they are recorded as distinct lines, the film is said to resolve the lines. We can, therefore, give considerable information regarding the quality of definition by a statement regarding the finest pattern of lines that it resolves. Figure 5 is a reproduction of one of the six charts of a test plate. To obtain readings up to 56 lines per millimeter, the chart is photographed at a distance of 26 times the focal length of the lens; the readings are then as indicated in lines per millimeter. To obtain readings up to 112 lines per millimeter, the chart is photographed at twice the specified distance and the readings obtained are multiplied by the factor 2. To obtain readings up to 168 lines per millimeter, the chart is photographed at three times the specified distance and the readings obtained are multiplied by the factor 3. In all cases the single test chart is located at the center of the lens field, as it is at this point that the average microfilm camera lens resolves the largest number of lines. The Kodak Micro-File Ektar Lens, 63mm, with a fixed mechanical aperture of $f/8$ is rated for 160 lines per millimeter. Kodagraph Micro-File Film is rated at 180 lines per millimeter with optimum exposure, with a subject contrast of 30 to 1 and with specified development in Kodagraph developer. Routine tests of the original

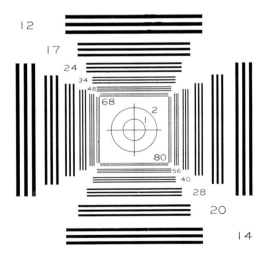

FIG. 6. National Bureau of Standards resolution test chart. (From Circular C-533.)

negative should resolve 112 lines per millimeter consistently; failure to do so indicates faulty equipment, procedure, materials or methods.

Figure 6 shows the latest National Bureau of Standards Test Chart, from Circular C 533 (1952), "A Method of Testing Resolving Power of Photographic Lenses"; this circular supersedes C 428, previously described. It includes one set of six high contrast charts and one set of six low contrast charts; the chart illustrated is one of the high contrast type. Note that the steps in this new chart are in the series 12, 14, 17, 20, 24, 28, 34, 40, 48, 56, 68, and 80 lines per millimeter.

The chart in Figure 7 is available from Ansco (Binghamton, New York). It is photographed at the reduction under test, and the photographed image is examined under a microscope; the rating in lines per millimeter is equal to that for the just-resolvable pattern multiplied by the reduction at which the chart is used. The reduction may be determined by measuring the length of the calibrating line in millimeters; the reduction is the ratio of the measured length to 100 millimeters. Thus, if the measured length is 10 millimeters, the reduction is 10, and the value obtained from the photographed chart is to be multiplied by 10. The numbers in this test series are: 1.0, 1.2, 1.6, 2.0, 2.5, 3.2, 4.0, 5.0, 6.3, 7.9 and 10.0 In the instructions furnished with the chart is the following: "Resolution, as measured on the film, is a test of the entire photographic system, including lens, exposure, processing, and other factors. These rarely utilize maximum resolution of the film."

In practice there is often wide variation in numerical values for resolving power obtained because of the variations in the conditions under which a test may be made. Some of these conditions are:

1. *The line-to-space ratio of the test object.* Emulsions which exhibit a characteristic called turbidity (image spread) will alter the line-to-space ratio of the photographic image compared with the test object, and emulsions lacking sharpness will show a fuzzy edge between the black line and the adjacent white space of the test pattern. Microfilm materials should be almost entirely free of this effect.

2. *The test object contrast* (assumed 30 to 1). The density of the black line is 30 times the density of the white space. A high value of test object contrast results in a high value of resolving power; a low value, in a lowered value; this condition is aggravated for an emulsion which lacks sharpness compared with an emulsion that has sharpness.

3. *Level of illumination* under which the test image is examined. (The effect of this is not serious compared with that of other conditions.)

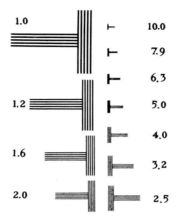

100 MILLIMETERS

FIG. 7. Ansco resolution chart. Resolution is expressed in terms of the lines per millimeter recorded by a particular film under specified conditions. Numerals in chart indicate the number of lines per millimeter in adjacent T-shaped groupings.

In microfilming, it is necessary to determine the reduction ratio and multiply the number of lines in the chart by this value to find the number of lines recorded by the film. As an aid in determining the reduction ratio, the line above is 100 millimeters in length. Measuring this line in the film image and dividing the length into 100 gives the reduction ratio. Example: the line is 20 mm. long in the film image, and $100/20 = 5$.

Examine T-shaped line groupings in the film with microscope, and note the number adjacent to finest lines recorded sharply and distinctly. Multiply this number by the reduction factor to obtain resolving power in lines per millimeter. Example: 7.9 group of lines is clearly recorded while lines in the 10.0 group are not distinctly separated. Reduction ratio is 5, and $7.9 \times 5 = 39.5$ lines per millimeter recorded satisfactorily. $10.0 \times 5 = 50$ lines per millimeter which are not recorded satisfactorily. Under the particular conditions, maximum resolution is between 39.5 and 50 lines per millimeter.

Resolution, as measured on the film is a test of the entire photographic system, including lens, exposure, processing, lack of critical focus, and exposure yielding very dense negatives are to be avoided. (Courtesy of Ansco.)

4. *The chromatic characteristics* of the light used to provide the test exposure. If light from either or both ends of the spectrum (red or blue) is used for exposing the film under test, an increase in resolving power occurs. This applies to negative microfilm because it is panchromatic; it does not apply to positive (such as Kodagraph Print film) because this is "color-blind," responding only to blue and ultraviolet light (360 to 460 millimicrons).

5. *Development conditions.* (a) Developer: some developers improve the resolving power of some emulsions; others reduce it markedly. (b) Development time: when development time increases, resolving power reaches a well-defined maximum and then drops off. (c) Developer concentration: an increase in developer concentration usually produces an effect equivalent to an increase in development time with a lower concentration. (d) Developer temperature: maximum resolving power occurs at a specific developer temperature; a loss in resolving power usually accompanies an increase in temperature.*

6. *Grain characteristics.* With small grain size and a correspondingly large number of grains, higher values of resolving power are obtained. Microfilm normally has small grain size and a correspondingly large number of grains.

Usually the correlation between conditions of test by suppliers of equipment, materials, and services and the actual conditions of use is quite poor. For this reason manufacturers' ratings of resolving power are frequently little more than a qualitative guide to the relative quality of a microrecording material or product.

Sharpness is such an important physical factor that some explanation of this little-understood characteristic is desirable. Assume that a sheet 8½ by 11 inches with an 8 by 10 inch checkerboard pattern upon it, each square of which is 2 inches on a side, is photographed on different microfilm materials. If after the film is developed, the image on the film is examined under a microscope (using a magnification so high that the effective size of the square as viewed through the eyepiece of the microscope is, say, 20 times the size of the original pattern), many films will show a fuzzy line of demarcation at the boundary, and very few films will show a sharp line even though the original checkerboard is still very sharp when examined with the same magnification. The difference is due to a difference in the sharpness of the emulsion, one of its most important physical characteristics.

To evaluate sharpness a microdensitometer† is used in the film

---

* This statement also holds for so-called "hot" processing, a processing condition designed to function most effectively at some temperature between 80 to 125° F. Conventional processing functions most effectively at 68° F.

† A microdensitometer is an instrument for measuring the density of a small area.

manufacturer's research laboratory to measure continuously the density (blackness) of microscopically small areas as the exploring head of the microdensitometer smoothly traverses the boundary between a white square and a black square of the checkerboard pattern. See Figure 8. Curve A is the trace obtained when the

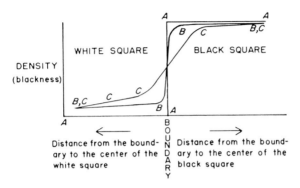

FIG. 8. Chart obtained by using microdensitometer to measure sharpness.

exploring head traverses a boundary on the original checkerboard pattern. Curve B is the trace obtained when the exploring head traverses a similar boundary on the checkerboard pattern on microfilm which utilizes a film emulsion with excellent sharpness. Curve C is the trace obtained when the exploring head traverses a boundary on the checkerboard pattern on microfilm which utilizes a film emulsion with poor sharpness.*

For best microfilm reproduction, the maximum sharpness possible is required, not only in the performance of the developed film, but also in the lens used in the microfilm camera. The sharpness characteristics of films and of lenses vary noticeably from product to product and between two different items of the same product, and, since no standard method for numerically evaluating sharpness has been adopted, this factor is best checked by making test exposures of the kind of document that the equipment and material to be used will be called upon to microfilm. The best test of a microfilm installation is the everyday microfilm that it produces.

---

* Sharpness may be defined as the slope of the curve at the boundary.

To aid in evaluating sharpness, the test image may be examined at, say, three times the magnification used as everyday routine in the microfilm readers; such high magnification can ordinarily show up quite readily the day-to-day vagaries of the overall sharpness of the recording process. If the routine use of microfilm readers effects an enlargement of the image presented for viewing to 1.5 times the size of the original document, it would be a good idea to view the image further enlarged (3 times 1.5, or 4.5 times original size) and compare it with the original test checkerboard pattern enlarged by a similar amount, 4.5 times, to make certain that the loss of sharpness may all be charged to the film and not to a poor checkerboard test pattern. Such simple comparisons can be accomplished by a serious user of microfilm without large investment in test apparatus; the prime requirements are a serious interest in the technology of the process and some ingenuity applied to simple apparatus.

LOSS OF DETAIL IN COPYING GENERATIONS

It should be evident that even the original microfilm negative does not record all the finest detail of the image being copied, even if the very best film, equipment, and methods are used. Since in a practical operation it is not reasonable to assume use of the very best of each element every time a particular function is performed, it may be stated unequivocally that every copying step involves a copying loss even though the loss may not be apparent to the naked eye. This loss can always be measured by comparing the original resolving power test pattern directly with its photographic reproduction; to see the difference clearly may require the use of additional magnification. The magnification should be of the same value for viewing both the original pattern and the photographic reproduction. Even the original microfilm facsimile negative cannot be expected to yield all the detail present in the original subject.

A second-generation microfilm such as a positive print from an original microfilm negative cannot be expected to yield all the detail in the first-generation microfilm original. If further generations of copies are derived from the second-generation positive print, it is quite evident that each succeeding generation will exhibit a loss of fine detail when compared with the preceding generation. A rough rule-of-thumb suggests a copying loss of approximately 30 percent in each copying generation. If there are 100 units of detail in an original microfilm negative, only 70 units will be found in the print, the second generation. It is reasonable to estimate a 30 percent loss per generation; thus the second generation can be expected to show 70 per cent of the detail on the original, the third generation can show 49 percent; the fourth generation 34 percent; and so forth. It is evident that it is not possible to copy through an indeterminate number of copy generations and still be certain that the end-use microcopy will be useful. Since it is foolhardy to ignore a quality loss of the order of 30 percent or more per copying step, a user of microfilm services should be interested in knowing how many steps there are (and what they are) of the process by which the end-use copies he expects to utilize are produced.

Since the copying loss from one copy generation to the next is quite large, it is a common microfilming procedure to make two or more separate microfilm original negatives of the original document. After these are processed, one or more is set aside for dead storage, where it is preserved in archival storage or the like, and the others are used for producing the end-use copies required by the users where and when such copies are required.

THE TERMINOLOGY OF MICRORECORDING— ORDER OR CHAOS?

As mentioned in an earlier chapter, serious conflict now exists in microcopying terminology. For the most part it results from the conflict between trade and proprietary names, generic terms and trade jargon. Although general usage and formal standardization will ultimately remove the conflicts, the situation has already become sufficiently serious to require prompt action owing to the rapid growth period through which microcopying is now passing. It would seem wise at this stage for the American Standards Association Committee on the Photographic Reproduction of Documents PH5 to collect and collate for publication as promptly as possible all terms presently used. Such an interim list project might profitably follow the procedures used so successfully by the Inter-Society Color Council for the publication of its interim glossary of color terms which made it possible to resolve equally serious conflicts in the field of color terminology. The terms should be listed and arranged in alphabetical order and the source of each term and its definition listed if known. The list should include all cross references for similar and related terms; no term presently used should be omitted. With all terms available to interested users in a single listing—and particularly to those who purchase microcopying equipment, materials, and services—general usage would become crystallized in a few years and certain terms would be recognized as preferred and others eventually fall into disuse. Terminology that is formally adopted in this way is terminology that is accepted because it has acquired acceptance; terminology that comes into use in any other way is likely to fall into disuse no matter how energetic its proponents may be in its behalf.

Part of the conflict in terminology arises because several commercial firms have applied for copyright protection of the trade names that they have chosen; part of the protection of the copyright rests in the right of such firms to restrict the use of such names solely to their products as proprietary trade names. Since an insufficient number of names has been coined to describe all the possible kinds of products and manufacturers and, because to some extent different copyright rules control copyright policy in different countries, trade names in one country may and frequently do have an entirely different meaning from those in another. Such matters can be resolved through the American Standards Association in the United States and later in the International Standards Organization and similar international standards organizations on a worldwide basis.

It is not the purpose of the authors to prescribe any specific usage, whether generic, trade jargon, proprietary trade name in one country or another, or other basis, but, rather, to arrive at some rationalized basis for describing the various forms of microtext and their applications, and for distinguishing among the various forms. Microcopy or microtext shall mean a microfacsimile in any of the available forms. If a microcopy is a transparency, the generic term would appear to be microtransparency. A microtransparency on 16mm, 35mm or 70mm film is microfilm. A microtransparency with its blacks and whites inverted in tonal scale is called a negative just as it is in motion pictures. If its blacks and whites are "right side up," it is called a positive. If a microtransparency is on sheet film of a size other than those specified for microfilm (which is customarily supplied in rolls for the photographing camera), it is called sheet film or microfiche. The term micro-opaque is used to describe an opaque in microrecorded form however made Micro-opaques may be produced by offset printing or they may be produced by photographic methods; Readex Microprint is an example of the former, Microcards and Microlex are examples of the latter. Readex Microprint and Microlex customarily have micro-images on both sides of the card; Microcards customarily have micro-images on only one side of the card; the other side is reserved for catalog information printed in the usual manner in full size on a conventional 3 by 5 inch card.

Microstrip and Microtape are proprietary terms describing a micro-opaque made by photo printing sensitized paper strips from microfilm. Both carry micro-images on only one side; on the opposite side is an adhesive that makes it possible to attach the micro-opaque to a file card or other mounting card or sheet. A difference between the two commercial products is that one uses a pressure-sensitive adhesive; the other requires moistening of the adhesive to make it adhere.

The conflict in terminology is not merely an academic matter that should be resolved at some vague date in the distant future; it is a practical matter that requires steps to be taken now. Some examples can best illustrate the problem. At the present writing (1956) Eastman Kodak appears to use the term microprint in a generic sense in connection with the Eastman Microprint Reader to describe opaque microtext such as photoprinted opaques on Microcards. In Publication No. 257 of the Federation Internationale de Documentation, the term Microcard is used to describe both micro-opaques and microtransparencies. In the United States the term Microcard is a registered trade name of the Microcard Foundation; similarly the name Readex Microprint is used as a trade name by the Readex Microprint Corporation. Microprint is also used as a trade name for equipment made by Dr. Rodehüser of Bergkamen-Westfalia, West Germany. The trade name Microstat is used for readers made by Dr. Böger of Lumoprint of Hamburg, Germany.

This explanation of terms has been given to enable the reader to follow the terminology used in describing apparatus and methods and indexing procedure. Since the section that follows deals with commercial processes involving trade names, section headings involving terms affected by conflicts in terminology are followed by an explanatory title.

SPECIALIZED FORMS OF MICROCOPYING

Microcards (Micro-opaques printed photographically from 16mm Microfilm Photographed with Special Format)

Microcards are index cards roughly $3\frac{1}{8}$ by $5\frac{1}{8}$ inches, the same size as a library card, on one side of which images are photographically printed from specially prepared microfilm, and on the other side of which catalog information and the like concerning the microtext is multilith-printed. As many as 60 pages of $8\frac{1}{2}$ by 11 inches of text or equivalent may be photoprinted from, say, 5 specially prepared 16mm microfilm negative strips each one of which carries 6 sets of exposures consisting of 2 pages of photographed text per exposure.

Photographic Operations in Preparing Microcards.* In the procedure described by Mr. Kuipers of Eastman Kodak, the microfilm record is photographed on unperforated 16mm film. The camera is a commercial Kodagraph Model D with 16mm parts modified so that the film-advance mechanism moves the film after each exposure with an advance of uniform length. The reduction depends upon the size of the document being photographed in order

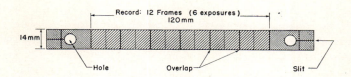

The above strip is cut from the following sequence of exposures made on 16 mm film:

Fig. 9. Standardized microfilm strip.

---

* Data abstracted from "Microcards and Microfilm for a Central Reference File," by J. W. Kuipers, *Ind. Eng. Chem.*, Vol. 42, pp. 463-467 (August 1950).

to produce a negative frame of constant size; the reduction usually falls in the range from 1:14 to 1:20. The maximum size of the original document to be recorded on a single frame is 8½ by 11 inches. As shown in Figure 9, twelve frames are exposed per strip and two frames per exposure with three blank exposures after each record sequence. During exposure, the light intensity is controlled so that the background density of the negative film strips will fall within the range 1.40 to 1.55 with accurately controlled consistent film development. After exposure, the 16mm film is processed in the conventional manner as a microfilm negative.

The processed film is inspected, punched with the holes, and slit to a width of 14mm. A simple hand-operated slitter is used to reduce the film width by 2mm; 1mm being removed from each edge on each of two passes through the slitter. The slitting operation requires only a minute or two for each 100-foot roll of film, the holes shown in the figure are punched in the film with a suitable hand punch. In final form, as shown in the illustration, the film strips are readily handled and kept in order by means of small peg boards.

The photographic printing of the Microcards from the 14mm film strips requires a special sensitized paper that is available in rolls or in card sizes; in a typical operation 200-foot rolls of paper are used. The microfilm strips are kept in proper alignment on the negative strip carrier by means of positioning pins and the holes in the 14mm film strips. The carrier contains a glass plate with the areas beyond the images of interest opaqued; this plate serves as a mask to provide white unprinted margins and white areas between strips on the Microcard. The negative strip carrier and its accessories contain all the photographic images required for photographic contact printing in a single exposure per Microcard; the usual contact printing and photofinishing methods result in excellent image quality on the special print paper. Automatic photographic contact-printing machines for producing quantities of Microcard duplicates are already available with a printing rate in excess of 600 per hour. When the background density of the negative is kept nearly constant as specified previously, the exposure of the printer requires little if any adjustment.

The rolls of paper, which are 5½ inches wide and may be 200

feet or more in length, are processed in a continuous processing machine similar to that used by large photofinishers. After processing, the paper rolls, which have also been ferrotyped, are chopped to size. Packs of approximately 100 chopped cards are given a final square cutting to accurate size on a large paper cutter.

At this point the cut Microcards are ready for imprinting the catalog information on the reverse side of the cards. This may be done with a Multigraph machine using a Multilith master of the unit index card which has been preserved for such use and kept in file. After this operation, the Microcards are ready for distribution.

When enlargements to approximately original size are required, paper prints may be obtained that are of acceptable quality; they are made from the master microfilm negative 14mm film strips. It is obvious that a special enlarger is required for the purpose that permits selection of the specific image of interest; the lenses and other optical elements of the enlarger are conventional in other respects.

There is no theoretical reason why film of other sizes such as 35mm and 70mm can not be used for Microcard purposes if the formats for those sizes are properly designed and suitable apparatus is manufactured. Some Microcards are being printed from 35mm film; up to the present there has been very little evidence of serious attempts to use 70mm.

Microcard reading machines are frequently designed with a magnification of about $25\times$ the effective enlargements of the Microcard image as presented in the range from 1.67 to 1.25 compared with the original document. A measure of the "compressibility" of the material may be obtained from the statement that a card file unit similar in size to the conventional four-drawer letter file will contain the Microcard record of some 350,000 pages of letter-size material—over one-third of a million letter-size pages.

Readex Microprint (Micro-opaque Offset Printed from Special Microfilm)

Readex Microprint is a process of printing, which for making end-use copies on large file cards utilizes a mechanical printing operation on paper such as offset printing rather than a photographic printing operation. Each card of the Readex Microprint Corp. of New York is 6 by 9 inches and contains 100 pages of 6 by

9 inch text on each side of the card; the two faces of the card accommodate 200 such pages. Microprint cards are made stiff enough to handle with ease, to insert into the Readex Reader, and to refile. The decimal arrangement of the text, 10 by 10 pages on each side of a card, makes document search simpler than some other forms of microrecording. Technical details of the process are not generally available, as they relate specifically to the manner in which original microfilms are made, and to the manner in which the end-use Microprint cards are produced from the microfilm. A separate file card is presumed for each Microprint card.

The Readex Microprint Corp. offers for sale Microprint copies of public documents; in documents of many pages such as books, where the 6 by 9 inch format is used, Microprint copies are often offered for sale for as little as one-half, and in some cases as low as one-fifth, the price of other forms of microdocumentation such as microfilm. The reduction used is quite large; the space reduction factor is therefore correspondingly large. The Microprint cards can be used in a reader such as the Readex Reader; so far the nature of the market exploited and the manner of its exploitation seem to suggest that it is likely that in the near future paper copies in original size may be made with a Readex Reader, as might be the case if a paper work copy of a particular page were needed.

Readex Microprint, being a paper and ink process for its end-use copies, is subject to the same deterioration and decay considerations as any other paper-and-ink process, and its cards may be laminated with acetate sheet just like any other paper document to be preserved. In particular, the archival properties of Microprint are no better or no worse than the chemical stability of its paper and ink materials. If the materials of Microprint are better than microfilm its stability will be better; if worse its stability will be poorer. Generally speaking there is reason to believe that safety film base such as that made currently in the United States like acetate lamination will have a measurably longer life than the better grades of paper commercially available; film emulsions as used on microfilm and Microcards from equal life to somewhat shorter. Microfilm and Microcards, when made of commercially available, high quality materials as made by the better manufacturers, will under identical conditions of good storage outlast poor paper by a wide margin, and probably outlast run-of-the-mill paper by a narrower margin. In the absence of specific technical data on the materials used, no more definitive statement is possible.

Since Microprint uses relatively large reductions and is an opaque, users should examine reader performance carefully, as image quality in terms of image brightness, contrast and detail will probably be the most important factor in overall performance.

Minicards

See Chapters III (pages 59 to 61) and IX.

A FINAL WORD ABOUT TERMINOLOGY

Once again it becomes necessary to warn the reader that the terminology of microrecording is not to be relied upon. Some groups are inclined to distinguish between photographic and nonphotographic processes and to classify the printed materials at all stages of the production process in accordance with this distinction, usually unstated. Other groups are inclined to ignore entirely any distinction between photographic and nonphotographic processes, also unstated, on the theory that a copy is a copy, however made, and what is significant about a microcopy is what it is and how it is used rather than how it is made. The former group can be said to be interested in the mechanics of production process, and the latter group in the end-use product and its performance for the user.

To a reasonable, unprejudiced person, *both* points of view are necessary. It is true that the nature of the end-use copy and its performance characteristics (which may be briefly described in terms of the reduction of the end-use copy compared with the original document, whether it is a transparency or an opaque) and its quality in terms of readability or suitability for further reproduction are of prime significance to the user of the end-use copy, but it is also true that others are concerned with the production process itself. The latter group is just as entitled to suitable nomenclature for the materials, processes, and methods as the former; a proper nomenclature anticipates the needs of *all* probable users. It can be confidently assumed that the adoption of a nomenclature list by the American Standards Association will be an indication that such fundamental requirements and all others fitting and proper will have been met. Submittal of prepared lists is therefore a step to the orderly organization of the nomenclature of this field. Such a step is currently being taken by the National Microfilm Association;* it is hope dthat all inteested parties will take part in this work.

Bibliography

M. d. Lafillye. *Dépêches par pigeons voyageurs pendant le siège de 10 jours de Paris.* Mame Fils, Tours, 1871.

"Microfilm tijdens het beleg von Parijs in 1870." *Nieuwe Rotterdamsche Courant,* Abendblatt C, Dec. 11, 1938.

P. Baron and L. Lobel. "Le Microfilm et ses applications." *La Technique Cinematographique,* pp. 81-82, 113-114 (1948).

Journal de Brevets. Brussels, No. 1, 1907.

Andre van Remoortel. "Le Microfilm en Belgigue." 16th Kongress der Federation International de Documentation, 1946.

Paul Otlet. *Traité de Documentation.* Editions Mundeanum, Palais Mondial, Brusells, 1934.

Ir. F. I. Vaes. "Ubersicht über die Geschichte des Mikrofilms und der Photokopie." *Zeitschrift Korte Mededeelingen des Nederlandsch Institut voor Documentatie en Registratur.*

De Ingenieur, 23.8.1935, S. A. 297.

"L'Utilisation du film comme support de la documentation." Conférences présentées au Symposium organisé par l'Office International de Chimie, le 31 mars 1935 a Paris.

Josef Goebel. Schrift, Letter, Mikrokopie. Mainz, 1940.

H. and J. Siedentopf. "Dokumentation durch Mikrokopie." *Phys. Bl.,* Vol. 3 pp. 267-270 (1947).

Wilhelm Redepenning. "Uber Probleme der Lesefilmtechnik." *Zbl. Bibliothekswesen,* Vol. 61, pp. 121-128 (1947).

Paul D. Green. "Ungeahnte Entwicklungsmöglichkeiten des Mikrofims." *Welt-Echo,* Bd. 3 (1948) Nr. ½.

The Photographic Journal, April 1937.

Wilhelm Redepenning. "Stand der praktischen Mikrokopie." *Phys. Bl.,* Bd. 4 (1948) H. 7, S.299-301.

Walter Brauer. "Das Mikrofot-Gerät der AEG," *Radio-Mentor* (1948) S.236-239.

Eggert. "Zur Frage der Dokumentation." *Phys. Bl.,* Bd. 3 (1947) S.394/395.

Eggert. Kongress der Federation Internationale de Documentation in Bern. *Recherches et Inventions,* (1939) Nr. 278 S. 73.

W. I. Faasch. "Kleinbildfoto und Dokumentation." *Foto-Kino-Technik,* Bd. 2 (1948) S.167-169.

German patents DRP 530,115, DRP 483,806, and DRP 702,310.

---

* Hendrix TenEyck. *Glossary of Terms Used in Microproduction.* National Microfilm Association, 1955.

"Microcards 100 to 1." *Newsweek*, p. 37, May 17, 1948.

Telegraf vom 14. 6. 1948 Nr. 136/3 und Neue Illustrierte.

"Das Mikrolit-Lesegerät." *Natur u. Technik*, Bd. 2 (1948) S. 380-383.

"Reading and Visual Fatigue." *Science* Bd. 106 (1947) S. 628/629.

"Das Mikrobuch." *Neue Berliner Illustrierte*, Bd. 3 (1947) 2. Januarheft.

"Den Vertrieb der Mikrobücher hat die Firma MIKROPHOT Kom.-Ges."
Dr. Heinz Lubeck, Berlin-Charlottenburg, Spandauer Str. 1.

"Die Rechte der Autoren und Verleger bei Vervielfältigung von Zeitschriften
im Wege der Mikrophotographie." *Gewerblicher Rechtsschutz und
Urheberrecht*, Bd. 50 (1948) S. 98-103.

Karl Hansen. "Aus der Praxis der Kleinbild-Reproduktion." *Foto-Kino-
Technik*, Bd. 3 (1949) S. 59/60.

R. Knapmann. "Dokumentation durch Mikrokopie." *Foto-Spiegel* (1948)
S. 4/5.

Lucia Moholy. "Mikrokopie in der Industrie." *Neue Auslese*, Bd. 3 (1948)
S. 50-53.

Lucia Moholy. "Das Kleinbild im Dienste der Dokumentarphotographie."
Blick in die Welt (1947) Nr. 8.

H. Lübeck. Grundsätzliche Fragen der fotografischen Mikro-Reproduktions-
technik." *Zbl. Bibliothekswes.*, Bd. 63 (1949) S. 17-29.

"Notes on Tropical Photography." Eastman Kodak Co., Rochester, N. Y.,
1949.

"Prevention and Removal of Fungus Growth on Processed Photographic
Film." Eastman Kodak Co., Rochester, N. Y., 1949.

Lucia Moholy. "Das Wunder des Mikrobuches." *Badische Neueste Nach-
richten*, Vol. 28, Feb. 1948.

Lucia Moholy. "Mikroliteratur—drahtlos!" *Natur und Technik*, Bd. 2 (1948)
S. 336/37.

Lucia Moholy. "Das Archiv unter der Lupe." *Der Morgen* (1948) Nr. 272.

F. Bruchman and U. Pfaff. "Die Fotomikrographie, *Die Technik*, Vol. 4,
No. 12, pp. 553-558 (1949).

J. Boyer. "Multiple Usages du Microfilmage en France." *Technique*, Vol. 26,
No. 7 (Sept. 1951).

Watson Davis, ed. World Congress of Universal Documentation and Other
Conferences, Paris, Aug. 1937.

Ralph Carruthers. "Microphotography: An Annotated Bibliography." *Bull.
Amer. Library Assoc.*, Vol. 31, No. 2 (Feb. 1937).

P. Poindron. "Microfilm in France." 15th Conference of Federation of International Documentation.

Walter Raths. "Recent Photo-Material for Documentation." 15th Conference
of Federation of International Documentation.

W. Schurmeyer. "Photomicrography in Germany." 15th Conference of
Federation of International Documentation.

D. Paterson and M. Tinker. *How to Make Type Readable.*

Maxwell Hicks Savelle. "History, Photography and the Library." *Library J.*
Vol. 60 (Nov. 15, 1935).

Orlin D. Trapp. *The Use and Production of Sound and Silent Filmslides.* Doc. 1439.

"Microfilming." Eastman Kodak Co., Rochester 4, N. Y.

L. E. Jones and G. C. Higgins. "The Nature and the Evaluation of the Sharpness of Photographic Images." *J. Soc. Motion Picture Tel. Engrs.,* Vol. 58, No. 4, pp. 277-290 (April 1952).

"Standard for Permanent Record Photographic Microcopying Film." National Bureau of Standards, Sept. 14, 1943.

J. W. Kuipers. "Microcards and Microfilm for a Central Reference File." *Ind. Eng. Chem.,* Vol. 42, pp. 1463-1467 (August, 1950).

R. H. Rasch and B. W. Scribner. "Comparison of Natural Aging of Paper with Accelerated Aging by Heating." *J. Research, Natl. Bureau Standards,* Vol. 11, pp. 727-732 (1933).

R. H. Rasch, M. B. Shaw, and B. W. Bicking. "Highly Purified Wood Fibers as Paper Making Material." *J. Research, Natl. Bureau Standards,* Vol. 7, pp. 765-782 (1931).

J. I. Crabtree, G. T. Eaton, and L. E. Muehler. "The Elimination of Hypo from Photographic Images." *J. Phot. Soc. Amer.,* Vol. 6, pp. 6-13, 42 (Oct. 1940).

J. I. Crabtree, G. T. Eaton, and L. E. Muehler. "The Removal of Hypo and Silver Salts from Photographic Materials as Affected by the Composition of the Processing Solutions." *J. Soc. Motion Picture Engrs.,* Vol. 41, pp. 9-68 (July 1943).

J. I. Crabtree and J. F. Ross. "A Method of Testing for the Presence of Sodium Thiosulfate in Motion Picture Films." *J. Soc. Motion Picture Engrs.,* Vol. 14, No. 4, pp. 419-426 (April, 1930).

J. I. Crabtree, G. T. Eaton, and L. E. Muehler. "The Quantitative Determination of Hypo in Photographic Prints with Silver Nitrate." *J. Franklin Institute,* Vol. 235, pp. 351-360 (April 1943).

E. K. Carver, R. H. Talbot, and H. A. Loomis. "(Motion Picture) Film Distortions and Their Effect Upon Projection Quality." *J. Soc. Motion Picture Engrs.,* Vol. 41, No. 1, pp. 88-93 (July 1943).

"Protection of Records." Consolidated Reports of the Committee on Protection of Records of the National Fire Protection Association, Reprinted, 1945, from Proceedings of Annual Meetings, 1923-1939.

"Protection of Microfilm Against Damage by Fire Advance Reports." *Natl. Fire Protection Assoc. Quarterly,* Vol. 35, No. 4, Pt. 2 (April 1942).

"Report of the Committee on Preservation of Motion Picture Film." *J. Soc. Motion Picture Engrs.,* Vol. 35, pp. 584-606 (Dec. 1940).

F. Rider. "The Microcard Code." *College and Research Libraries,* Vol. 6, Pt. II, No. 4, pp. 441-6 (Sept. 1945).

L. J. van der Wolk and J. C. Tonnon. "The Microcopy on Flat Film as an Aid in Documentation." *Rev. Documentation,* Vol. 17, 1950, Nos. 5 and 8, pp. 134-141, 216-238.

H. R. Verry. "Unesco's Survey of Microfilm Use, 1950." *Unesco Bull. for Libraries,* Vol. 5, pp. 161-166 (May 1951).

"Tagung Mikrobuch am 22.1.1948 in . . . Wetzlar." Report published by the
library of Messrs. E. Leitz, Wetzlar, 1948, 10 pp.

W. Best. "Neue deutsche Aufnahme-und Lesegeräte." *Rev. Documentation,*
Vol. 17, No. 4, pp. 97-101 (1950).

H. H. Fussler. *Photographic Reproduction for Libraries.* University of Chicago Press, Chicago, Ill.

H. W. Greenwood. *Document photography, individual copying and mass
recording.* London, 1943.

R. de Sola. *Microfilming.* Essential Books, New York, 1944.

D. T. Richnell. "Some Aspects of Microfilm Reproduction and Reading in
British Libraries." Papers of Scarborough Conference, Library Association, 1948, pp. 32-39.

D. F. Noll. "Microfilming of records." U. S. War Dept. Technical Manual,
TM 12-257, March 1946.

R. C. Gremling. "You Can Afford Microphotography." *Library J.,* Vol. 75,
pp. 246-247, 334, 336 (Feb. 15, 1950).

Fremont Rider. "The Scholar and the Future of the Research Library."
New York, 1944.

E. B. Power. "The Use of High Reduction Microfilm in Libraries." *Amer.
Documentation,* Vol. 1, pp. 139-143 (Aug. 1950).

G. W. Bacon. "Handling Microcards in Libraries." *College and Research
Libraries,* Vol. 11, pp. 372-373 (Oct. 1950).

G. W. W. Stevens. "Some Practical Aspects of Microphotography." *Phot. J.,*
Vol. 84, pp. 108-111 (April 1944).

H. M. Silver. "'Near-Print' Draws Nearer." *J. Documentation,* Vol. 5,
pp. 55-68 (Sept. 1949).

A. de Waele. "The Duplication of Documents, etc. by Photographic Methods."
F.I.D. Communications, Vol. 6, pp. 15-16 (1939) (Gesteprint; Forograph).

M. E. Schippers. "Federative Documentary Organization with the Aid of
New Technical Means." (Ondoprint). *Trans. Internt. Fed. Documentation,* 14th Conference, 1938, Vol. 2, pp. 230-232.

"Stenafax Facsimile." *Amer. Documentation,* Vol. 1, p. 170 (Aug. 1950),
(stencil reproduction by electronics).

C. A. Harrison. "The Fairchild Photo-electric Engraver." *Penrose Annual,*
Vol. 45, pp. 104-105 (1951).

R. M. Schaffert and C. D. Oughton. "Xerography." *J. Opt. Soc. Amer.,*
Vol. 38, pp. 991-998 (Dec. 1948).

R. S. Schultze. "Literaturflut und mechanisierte Auskunftserteilung unter
Berücksichtigung der modernen Einrichtungen des Auslandes." *Nachr.
Dokumentation,* Vol. 1, pp. 10-16 (June 1950).

V. D. Tate. "The Library and the Technique of Research." *M.I.T. Library
Annual,* 1948, pp. 43-51.

H. T. Engstrom. "Microfilm Selection Equipment in Information Work."
Ind. Eng. Chem., Vol. 42, pp. 1460-1461 (Aug. 1950).

J. W. Perry. "New Horizons in Scientific Information Techniques." *Chemisch
Weekblad,* Vol. 45, pp. 522-524 (Aug. 13, 1949).

D. R. Jamieson. "Mechanized Bibliographic Aid." *Library Assoc. Record,* Vol. 53, pp. 216-221 (July 1951).

E. C. Berkeley. *Giant Brains; or Machines That Think.* Wiley, New York, 1949.

R. R. Shaw. "The Rapid Selector." *J. Documentation,* Vol. 5, pp. 164-171 (Dec. 1949).

C. S. Wise and J. W. Perry. "Multiple Coding and Rapid Selector." *Amer. Documentation,* Vol. 1, pp. 76-83 (April 1950).

"Clearing House for Extensive Microfilming Projects (at the Union Catalog Division, Library of Congress)." *Amer. Documentation,* Vol. 1, p. 164 (Aug. 1950).

L. K. Born. "A National Plan for Extensive Microfilm Operations." *Amer. Documentation,* Vol. 1 pp. 66-75 (April 1950).

"Microfilms and Microcards: Their Use in Research, A Selected List of References." The Library of Congress, Washington, D. C., June 1950.

Daniel F. Noll. "A Selected Bibliography on Microphotography." *U. S. Natl. Archives 1948,* pp. 150-153 (National Archives Publ. 49-5).

Vernon Tate. "From Binkley to Bush." *American Archivist,* Vol. 10, pp. 249-257 (July 1947).

Clapp, Henshaw and Holmes. "Are Your Microfilms Deteriorating Acceptably?" *Amer. Library J.,* Vol. 80, No. 6, pp. 589-595.

R. Gilliam Rudd. "Some Factors Influencing the Quality of Microfilm Images." *Proc. Natl. Microfilm Assoc. 2nd Annual Meeting, N. Y.,* March 19-20, 1953, pp. 44-58.

C. E. K. Mees. *The Theory of the Photographic Process.* Macmillan, New York, 1954 (2nd ed.).

James and Higgins, *Fundamentals of Photographic Theory.* Wiley, New York, 1948.

Roebuck and Staehle. Photography, Its Science and Practice. Appleton-Century, New York, 1942.

W. Clark. "Cellulose Photographic Film," in *Dictionary of Applied Photography,* Vol. 2, 4th ed. p. 446, 1938.

G. E. Matthews. "Chemistry of Photography." *The Complete Photographer,* Issue 11, pp. 702-718.

V

CAMERAS

BASIC REQUIREMENTS

Photographing a document requires:
(1) setting the document in place within the lens field of the camera;
(2) illuminating the document; and
(3) photographing the document by exposing the film to the illuminated document and the identification data associated with it for the required length of time at the required light level.*

PERFORMING THE NECESSARY OPERATIONS SO THAT THE EQUIPMENT IS READY TO PHOTOGRAPH THE NEXT DOCUMENT

Large or small, all microcopying camera equipment performs the functions mentioned above. In the smaller kind, many if not all of these operations must be performed manually by operating a control or controls associated with each of the functions in the correct order and at the right time. In the larger kind, which may cost as many thousands of dollars as the smaller costs hundreds, a single button may cause all the required operations to occur in the correct sequence for the correct time interval and at the right time for all the documents to be photographed at the time of interest. Equipment used to photograph large numbers of documents of

---

* Different settings of focus and lens aperture will probably be required if different lenses are used to photograph the document and the identification data of the document. When different lenses are used, both document and caption are usually photographed simultaneously, the illumination level for both being the same. Some camera equipment, notably sheet film equipment, uses different lenses but most microfilm camera equipment uses special caption materials so that the identification caption data will be of appropriate size on the film.

the same or similar kind every day in repetitive fashion usually has numerous automatic devices, such as document feeders, which, when running, require the operator to do little more than keep a hopper filled with documents to be recorded. One class of larger automatic equipment is of the intermittent-operation type in which a cycle of events is repeated intermittently every time a document is to be recorded. In some, the operator must push a button for each document; in others he pushes the button only once to start the machine, and it stops automatically when the hopper is empty or when the camera needs to be reloaded. A second class of automatic photographing equipment is the continuous-flow type where the film moves steadily in the camera, and the documents move steadily in suitable similar fashion on a continuously moving conveyor-like belt before the camera or over a photographing aperture upon which the camera is focused.

The control apparatus for automatic equipments may be quite complex and quite expensive; the control equipment may be designed and built as an integrated part of the basic mechanism. In the Diebold continuous-flow microfilm camera No. 90-03, equipment of the second class, the continuous-flow class, for example, 500 checks or 150 letters may be recorded per minute. A photoelectric cell triggers an electronic switch as a document spacing control; the switch is actuated by the leading and the trailing edges of the document copy. In this Diebold camera equipment, there is a two-sheet cutoff which automatically stops the machine if two documents are present in the lens field at the same time; this limits the machine to recording one document at a time. When the end of the film roll is reached in the film magazine, an electrical interlock automatically turns on a warning light and at the same time the conveyor stops and cannot be restarted until a fresh roll of film is loaded in the camera.

Accessories and auxiliaries can be added to the Diebold camera equipment of the flow type (to the Diebold 90-46, for example) that permit the combination to be used as a flow enlarger. When so used, the machine will permit the enlargement of a roll of microfilm negative to a large roll of sensitized paper to reproduce the documents from the microfilm at original size or larger, as desired. Such complex and specialized yet versatile equipment can be justified only when the work load of the machine in documents per hour is quite high, and the need for such a workload continues fairly constant from day to day. It would not be justified for a small library, for example, where the librarian might be called upon to provide occasional document copies, say a few a week; its price is $2650.00.

At the other end of the cost scale is the Polaroid Copymaker, definitely useful equipment for photographic copying of documents. The Copymaker is a holder for a Polaroid Land camera that provides a photographing stage upon which copy or objects to be photographed may be placed. Since the Polaroid Land camera is used, no special developing is required, as a completely processed print can be obtained from the film holder of the camera within some 60 seconds after the exposure is made; the processing occurs within the camera. The Model 205 Copymaker provides:

(1) polarized illumination to reduce "hot spot" reflections even from shiny objects;

(2) an automatic indicating scale which shows the proper platform setting, and the correct camera focus setting and lens aperture setting;

(3) an exposure guide that indicates the correct exposure for each platform setting and for the different kinds of copy work;

(4) an adjustable platform that accommodates originals of different sizes from 3 by 4 inches to 11 by 14 inches;

(5) an electric timer for presetting the exposure time;

(6) a circular fluorescent lamp that provides uniform diffuse illumination at every platform level.

The price of the Model 205 Copymaker is $67.50; the Polaroid Land camera is $89.75 additional. An 8-exposure film roll costs $1.75. The picture size is $3\frac{1}{4}$ by $4\frac{1}{4}$ inches. Using the largest size copy (14 inches) for which provision is made, the maximum reduction obtained is about 1:4. Since the format and the reduction used do not meet the requirements set forth in the American Standards reproduced in Appendix C, the Polaroid Copymaker may not be called a microfilm camera in the strict sense.

Although roll film camera equipment is the most important for recording original microrecords in the United States, there is no reason why the recording of micro-images on sheet film (microfiches) will not prove much more useful in the future than it is now. Just how far and how fast progress will be made will depend in some measure on the convenience of indexing, storing, and like factors. There would seem to be little reason, for example, why microrecords should not be stored in the same sheet sizes and in the same cabinets as original documents themselves; such storage would be economic if the volume of documents per subject were quite large. If, hypothetically, a business office uses stationery 8½ by 11 inches, it might use an opaque card such as a Readex Microprint card with 10 by 10 documents recorded on each side of the card; 200 letter-size sheets would then appear per card with 100 sheets per side. Cards, carbon copies of letters, and original letters might all be kept in the same single file, suitably indexed.

Although no product such as the hypothetical one just described is being marketed commercially, a variant is in almost as wide use in Europe as Microcard and Readex Microprint are in the United States. Microfiches, usually transparencies on sheet film, are filed in pretty much the same way as index cards. They are used in a variety of sizes ranging from 75 by 125mm to 228 by 152mm. Each microfiche contains a variable number of images depending upon the reduction ratio employed for recording. UNESCO* has suggested that 75 by 125, 105 by 148, and 228 by 152mm sizes be standardized not only for transparencies but also for opaque copies from these sizes as well. Microfiches are most widely used in the Netherlands and Germany; they are also used to an important extent in France. In one commercial equipment† 3 to 10 images are recorded per horizontal row and 2 to 7 rows of images per 75 by 125mm frame (fiche). The reduction ratios used with this equipment range from 1:6 to 1:24. Titles for the exposures are photographed through a separate camera objective of 100mm focal length.

Needless to say, there is a very wide variety of combinations of equipment performance, equipment features, and automatic controls which may be measured in terms of equipment complexity, equipment quality, equipment reliability, ease of operation and the like, all of which are reflected in the first cost and the operating costs. In the very simplest case where a photographic copy of a

---

* UNESCO Bulletin for Libraries, Vol. VI, No. 2/3, February-March, 1952, p. E34.

† Manufactured by Les Appareils Controleurs, Paris.

document is needed in a noncritical application, it has not been uncommon for an amateur photographer, in satisfying an occasional need, to use his still camera for the purpose.

LENS PERFORMANCE

Despite the obvious simplicity and low cost of this approach, it must be emphasized that neither the lenses nor the films ordinarily used in still cameras have the ability to record fine detail accurately with suitable reduction ratios with the sharpness and without the image distortion of which lenses and films designed specifically for microfilming purposes are capable. In terms of detail rendition, for example, microfilm lenses are customarily designed (in the best commercial makes) for approximately a two-to-one advantage over a very good still camera lens. The Kodak Microfile Ektar, for example, which is designed as an $f/4.5$ lens with a fixed mechanical aperture of $f/8.0$, is rated to yield a resolution of 160 lines per millimeter throughout most of its field. In a very good still camera lens, say $f/1.5$ at full aperture, a resolution of 60 lines per millimeter in the corners of the image is considered good performance, even if the lens is stopped down (the mechanical iris aperture closed) to the point where the greatest resolving power is obtained from that lens.

Since the lens is so very important in recording fine detail, it is worthwhile to go into some detail regarding it. ASA Z38.4.19-1948* lists the American Standard Nomenclature for Parts of a Photographic Objective Lens. The equivalent focal length of a lens determines the reduction ratio at which the lens can be worked; ASA Z38.4.21-1948* describes the American Standard Methods of Designating and Measuring Focal Lengths and Focal Distances of Photographic Lenses.

The theoretical photographic speed of a lens is determined by its relative aperture, a measure of the diameter of the entrance pupil of the lens in terms of the equivalent focal length of the lens; for a lens with a ratio of 1:2, the relationship is written $f/2$. The symbol f (lower case) is used to represent relative aperture; the symbol F (upper case) is used to designate the focal length of a lens. ASA Z38.4.20-1948* describes the American Standard Meth-

---

* Reproduced in Appendix C, pages 387 to 393.

ods of Designating and Measuring Apertures and Related Quantities Pertaining to Photographic Lenses.

In practice, every photographic lens exhibits light losses due to reflection, refraction, and absorption at each surface that the light traverses; for this reason the relative aperture of a lens is always larger than its actual light transmission t, which is the practical value of light transmission that accounts for the light losses. For a well-coated lens, the loss at each surface of which there are two per element may be as small as $1\frac{1}{2}$ to 2% of the incident light; for an uncoated lens, the loss at each surface may be as high as 4 to 5%. It is quite obvious, therefore, that a multi-element lens, say with seven elements, will permit appreciably less light to pass to expose the film than a simpler lens, say of three elements; the difference will be especially large when the lenses in question are not coated with low-reflectance coatings.

Since the primary reason* for designing multi-element lenses is to increase photographic speed compared with lenses of a smaller number of elements, and since the use of additional lens elements not only reduces the light transmission of the lens but also increases the possibility of internal reflections within the lens, which reduce its ability to record fine detail, it is apparent that lens designers are acutely aware of design compromises that they must make between increasing the photographic speed of the lens being designed and reducing the quality of its definition. A Tessar lens of $f/2$, for example, having only three separated lens components and consequently three pairs of glass-air surfaces, will show a 20% increase in light transmission over that of a modern uncoated $f/2$ lens with five separated components with five pairs of glass-air surfaces. If all surfaces of this modern five-component lens are treated appropriately with reflection-reducing coatings, for example with calcium fluoride, the coated lens will transmit 50% more light than the same lens uncoated. Such a coating not only reduces the light loss within the lens but also reduces somewhat its internal reflections.

In practice, the performance of a very good uncoated lens is aided more in terms of lens performance improvement by the process of coating than is the performance of a poor lens; the

---

* This usually applies especially to lenses of short focal length (25mm or less).

amount by which it is aided depends upon how much better the lens is. For this reason a coated lens of good design will show much better definition at a specific lens opening than a coated lens of poor design. Coating tends to accentuate the differences in quality between lenses (apparently similar, good vs. bad) but tends to make the light transmission of both good and bad lenses of a specified number of elements alike.

National Bureau of Standards Circular C428, "A Test of Lens Resolution for the Photographer" (Government Printing Office, Washington, D. C., 1941), discussed in Chapter IV, provides a set of charts by which the resolving power of a photographic lens may be numerically measured with respect to a definite scale of values, and includes a detailed description of the procedure and technique to be followed in order that comparative values may be obtained by different observers. The charts supplied are printed from plates by the U. S. Bureau of Engraving and Printing; the plates for this printing were ruled by means of a dividing engine. The process of printing employed is identical with that used in the production of postage stamps; the charts, when magnified, will not appear fuzzy at any order of magnification likely in lens testing, such as 5×.

The evaluation of lens performance is so important that some of the data and text of NBS Circular C428 deserves to be cited or paraphrased:

Lenses of different types or makes may show important differences in performance arising from differences in vignetting. For a given setting of the lens diaphragm (in the event that the setting of the lens diaphragm is adjustable), the effective exposure is necessarily less at the corners of the photographic plate than at the center (except with unusual designs not ordinarily encountered with microfilming equipment). In some instances in order to produce a compact lens (of smaller diameter), or in order to lessen the cost of production, the outer components of the lens are unduly reduced in diameter. This can be done to the extent that the speed of the lens, as far as the center of the field is concerned, is not reduced, but there is excessive vignetting and the exposure received by the corners of the field is much less than for a lens of the same nominal speed, but with the outer components of more generous (larger) diameter.

A great variety of lenses is now available, and lenses identical in focal length and speed but of different makes and qualities sell at widely different prices. When such a series of lenses is tested, the most marked difference in performance is found to lie in the sharpness of the images produced; and this one characteristic is probably the best single criterion for determining the quality of the lens. Lens makers have not yet adopted a method of specifying the quality of their lenses that is helpful to the purchaser. This is not surprising because a precise specification of lens quality is attended with many difficulties.

It is common practice to describe a lens as being free or sensibly free from the different aberrations such as chromatic and spherical aberration, coma, astigmatism, curvature, and distortion. No lens can be entirely free from these aberrations. In any lens that covers an extended field of view some of the aberrations are always present to such an extent that they are sensible at some part of the field, either at unit magnification on a positive print or at an enlargement of four or five times the original size of the test pattern. Lenses are sometimes characterized by a statement that the diameter of the circle of confusion has a stated value, say 1/250 inch. Although this statement appears quantitative, it does not give complete information; if the measurement is made upon the photographic image of a star, real or artificial, the diameter of the recorded image is so largely a function of the brightness of the star, and the duration time of the photographic exposure, that it tells little about the performance of the lens per se.* Where statements are made about the size of the circle of confusion of a particular lens by the lens manufacturer, it is probable that the stated value was not determined by measurement at all, but determined, rather, by calculation based upon the results of ray tracing required for the detailed determination of the factors involved in the lens design. Such a calculated value ignores entirely the quality of workmanship of the lens under consideration. In recent years manufacturers have recognized the shortcomings of this quality measure and, to an increasing degree, have refrained from using it as a quality index.

Different numerical values for resolving power are obtained for different values of process and image contrast. In Bureau of Standards Circular C533 (1952) two sets are provided, one of high contrast and one of low contrast. The former is especially useful in connection with the reproduction of type, line cuts, etc.; the latter with continuous tone photographs. Such charts are a must in evaluating performance.

Despite the rapid progress in photography and cameras before World War II, the American Armed Forces found considerable

---

* For a number of years the National Bureau of Standards has tested airplane camera lenses; such lenses have many performance requirements in common with lenses for microfilm cameras. The special camera used is described in the *Journal of Research of the National Bureau* of Standards, Research Paper RP984 (1937), ''Precision Camera for Testing Lenses,'' a reprint is obtainable from the Superintendent of Documents, Washington, D. C. at a nominal cost.

difficulty with the calibration and marking of lenses and camera equipment. To a great extent these standards have corrected the difficulty: American Standard Z38.4.3-1947, Distance Scales Marked in Feet for Focusing Camera Lenses;* American Standard Z38.4.13-1948, Distance Scales Marked in Meters for Focusing Camera Lenses;* American Standard Z38.4.7-1950, Lens Aperture Markings;* American Standard Z38.4.4-1942-R1947, Focal Lengths of Lenses, Marking;* American Standard PH3.5-1952, American Standard Exposure-Time Markings for Between-the-Lens Shutters Used in Still Picture Cameras;* American Standard PH3.3-1952, Exposure-time Markings for Focal Plane Shutters.* Although microfilm cameras do not have the wide range of exposure times available in conventional still cameras, the performance requirements specified in Standard PH3.5-1952 for the exposure time values found in microfilm camera equipment should be considered to apply until such time as special standards are issued specifically covering microfilm cameras.

American Standard PH3.14-1944, Dimensions of Front Lens Mounts for Cameras,* and American Standard Z38.4.11-1944, Threads for Attaching Mounted Lenses to Photographic Equipment,* although written particularly for still camera lenses, may be considered to apply to microfilm cameras where the types of mounts and their dimensions are comparable to those shown in the standards. Since many microfilm cameras have specialized requirements that arise out of their need for high-speed operation, lens mounts and lens mounting arrangements may differ markedly from the standards shown. In this regard microfilm cameras are like still cameras and motion picture cameras; bayonet-type lens mounts with accurately machined mounting flanges are not unusual in the more costly camera equipment.

Resolving Power

If one attempts to photograph a pattern of parallel lines, it will be found that the lines, if too close together, will photograph as a gray patch and the individual line cannot be distinguished. If however, the lines in the object are so far apart that they are

---

* Reproduced in Appendix C, pages 394 to 402.

recorded as distinct lines, the lens is said to resolve the lines. A given pattern of lines will appear finer and more difficult to resolve as it is placed more distant from the lens. If the distance between the just resolvable lines on the test chart is measured, this value has meaning only when the distance from the lens to the chart has also been measured.

In practice, the user is concerned not with the fineness of detail in the object being microfilmed, but only with the fineness of detail upon the microfilm negative and/or copies and prints from that negative, whatever they may be. Since at this point examination of a print of a microfilm negative or an enlargement paper print from the microfilm negative would introduce additional unknown variables of the quality losses* of the copying process, only the original microfilm negative should be examined to evaluate the performance of the lens, the microfilm camera, and its film. This can be done with a conventional compound microscope, or with a projection microscope; it will be useful to examine the microfilm negative with a microscope enlargement of several different values: (1) approximately at one-half the reduction ratio of the microfilm, (2) at equal value, and (3) at a value of some four or five times the reduction value. For examining the image at lower values of magnification, the microfilm readers that are available may be quite useful. The NBS chart may be examined with a hand glass of about 5× magnification for direct comparison of the original and the facsimile of the microfilmed test that is examined under the microscope under the greatest enlargement recommended so that the two will be of the same size when compared.

When conducted as described, the resolution test is dependent not only upon the lens but also upon the camera construction and the characteristics of the photographic film. A lens cannot be expected to produce negatives of the first quality unless it is mounted in a camera that holds the film, free from curvature, in

---

* When the quality losses in the copying process are being investigated, it is necessary to examine every generation or stage in the copying process by comparing the film or other material of which the copy is made under such magnification as will permit a direct comparison of the image with the original subject with a one-to-one size relationship between the two items being compared. It will be rare indeed that the difference between original and copy will not be immediately apparent, or that the difference between any two generations will not be immediately apparent.

a plane normal to the axis of the lens. Consistently good negatives cannot be produced unless the camera functions, such as its focusing, are sufficiently free from lost motion to permit a given camera adjustment to be repeated with certainty. Even with an excellent lens and camera, the resolution may be limited by the type of film used; for this reason only microfilm negative of highest quality should be used in photographing the original, as other forms of negative film have appreciably lower resolving power values. With the better lenses, the limiting resolution in the center of the field is most frequently determined by the film if other than microfilm negative is used.

The resolving power of a practical lens is not the same across the entire negative; usually it is greater at the center and decreases along any radius. Although the decrease is often assumed to be symmetrical about the center axis of the lens along different radii, the assumption is not valid because of unavoidable errors in workmanship. In practice, the geometrical center of a lens element and its optical center fail to coincide by a small but significant amount; a considerable percentage of the manufacturing cost of an objective lens such as a microfilm camera lens is involved in centering and locating the individual glass elements properly within the metal lens barrel housing. Some of the techniques for accomplishing this difficult task in commercial practice are outstanding examples of sheer ingenuity; when resolving power tests are made, the variations of decreases in resolving power value along different radii are frequently of the second order of importance and quite small.

At this juncture it is well to point out the usual difference in lens mounting technique used in many still cameras as compared with many motion picture cameras; in certain cases it has a distinct bearing upon the variations of resolving power of lenses along different radii. The usual still camera lens in a bellows-type camera is mounted in such a manner that the lens moves backward and forward along the optical axis (by extending the bellows) *without* any rotation of the lens at all with respect to the optical axis. The usual American motion picture lens is mounted in the motion picture camera in such a manner that the lens is rotated along a special screw thread to cause it to move backward and forward along the optical axis when it is rotated. Thus, in the still camera (bellows type), the bottom of the lens always has a fixed rotational relationship to the bottom of the picture. In most motion picture cameras and certain miniature still cameras, what is the bottom of the lens for a picture at one focus setting will be somewhere else for another focus setting; the film does not see the picture through the same parts of the lens at its different focus settings. Occasionally, when a designer of microfilm equipment designs the lens mount for the camera, he chooses his design without thinking very seriously about the lenses that his camera will use. If the generalized form of his finished equipment happens to be similar to a still camera or enlarger in appearance, he may instinctively choose the first type of design; if it happens to be similar to a motion picture camera form or a 35mm miniature camera form in appearance, he may choose the second. Because the magnitude of the variation in lens resolving power along different radii is the important factor, the use of one mount type or the other is no assurance in the case of a microfilm camera that the overall performance is either better or worse with one type of design or the other. The only way to compare one construction with another is to make comparative resolving power tests of the films produced by them; too many practical design and workmanship quality factors enter that cannot be evaluated without such a test.

In practice, it is usually considered convenient and adequate to measure the resolving power of the lens at 5-degree intervals across the lens field. At a camera distance of $26F$ (26 times the focal length of the camera lens) charts are located at the distances shown in the accompanying table; in all cases the distance from

Degrees	Distance from the center axis, ° F.
0	0
5	2.28
10	4.58
15	6.96
20	9.46
25	12.12
30	15.01
35	18.20
40	21.82
45	26.00

the center axis is given as a factor multiplied by the focal length of the lens used. When the charts furnished with the NBS Circular C428 are used as above, the maximum value that can be read from the chart is 56 lines per millimeter. To test at higher values of resolving power with the same charts, it is necessary merely to multiply the values on the charts by the same constant as is applied to the table of distance values. If we use the constant of 3 in the table, multiplying each distance value above by the factor 3, the values read on the resolving power charts shall likewise be multiplied by the factor 3. If the factor 3 is used, the maximum value of resolving power that can be measured is 168 lines per millimeter; this is 56 lines per millimeter multiplied by 3.

In making tests, it is customary to set up a line of test charts, mounting them on a long strip of wood such as wood moulding, for example, and spacing the charts at a distance equivalent to the value of 5 degrees specified. One chart will be on axis at the center, the next pair at 5 degrees, one to the left and the other symmetrically to the right of the center chart by an amount equal to 2.28 times the focal length of the lens (for a maximum reading of 56 lines per millimeter) or at a higher multiple as desired. The next pair is set at 10 degrees, one to the left and the other symmetrically to the right, and so on. Four tests are usual:

(1) with the chart strip horizontal, with the center chart at the center of the field;

(2) with the chart strip vertical, with the center chart at the center of the field;

(3) with the chart strip running from the upper right corner to the lower left corner, with the center chart at the center of the field; and

(4) with the chart strip running from the upper left corner to the lower right corner, with the center chart at the center of the field.

In all cases the chart strip is equally distant from the plane of the camera; for further details of the test, refer directly to NBS Circular C428.

Since good microfilm negative film is rated at 180 lines per millimeter, and good microfilm lenses are rated at 160 lines per millimeter, it would seem reasonable at first glance to expect that resolving power values of three times the 56 lines per millimeter value, or 168 lines per millimeter, obtained from the NBS chart used at 3 times the reference distance of 26 times the focal length of the lens ($78F$) might be expected. Actual performance of commercial equipment when operated commercially falls quite short of this value; just how far can be determined only by test. When microfilm camera equipment consistently shows resolving power values at the top of the scale in day-to-day operations, it is reasonable to expect that it is operating with satisfactory quality and meeting the claims that its manufacturer has made. If it does not, a study of such tests as these and similar tests of the other important elements is capable of revealing the cause of the shortcomings.

The quality shortcomings of still camera films, lenses, and the like, when measured in terms of loss of detail-rendering ability compared with equipment designed specifically for microfilming purposes, are so large in magnitude that they cannot be successfully ignored regardless of how suitable such still cameras and films appear to be for their intended purposes.

Microfilm negative raw stock has a 3 to 1 advantage in resolving power over the best commercial picture negative film for motion pictures and still pictures; such films are rated at 55 to 60 lines per millimeter compared with a rating of 180 lines per millimeter for Kodak Microfile, for example. To effect significant savings in costs implies the use of large reduction ratios in microfilming; such ratios are quite impractical with anything less than the best performance from the films and lenses used.

Since the detail-rendering ability of microfilm negative is greater than the detail-rendering ability of most available lenses, it is apparent that, with good film processing, it is the equipment and its operation that will probably fail to meet the quality demands of the user. Allowance must also be made for the fact that the quality obtained from readers is ordinarily not as high as that obtained from camera equipment because readers must be made at much lower cost. Since the average reader does not have a perfect lens and optical system, it too shows a lower resolving power rating in the corners than at its center. In practice, the quality of a viewed portion of the image may be marginally satisfactory at the center of the image field and unsatisfactory when that portion is moved upward or downward and appears at the image borders. This effect must be anticipated so that the images at the corners in

the reader will not be unsatisfactory; the image on the film must
be sufficiently better than marginal to assure the readability of the
image in the corners of the reader.

Where the larger reduction ratios are used, proportionately
greater care and accuracy are demanded of the equipment than
when smaller reduction ratios are used. With extreme care, using
high definition equipment and excellent processing, a reduction
ratio of 1:60 is feasible, but, more often than not, such a high ratio
is not commercially practical. In the case of newspapers microfilmed on 35mm film by commercial microfilmers, for example, a
1:16 ratio is frequently used rather than the 1:19 ratio; for a critical user, even at this low ratio marginal image quality occurs occasionally at some portion of the image when a print from a microfilm negative is viewed on a conventional microfilm reader. It is
not unusual, for example, for such marginal quality to occur more
frequently at the corners of the image than at the center; if the
fault is in the camera, such performance would suggest that the
microfilming camera lens might well be a contributing cause. If
such marginal quality occurs more frequently at the center of the
image, for example, such performance might suggest that the focus
setting for the microfilm camera might well be a contributing cause.
If such marginal quality should appear at random places within
the image area, possibly the printing of the positive from the microfilm negative was a contributing cause, or the film gate of the camera was defective.

If the very best combination of raw films, equipment, adjustments, and operating skill are present, it is reasonable to expect
no occurrences of marginal performance; in such event not even
occasionally should poor quality images or copies be present.
Since, up to the present, marginal performance has occurred occasionally in day-to-day microfilming of complete newspapers, some
newspapers have installed equipment for 70mm microfilming for
their reference file clippings. The effective reduction ratio for the
70mm film as used is about 1:10 rather than 1:16; storage costs
are therefore increased proportionately per square inch of copy
microrecorded. Since the vagaries of equipment, its adjustment,
its operation, the negative developing, the printing of the positive
and the development of the positive all contribute to effect at each
step a quality loss in the image presented to the user, it may be

said that the sum total of all such vagaries rarely results in marginal
quality with 70mm film; it does result occasionally with 35mm
film. Since the reference file clippings, because of their classification by subject or name and their indexing, constitute a more
valuable form of data storage in terms of accessibility to the user
(since unrelated matter has been discarded before microfilming),
the elimination of occasional fuzzy images of marginal and poor
quality, even though they occur but occasionally, may far more
than justify the additional storage cost implied by the small reduction, and the higher cost of microfilming per square inch of text.
Such data may be considered more highly refined. Phrased still
another way, in the case of documents and clippings, the increase
in cost that results from the 1:10 reduction used on 70mm film is
reflected in an increase in storage space of about one-half over that
of 35mm film used at the ratio of 1:16 and an increase in the cost
of film used. This additional cost is more than offset by the greater
value of the data stored per unit stored, regardless of whether the
unit is measured in terms of unit area, unit number of words, say
per thousand words, or other unit of measure. Document data must
be refined if they are to be used for a specific purpose, and they
must be refined in accordance with the requirements of the intended use.

Although reduction ratios of 1:60 and as high as 1:100 are
feasible, such high ratios are not ordinarily commercially practical
for run-of-the-mine documents; in practice, a reduction of 1:40
is more practical for a second-generation end-use copy such as a
print. At this value it is not probable that every letter of every
document so recorded will be crystal-clear in a print; occasionally
some portions of some images will probably be somewhat fuzzy, and
a few images may be somewhat fuzzy in quality. To prevent fuzziness, even in a small portion of the image, a low reduction ratio of
the order of 1:10 is necessary in the "average" operation with present commercial processing. There is little doubt that, as microfilm
and microrecording become more widely used, these ratios will
move upward in value; with very great care, for instance, it would
seem likely that what is now being done with 70mm film will, in
the next decade, be approached with 35mm film; what is now being
done with 35mm will in all likelihood be approached with 16mm
film. Since increased savings in storage costs depend squarely

upon the use of the larger reduction ratios, the cost savings possible would seem to be well forth the effort. Since the important savings occur in live storage and not in dead storage, accessibility in terms of convenient filing and rapid search will be of great importance. Airborne dust is probably the most serious obstacle.

Since the lens in the microfilming camera and its setting accuracy play such an important part in the maximum value of reduction that is practical with a particular kind of equipment, it would be unwise to purchase any microfilming camera equipment, especially if it is to be purchased outright, without making some resolution tests on it as it will be used. Although the lenses furnished by microfilm equipment manufacturers are generally of good quality, it is not unusual to find significant quality differences between one lens and another of the same type used in camera equipment. As mentioned in the previous chapter, a resolving power test of the camera lens as mounted in the camera equipment to be purchased should give an indication of what the resolving power of the lens actually is. The National Bureau of Standards charts from Circular C428 would be photographed at 3 times the recommended distance of 26 times the focal length. With commercial equipment it is probable that the resolving power determined from the reproduced chart will be noticeably less than the largest value of 168 lines per millimeter; it may prove as low as 100 lines per millimeter. To relate the results from the charts with practical microfilming, the charts should be photographed over the same range of reduction ratios and at the same settings at which the equipment is to be used. When the microfilm chart test is processed, it should be processed in just the same manner as production microfilm so that chart tests may be matched with production microfilming as a quality guide. Generally speaking, assuming consistent operation, the certainty with which clear and sharp images will probably be produced can be indicated by the ratio of the resolving power of the lens as determined by the method suggested above to the reduction ratio at which the microfilming camera equipment is regularly used.

CAMERA SPOOLS

Although many cameras accommodate a roll of raw stock in the feed side of the camera magazine larger than 100 feet, exposed film is usually taken up on 100 foot film camera spools. American Standard Z38.1.52-1951* describes the standard camera spool for 16-millimeter film; American Standard Z38.1.54-1951* describes the standard camera spool for 35mm film; and American Standard Z38.1.55-1951* describes the standard camera spool for 70mm film. Camera spools are quite different from reels used to mount processed microfilm; they are more sturdy, much more accurately made, and more costly.

FACTORS AFFECTING IMAGE QUALITY IN PRACTICE †

Since no end-use copy made from a microfilm facsimile negative original can ever equal the quality of that original because each step in the photographic copying process is accompanied by a photographic loss, the quality of the facsimile negative original is of primary importance. In practice, several factors affect it to a marked degree, causing marked reduction of the quality of which it is capable under suitable operating conditions.

The starting point is the lens. Lenses for microfilm should be:

(1) free from aberrations common to many types;

(2) all glass-air surfaces should be coated to reduce stray light transmitted to the dark-image regions of the lens;

(3) the sharpness should be high, and the resolving power 100 lines per millimeter or more (sharpness is more important than resolving power);

(4) the field should be flat;

(5) the lens should be operated at optimum aperture where the detail-rendering ability of the lens is a maximum (to accomplish this some manufacturers fit to the lens a fixed diaphragm of the appropriate value).

Often a lens-film combination which does not resolve the individual line of a series of narrow parallel lines may satisfactorily record a single line of the same width; such a combination has good sharpness.

---

* Reproduced in Appendix C, pages 403 to 408.

† Some of the material in this section has been adapted from Proceedings, Second Annual Meeting, The National Microfilm Association, New York, March 19-20, 1953, from a paper, "Some Factors Influencing the Quality of Microfilm Images," by R. G. Rudd, Communication 1586, Kodak Research Laboratories, Eastman Kodak Co.

In the average case the improper use of a good lens will cause less loss of image detail than the proper use of a poor lens.

Dust or smudge or finger prints collected on a lens (from city smog, for example), may reduce the detail-rendering ability of a lens by as much as 50% and even more. The result is an increase in lens flare and a loss of light; the loss of light is far less important than the loss of image detail.

When humidifiers are used (during cold weather, for example), the minerals in the water have been known to deposit a heavy coating of such dissolved minerals as a thin layer on a camera lens overnight; this may be avoided if distilled water is used in the humidifiers.

A lens should be cleaned only when it is dirty. A lens should not be scrubbed. To examine it, a fountain-pen flashlight is used about 6 inches away from it, viewing through the lens from the other side; this is known as dark field examination. To clean, paricles are first blown away with a syringe such as a rubber ear syringe; the objective is to use a small orifice to increase the air velocity sufficiently to blow off surface dust. Then it is polished with the lightest pressure possible, using lens tissue with lens cleaner. The fountain-pen flashlight inspection must be made both during and after the cleaning process to assure that cleaning has been accomplished as intended.

A good facsimile of a document such as a microfilm negative will usually be more legible when enlarged to original size than the original document itself under identical viewing conditions. Microfilm when well exposed and processed usually has a higher contrast than the original document. Exposure level is critical, and processing must be consistent.

At the usual values of reduction encountered (less than 1:30), the grain size of microfilm is so small compared with the smallest detail of the document image that it will not be observed at all. At higher reductions (1:100, for example) the loss of quality in the image under best conditions that is due to the grain of the film depends upon the ratio of the image detail to the grain size. In practice, even microfilm emulsions, as fine as they are in grain size, have slight yet significant turbidity; owing to emulsion turbidity, fine lines of a document are reproduced somewhat finer and broad lines somewhat broader than their counterparts in the original document. Only the Lippman emulsion has zero turbidity, but it is impractical to use a Lippman-type emulsion for commercial micro-filming at present because entirely too much light would be required for illumination of the document and for related reasons. Turbidity is a function of grain size; since microfilm is the finest-grained material regularly marketed for commercial purposes, its turbidity is the lowest among commercial materials. Since the photographic speed of fine-grain materials can be increased by improvements in the negative films themselves and in the developing of those films, we can expect in the future that it will become more and more practical to use finer and finer grained films with still lower and lower values of emulsion turbidity than today's excellent microfilm negative materials. Recent progress in the research laboratory in the physics and chemistry of sensitized films has shown that it is possible to increase the effective photographic speed of today's materials (implying an equivalent reduction in the amount of light needed for document photographing) by values between 10 and 20 without significant increase in graininess. Obviously all that is needed to get these developments out of the laboratory and on the market is a willingness on the part of the user to pay a somewhat higher price for a further improved film and a somewhat higher price for the improved chemical development of it; normal American business competition will make these advances available as soon as they show signs of becoming commercially profitable.

To obtain uniformly high quality of the photographic image on the original negative requires adjustment of the exposure (usually accomplished by changing the brightness of the illuminating lamps) in accordance with the contrast of the original document itself. If the text is bold black, more light is required than if it is handwritten or lightly printed. For practical purposes the classifications of the original documents into a small number of contrast groups is ordinarily entirely adequate to provide such a high degree of negative uniformity that copies may be made from different frames of such a negative with the identical copying equipment settings and the identical processing (developing) characteristics. This recording procedure can produce the most consistent end-use copies of the highest and most consistent quality from copy to copy, from day to day, and from year to year as well as from place to place. Generally speaking, the greater the reduction at which documents are photographed, the more accurate must be the exposure control and the greater the number of contrast groups into which the original documents must be classified. To aid in the classification of documents with respect to contrast and to aid in the precise determination of exposure levels, much of the most costly equipment is equipped with exposure meters, brightness meters, and the like. In practice some 5 to 7 contrast groups are widely used. The accompanying table lists suggested reference values for a five-group

Group	Relative exposure, %	Negative background density
1 (printed books, typewritten matter, etc.) .	100	1.7
2 (fine printing, writing with a soft pencil, lightly typed letters, etc.)	95	1.60
3 (penciled engineering drawings; faded printing, thin colored lines, very fine printing)	87	1.40
4 (lightly handwritten manuscripts, faint printed documents)	80	1.25
5 (photostats, paper-negative copies, etc.) ..	180	

series. These values assume a film with a base density of 0.28; such film is known in the trade as "gray base film" and is the type customarily furnished for microfilm negative use. In controlling quality, the reference density of such film as developed is 1.7 and test exposures are made to produce this density with "standard" (controlled) development. Negatives made as recommended can ordinarily be printed under identical printing conditions with a high degree of uniformity and a high level of photographic quality.

In practice, vibration of the microfilming camera with respect to the document it is to photograph is often a serious source of quality loss in otherwise excellent photographing equipment; this is especially true of portable equipment. It is impossible to make very rigid equipment portable, or portable equipment very rigid; rigidity is accomplished only at the expense of appreciable weight, even in the most efficient design. For this reason portable equipment is rarely used at a reduction greater than 1:20 in practice; the same equipment in permanent form may often be used successfully at reductions as high as 1:40. One research investigator [*] who

---

[*] Henry Roger, Sandy Hook, Conn.

regularly photographs at reductions exceeding 1:100 moved his photographic laboratory to the country where there would be no heavy traffic, and put his equipment in the basement mounted on a large cement block floor that was supported by a large rock shelf in the ground. Only in this way was it possible for him to eliminate vibration effects satisfactorily with his very well-designed equipment. Remembering that vibration is a serious yet frequently ignored source of loss of quality in the microfilm negative facsimile image, very material improvement in image quality can often be obtained even with portable equipment, if it is carefully set up when it is to be used. Frequently a little ingenuity on the part of the person setting up portable microfilming camera equipment may be the equivalent of several thousands of dollars invested in better equipment that is less subject to vibration but is set up with less care.

In practice, a very important limiting factor in the use of large reduction ratios is ordinary atmospheric dust, especially at the point of end use. If a blotch of dust in a reading apparatus should obscure a significant word in text or significant figures in formulas, the microrecord may be of very little value to the user. When the reduction ratio employed is small, the blotch of dust may not be so annoying, but, when the reduction ratio becomes large, the blotch of dust may become so large relative to the text as to obscure not only single letters or numbers, but even words or terms. Commercial contract companies, knowing the importance of dust-free operations, usually take great pains to avoid or eliminate dust in their own operations; practical experience and well-remembered unpleasant accidents exert a strong influence on the degree of caution used.

For print of high quality such as that produced, say, by photo-engraving, when viewed with the naked eye under "average" advantageous viewing conditions, a value of some 5 lines per millimeter may be assumed to be a limiting value of resolving power. As a very rough rule-of-thumb, it would seem reasonable to require that microrecording materials as used show a minimum resolving power rating of 5 lines per millimeter multiplied by the reduction ratio used; this value would apply to reproductions of such quality as to be suitable for further reproduction, say, in a book. A readable copy might be rated at half that value; a good copy not suitable for reproduction at three-fourths of that value. The application of such a rule-of-thumb leads to interesting speculation when interpreted in terms of the practical reduction ratios realized.

In the section on microcopying in the F.I.D. *Manual on Document Reproduction and Selection* there are some estimates relative to reduction ratios suitable for international exchange. At no point is the text clear as to the number of generations of copies to be anticipated; in the absence of such data, one may guess that only the microcopy facsimile original and a print from it are assumed. Reduction ratios between 1:12 and 1:15 are suggested for international exchange; 1:20 is reported as possible under good conditions. Multiplying these values respectively by 5 lines per millimeter, resolving power values of 60, 75, and 100 lines per millimeter respectively must be obtained. In the same manual, in the section on high reduction, it is stated that a reduction of 1:300 is possible; 1:80 is feasible and 1:30 is the maximum that is in wide use. Again multiplying by 5 lines per millimeter, values of 1,500, 400, and 150 lines per millimeter respectively are obtained. If it is remembered that Microfile negative is rated at 180 lines per millimeter, microfilm positive at 145 lines per millimeter, and a Kodak Micro-File Ektar lens at 160 lines per millimeter, it may be inferred that the capabilities and limitations of microrecording will be better understood when published data specify precisely the number of copy generations anticipated in the process being described and the conditions under which such results are obtained.

Arbitrarily it has been suggested above that a readable copy might be rated at one-half the 5 lines per millimeter value, and a good copy at three-fourths that value. Such an arbitrary breakdown into quality degradation grades implies that a statistical quality degradation study might well be made which would describe the quality grades of reproduction actually distinguishable in microrecording. Although at the present time a user may not be able to distinguish more than three grades, a statistical study properly conducted would be certain to reveal that interested and qualified persons can recognize a larger number. Since it is quite evident that price differences should be directly reflected in the quality grades, such a study will hasten quality standardization. It would not be surprising to find the same number of steps of quality degradation and the same verbal descriptions of them as were found in an elaborate statistical study of the quality of television pictures by the Bell Telephone Laboratories.

Since microrecording has fundamentally the same reproduction problems as television and motion pictures, being photographic processes, all would appear to be subject to the same fundamental methods of analysis. A description of the study for television appears in the *Proceedings of the Institute of Radio Engineers.** This fundamental and thorough study suggests that quality may be rated quite accurately in accordance with an empirical quality degradation scale with word descriptions accurately related to a seven-number scale as follows:

    (1) not perceptible degradation;
    (2) just perceptible;
    (3) definitely perceptible, but only slight impairment to picture;
    (4) impairment to picture, but not objectionable;
    (5) somewhat objectionable;
    (6) definitely objectionable;
    (7) not usable.

COMMERCIAL EQUIPMENT

Prices for microfilming equipment range from some $500 for the simplest equipment such as the Graflex Photorecord to well over $5000 for standard models. Since the more costly equipment (priced above $1000) can afford to use a very good lens and accurate means of setting it, a major portion of the cost above that figure may be attributed to convenience of operation and speed of operation as well as to convertibility of the specific equipment to other purposes, for example, conversion of a flow-type camera to a flow-type enlarger by the addition of accessories designed specifically for the purpose. Each manufacturer has emphasized certain features in his advertising over others; a detailed study of the advertising leaflets rarely provides sufficiently complete technical data to make it possible to choose a specific piece of equipment for a specific purpose among those offered for sale. Actual use over a period of time would seem to be the most prudent method of choosing among competitive equipment in the average case; this is

---

* Mertz, Fowler, and Christopher, ''Quality Rating of Television Images,'' *Proc. I. R. E.*, Vol. 38, pp. 1269-83, 1950.

especially true for installations where large output in documents per hour is an important factor. In many cases equipment can be rented from the manufacturer's sales agent for something like 3% of the list price per month; in many cases the rental may be applied to the purchase price if the purchaser arranges for it at the time the rental agreement is made. This percentage frequently applies to equipment in the price range of $4000 and up; the percentage may run somewhat higher on smaller equipment.

Microfilming equipment may be classed broadly into two groups based upon the manner in which the basic mechanisms are housed:

(1) flat-bed equipment and

(2) cabinet or desk-housed equipment.

Much of the higher-priced equipment is of the latter class, in which automatic electrical controls and automatic document feed and the like account for a large portion of the total cost of the equipment. 70mm and to some extent 35mm equipment is made in flat-bed form; such equipment usually has the camera or cameras mounted at the top of a rigid column facing downward to an easel or copyboard where the document to be photographed is located. In general appearance, such equipment looks somewhat like a big enlarger for still pictures.

Cabinet or desk-housed equipment is frequently of the rotary type. In the so-called rotary equipment the document is photographed on the microfilm or other original while it is passing through the machine; in some equipment of this kind the film moves through the camera aperture at a speed that is proportional to the speed of the document past the illuminated stage where it is photographed. The latter type of equipment is often called flow-type equipment.

In intermittent-cycle equipment, that is, equipment that performs the required functions sequentially in order to photograph a particular document, there are two general formats of images produced on the film:

(1) a format of standard width (usually full width, half width, or one-third width) and of variable length along the film depending upon the equivalent length of the document, and

(2) a format also of standard width and of fixed length along the film independent of the equivalent length of the document.

Frequently, the photographing camera is equipped with means to project a light beam through the camera lens to the copy, often called a field indicator, so that the copy may be accurately aligned with respect to the camera field. If the document is short compared with the full length of the projected light beam, adjustable length format cameras have means to mask the light beam from the bottom of the document upward so that the light beam just covers the document. The shutter that limits the light beam will similarly limit the aperture size of the camera after the field indicator light has been turned off. In this manner the amount of film actually used for the exposure matches closely that required by the specific document size. When the film is advanced prior to the next exposure, it is advanced just the amount required by the previously limited adjustable-length format field and by the required margin. In the second type of format, the length allotted along the film is fixed and is independent of the equivalent length of the document. The latter arrangement is frequently used for documents of standardized sizes where substantially all documents to be recorded are of preselected standard sizes. This would be typical of bank checks, business correspondence of standard $8\frac{1}{2}$ by 11 inch size, statement forms of similar size, and the like. For identification, we might call the first type adjustable-length format, and the second, fixed-length format.

At the lower end of the microfilming equipment cost scale is the Graflex Photorecord, the equipment shown in Figure 1 of Chapter IV, page 69. This is essentially a still camera, stand, platen, and lighting assembly that provides images on 35mm perforated film; the film is wound on a daylight loading spool in a manner similar to that for still cameras. The time range of the shutter is from 1/25 to 1 second; a single roll of 35mm film accommodates 800 exposures of 1 by $1\frac{3}{8}$ inches or 1600 exposures of 1 by $\frac{3}{4}$ inch. The film advance from one frame to the next is automatic; the shutter is air-operated. Four 150-watt 1000-hour reflector flood lamps are used for document illumination; the maximum document size recommended is 17 by 22 inches. Larger sizes may be accommodated if the reproduction quality of the copy is very good; in practice it would seem unwise to exceed the specified maximum. The document is set within the field of view of the camera by means of a "field indicator," a light beam projected through the optical system of the camera which permits accurate lineup of the document with respect to the photographed field; a ground glass is used for accurate focusing. The price of the Graflex Photorecord is about $400; the air-supply unit required for operating the shutter is an extra. Since the maximum document size recommended is 17 by 22 inches and the image size is 1 by 1⅜ inches, the maximum reduction at which this camera is recommended by its manufacturer is about 1:16.

The Griscombe desk microfilm cameras (Models D-1, D-3, D-4) are mounted in a desk about the size of a stenographer's desk 27 by 30 by 30 inches; prices for these models range from $700 to $750. These cameras hold 100 feet of 16mm film; the D-1 is designed for a reduction ratio of 1:17; the D-3 and D-4 for a ratio of 1:20. Both are of fixed aperture length format. The operator places the copy manually on the filming aperture, then presses a button. Four ordinary 60-watt lamps provide the required illumination; film is quickly loaded and the equipment set into operation. To photograph the reverse side of a document, it is merely necessary to turn over the document after photographing one side, and to press the button again. No provision is made for a second camera such as might be desired if one microfilm negative were to be placed in archival storage and a second microfilm negative used to provide prints and other copies for users.

Somewhat farther upward in the price scale are the 35mm "flat-bed" microfilm cameras such as the Eastman Kodagraph Micro-File Machine Model E (Fig. 1). This is an adjustable length-format portable machine consisting of:

(1) a Kodagraph Micro-File film unit (microfilm camera); convertible to 16mm if desired (the basic photographing camera used in the Eastman Kodak "flat-bed" equipment);

(2) a tripod mounting for the camera, the lamps for illumination and the copy board, and

(3) a control cabinet.

This equipment is intended for operation at a reduction of 1:10; if the copy is attached to a wall or to an upright board, the equipment may be operated at a reduction of up to 1:30

FIG. 1. 35 mm ''flat-bed'' microfilm camera (Eastman Kodagraph Micro-File machine, Model E). (Courtesy of Eastman
Kodak Co.)

if the mounting does not permit "jiggling" of the camera (the
result of vibration) with respect to the copy. It is very important
to recognize that vibration of the camera or copy with respect to
one another becomes more and more serious as the reduction ratio
is increased. Where the larger reduction ratios are used in commercial equipment, the mounting of the camera and the copy
platen must be quite rugged and vibration-free if there is to be
no "jiggling" of one with respect to the other. Should "jiggling"
occur during the exposure interval, there will be a significant loss
of resolving power. Since it is of little value to have excellent
lenses and excellent films if the camera "jiggles" with respect to the
copy, firmness and absence of such "jiggling" is very important
indeed. The price of Model E is about $1765. For permanent
installations and the like, the Kodagraph Model D operates normally in the range from 1:10 to 1:20; it may be used up to 1:30.
Its price is about $2285. The Kodagraph Model C-1 is intended for
use at reductions up to 1:30; the column upon which the camera
is mounted is extra rugged. The camera exposure oscillates from

left to right on alternate exposures so that pages of a book may be readily microfilmed. The price of Model C-1 is about $4565.

From this point onward in 35mm and 16mm microfilm camera equipments, apparatus is designed for specialized purposes; in most cases automatic document feeders for specific sizes of documents for fixed-length format are an outstanding feature.

The Burroughs equipment (made by Bell and Howell) (Fig. 2) includes a Microfilm Recorder for 16mm film only; three

FIG. 2. Burroughs recorder with Arco feeder. (Courtesy of Burroughs and Bell & Howell.)

arrangement patterns with reduction ratios of 1:18, 1:30, and 1:37 are available; mechanically interchangeable cameras are used, one for each ratio. The machine may be hand or automatically fed; checks and the like can be run at speeds up to about 400 per minute; documents such as ledger accounts can be run up to 150 per minute. A rheostat for illumination control is provided. The price of this unit is about $4050; it is available for either direct-current or alternating-current operation. A second microfilming camera may be purchased if duplicate microfilm negatives are desired.

Remington-Rand furnishes competitive microfilm camera equipment; the Dual-Film-A-Record can use either 35mm or 16mm film and can operate at reductions of 1:24, 1:32, and 1:37 as desired by changing lens assemblies. Both sides of records such as checks can be photographed simultaneously side by side, one side only down half the film, the other half up. Film-A-Record Model 6 operates at a reduction of 1:17 or 1:23, depending upon the type chosen; the twin camera with its two lenses can make two photographs of a document simultaneously on two separate rolls of film. With the Dual Film-A-Record, up to 500 checks per minute or 125 feet of paper documents may be hand fed. Such features as light intensity control by a rheostat for illumination, photographing the date of microfilming, counting the documents, stacking the documents in a hopper in the same order in which they are fed, stopping automatically when a lamp burns out are found in these machines. The price of a Remington-Rand Dual Film-A-Record is about $2350.

Diebold, makers of equipment under the trade name Flo-Film, produces a variety of microfilming, developing, printing, and enlarging equipment; most of the equipment is of the continuous flow type. Their portable camera is about the size of a suitcase, it weighs 20 pounds, it uses a reduction ratio of 1:24, it has an 11-inch throat for documents up to this maximum dimension, it uses 16mm film in a daylight-loading magazine, and it costs about $750. Their continuous flow camera 90-05 for wide drawings, maps, ledger sheets, and newspapers provides reduction ratios from 1:20 to 1:35, depending upon the document widths, which range from a maximum of 24 inches for the smallest ratio to 42 inches for the largest, is 52 by 41 by 20 inches in size and weighs 608 pounds, recording documents at a rate of either 20 or 40 feet per minute depending upon the setting of a switch. The conveyor for the documents is chain-driven from a single-phase, alternating-current, two-speed reduction motor. Equipment can be furnished to convert this highly automatic machine to a flow-enlarger to use either sheets or rolls of photographic paper. The machine proper is equipped to handle either 16 or 35mm unperforated film in 100-foot rolls; it is also so arranged that the machine proper may be used as a printer for either 16 or 35mm unperforated film. With a single lens for one reduction ratio as selected, the price of the Flo-Film 90-05 camera is about $6900, which includes the estimated cost of installation by factory service men within a short radius of the factory at Norwalk, Connecticut. Lenses for other reduction ratios are available at approximately $200 per lens set.

Although called a camera, this equipment may be used without addition of parts as a microfilm printer; with auxiliary equipment it may be used as a flow enlarger. This machine does not provide facilities for developing either microfilm or paper enlargements; such processing must be accomplished by other machines. Diebold furnish their Model 9107 film processor for developing 16mm and/or 35mm film; they furnish their Model 9140 paper processor for paper rolls up to 14 inches wide and 350 feet in length.

Alsaphot of Paris, France, has built a combination instrument, Soretex, using perforated 35mm film with an image format of 22 by 32mm that functions as a camera, enlarger, film printer, reader, and projector for images on the wall. Such a combination instrument, which is sold at a modest price, would find application where the volume of microrecorded material to be handled is limited, yet where there is need for performing all the functions within the organization. Processing equipment for the film and for the paper enlargements must be purchased separately.

Several manufacturers, notably the Microtronics Division of Photostat Corp. (Rochester, New York), and Photographic Products, Inc. (Hollywood, California) under the trade name Varifile, have specialized in the manufacture of 70mm equipment. The image on the film is usually fixed in size ($2\frac{5}{8}$ by $3\frac{1}{2}$ inches); approximately 300 images appear on a 100-foot roll. In the Microtronics equipment as a typical example, the maximum copy size is 36 by 48 inches. The reduction ratio used ranges from 1:4 to 1:14; full image coverage is obtained from original copy sizes from $8\frac{1}{2}$ by 11 inches to the maximum mentioned. The illumination is provided by four 42-inch Slim-Line fluorescent green tubes; a 25% variation of intensity is accomplished with a Variac (variable voltage control of the multi-tapped transformer type). Figure 3 shows the Microtronics 70mm camera; the price is about $3600 as shown. The two major manufacturers of 70mm equipment design most of their cameras so that they may be changed over for 35mm film if desired; this follows the similar practice of the major manufacturers of flat-bed 35mm camera to design their equipment so that it may be changed over for 16mm film if desired. Full details on such features should be sought directly from the manu-

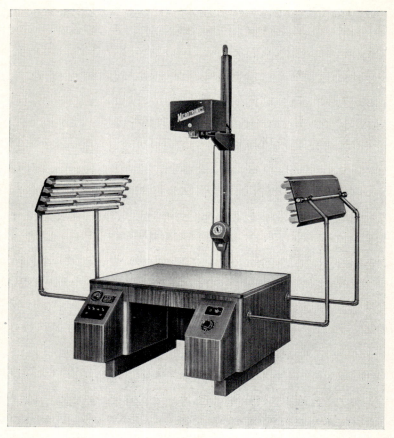

Fig. 3. Microtronics 70mm camera. (Courtesy of
Microtronics Division of Photostat Corp.)

facturers concerned; as the progress being made in the field is
quite rapid, design improvements are occurring almost daily. This
makes it impossible for any textbook to be completely up-to-date on
all features of commercial equipment.

Being fully aware of the great importance of fine detail on
engineering drawings and the like, manufacturers of 70mm microfilming equipment have striven to avoid entirely situations where
end-use copies of their negatives show hazy or unclear images regardless of how produced. For this reason the reduction at which

the original is made on 70mm film is limited to 1:14; enlargements direct from such negatives should never produce any hazy images unless the original drawing itself was poor. Since there are cases where dispersal of drawing files may be needed, which need might well be determined only after the original 70mm photographing had taken place, this modest reduction ratio combined with accurate photographing and well-controlled processing of the films and paper concerned makes it feasible to produce fourth-generation copies should the need to do so arise. The number of man-hours required to produce a drawing and the scarcity of the engineering skill required for the design of the item shown on it justify the "better be safe than sorry" attitude as the guide to the choice of the reduction ratio to be utilized. Until better measurement and testing methods, better and more complete and more numerous standards, and better operating techniques are more widely used, it is unwise to "go overboard" on high reduction ratios regardless of the very strong temptation to do so that exists in large cities where floor space is costly and a large number of documents is accumulated each day in the normal course of business.

So many factors govern the choice of the particular equipment for the particular installation that a book such as this can do little more than provide a guide to the criteria in equipment selection. Equipment manufacturers have given their cooperation unstintingly in providing data and information about their products. Because of the wide variety of products and the large number of manufacturers, only a single representative equipment in a broad class has been shown, owing to the practical limitations of space. For a user's purpose competitive equipment of the same general class may actually be better; whether it is or not will depend upon the specific needs of the application and the specific characteristics of the equipment and the personnel available to deal with them.

It must be recognized that it is almost impossible to cover in any significant manner the details of how microrecording is accomplished and used in all its important applications; a book would be required for each separate specialty field. Despite the fact that no attempt is being made to do so, some mention should be made of the microrecording of radiographs (x-ray photographs) and the like because of their great importance in the field of medicine and because of the great advances in public health that have been attained in the United States under the guidance of the medical profession. Since it is becoming more and more common for private medical clinics to assemble complete medical histories of the patients who are examined at such clinics, and since x-ray plates (as they are often called) are quite large and occupy a large amount of space for filing, it has been found that 35mm microfilm is capable of recording satisfactorily substantially all the significant detail recorded on the conventional 14 by 17 inch plate (it is often called a plate despite the fact that it is actually a film). A 35mm Kodak Radiograph Micro-File machine, made by Eastman Kodak Company (Rochester, New York), is designed to copy such radiographs on 35mm film, using a special 35mm Kodak Micro-Film, Type X. This film is a low-gamma film which with recommended development will satisfactorily reproduce Radiographs when that negative is printed on Eastman Type 7302 or 5302 Fine Grain Positive Release film. The price of the Kodak Radiograph Micro-File machine is about $3000. Details about the machine and its use, and details about making copies of radiographs will be found in *Medical Radiography and Photography,* Vol. 27, No. 4, 1951, published by Eastman Kodak Company, Rochester, New York. Although the art and science of photography have not reached the point where it is practicable as a routine procedure to make all radiographs directly on microfilm, wider use of it to provide detailed individual clinical records accumulated over a period of time will speed the day when the original itself will be directly recorded on microfilm in most places where radiographs are taken.

Table I lists a number of manufacturers and their products in different parts of the world. It must be recognized that this list, extensive as it is, is far from complete. Additional data will be found in a new publication, F.I.D. Pub. 264, of the Federation of International Documentation, 6 William Witsenplatz, The Hague, Netherlands, "Manual on Document Reproduction and Selection," Part 1, which is available in looseleaf form with supplements. This book includes manufacturers' data sheets in looseleaf form on certain of the equipment available, and should act as a valuable supplementary source book for collected commercial data as well as for data on the costs and methods of other forms of duplication such as typing, stencil, and offset printing.

TABLE I. Microfilm and Microfilm Cameras

p	= perforated	R	= to cover reduction shown	Fl	= Dutch florins	fr	= French francs
∞	= infinity (continuous flow)			DM	= German marks	£	= pounds sterling
up	= unperforated	$	= dollars (U. S.)				

Prices stated are approximate as of 1954 and do not include taxes, which may be as much as one-third of the sales price.

Type	Price	Film, size in mm	Reduction ratio	Image size, mm	Lens	Capacity	Remarks
United States							
Burroughs Recorder (1)	$4000	16p 16up 8up	1:30 1:18 1:37	13 x 16 8 x 10 6 x 8	R	100 ft	Portable automatic feeder holds up to 500 check size documents. 12,000-17,000 items photographed per hour.
Burroughs BH205 (1)	—	—	—	—	—	—	Indexing meter and dial to compensate for document color variations. Automatic feeder.
Portable (2) FloFilm	$750	16up	1:18	—	—	—	Daylight magazine loading. Wt. 20 lb| 11-in. throat.
FloFilm Model 90-05 (2)	$5950	16up 35up	1:35 1:30 1:24 1:20	15 x ∞ 32 x ∞	R	100 ft	Convertible to printer or enlarger. No limit to length of document copied. 42-in. throat.
Duplex Model 90-03 (2)	$3950	16up 35up	1:36 1:26 1:21 1:30	— 15 x ∞ 32 x ∞	R	100 ft	Can also be used as printer. Photographs documents on 1 or both sides simultaneously. 14-in. throat.

TABLE I (*Continued*)

United States (*Continued*)

Type	Price	Film, size in mm	Reduction ratio	Image size, mm	Lens	Capacity	Remarks
FloFilm Model 90-46 (2)	$2650	16up 35up	1:24 1:11 1:5.5	15 x ∞ 32 x ∞	R	100 ft	Convertible to enlarger. 14-in. throat.
Kodagraph Model C.1 (3)	$4565	35up 16up	1:12 to 1:30	32 x 44	Ektar 4.5 $F = 63$ mm	100 ft	Designed for microfilming large single sheets and large bound vols. Flat bed.
Kodagraph Model C.2 (3)	—	35up	1:30	32 x 44	Ektar 4.5 $F = 63$ mm	100 ft	Similar to C.1 but for large drawings with special copy-board. Flat bed.
Kodagraph Model D (3)	$2285	35up 35up 16p 16up	1:10 to 1:30	32 x 44	Ektar 4.5 $F = 63$ mm	100 ft	Field indicator, Exposure meter. Flat bed.
Kodagraph Model E (3)	$1765	35up 16up	1:8 to 1:30	32 x 22	Ektar 4.5 $F = 63$ mm	100 ft	Portable model. Supplied in 2 cases. Total wt. 95 lb.
Recordak Duplex RD (3)	$3100	16up	1:18 1:24 1:35	—	—	100 ft	Like Commercial. Can also record on ½ the film width. Desk type.
Recordak Triplex RF, RF 1 (3)	$2100–$2400	16up	1:19 1:24 1:35	—	—	100 ft	Like Duplex except document reverses for front and back photo. Desk type.

TABLE I (Continued)

| | | | United States (Continued) | | | | |
Type	Price	Film, size in mm	Reduction ratio	Image size, mm	Lens	Capacity	Remarks
Recordak Bantam RH (3)	$1800	16up	—	—	—	100 ft	With one lens kit. Desk type.
Filmsort Camera (4)	—	35up	—	—	—	—	Specially designed for Filmsort equipment.
Graflex Photorecord microfilm camera (5)	$391	35p	1:18	24 x 36 / 18 x 24	$f/4.5$ / $F = 75$ mm	—	Copy laid over glass. Pneumatic shutter.
Recordak Junior (3)	$975–$1550	16up	1:19 / 1:24	—	—	100 ft	Combination camera-reader. Reader enlargement 24×. Desk type.
Recordak Commercial A, B, BA, C, C.1, RE, RE.1 (3)	$600–$1625	16up	1:24	—	—	100 ft	Index marking system. Can photograph both sides simultaneously. Desk type.
Griscombe D5 (7)	$795	16up	1:21.5	11 x 2½– 11 x 14	—	200 ft	Single control and exposures up to 50 per minute.
Griscombe 16P (7)	$1195	16up		Up to 14 x 21 in.	—	200 ft	Portable unit in carrying case, complete with lights and control panel.
Griscombe D6 (7)	$895	16up	1:25	14 x 21 in.	—	200 ft	Single control and exposures up to 50 per minute.

TABLE I (Continued)

United States (Continued)

Type	Price	Film, size in mm	Reduction ratio	Image size, mm	Lens	Capacity	Remarks
Griscombe 35B (7)	$800	35	12:7	15⅝ x 18½ in.	—	100 ft	Operated electrically on 115 v. 60 cycles or 220 v. 60 cycles. Both on special order.
Griscombe 35A (7)	$895	35	1:16	20 x 24 in.	—	100 ft	Fixed focus and electrically operated. Geared for photographing vital statistics, county record materials and data.
Graphic Microfilm (6)	—	70up 35up	—	—	—	—	Turret head. Both 70mm and 35mm film rolls.
Griscombe DI (7)	$950	16up	1:17	11 x 14 in.	Fixed	100 ft	Desk type. Fixed focus. Fixed aperture.
Griscombe D3 (7)	$950	16up	1:20	—	Fixed	100 ft	Hand fed. Fixed illumination.
Microtronics (8)	$3495	70up	1:14	2⅝ x 3½ in.	—	100 ft	Fluorescent lighting consisting of 42-in. green lights.
Micro 35 (8)	$960	35u	1:16	1¼ x 1-7/16 in.	Fixed focus	100 ft	Flat bed. Removable magazine with knife. Convertible to 16mm.
Bolsey Microfilmer and reader (9)	$195	35p	1:10	24 x 36	—	40 exposures	Small portable apparatus. Can be used as reader. Wt. 18 lb.

TABLE I (Continued)

Type	Price	Film, size in mm	Reduction ratio	Image size, mm	Lens	Capacity	Remarks
				United States (Continued)			
Beattie Varifle Standard (10)	$1300 $1978	70up	1:9 1:25	2½ x 3⅜ in. 2½ x 1⅝ in.	$F = 114$ mm $F = 65$ mm	100 ft	Portable. Convertible to 35mm. Flat bed. Table top.
Master Model (10)	$2518	70up	1:13 1:35	—	$F = 65$ mm	100 ft	Same as Beattie Varifle Standard and with full-size table.
Film-a-Record Model 4 (11)	$985	16up	1:21	Full width	—	100 ft daylight spool	11-in. throat. Single roll only. Adjustable illumination.
Film-a-Record Model 8 (11)	$1125	16up	1:25	Full or ½ width	—	200 ft daylight spool	Portable. Optional ratio 1:40. Single or double row image. 12-in. throat. PB automatic feed attachment optional.
Film-a-Record Model 12 Dual (11)	$2350	35p 16up	1:24 1:32 1:37	Full or ½ width	—	200 ft daylight spool	Both sides simultaneously or two copies on separate 16mm. rolls simultaneously. 15-in. throat.
(12)	—	Sheet film	—	—	—	—	Sheet film. Detailed specifications not yet available.
				West Germany			
Lumoprint M.F. 36 (13)	3,820 DM	35p 35up	1:17.5 1:13	24 x 36 32 x 45	Tessar $f/4.5$ $F = 75$ mm	50 m	Visible and audible film control. Indicators. Automatic lighting. Magnetic shutter.

TABLE I (*Continued*)

West Germany (Continued)

Type	Price	Film, size in mm	Reduction ratio	Image size, mm	Lens	Capacity	Remarks
Lumoprint M.T. 3 (13)	$660	35p	1:17	18 x 24	Tessar $f/4.5$ $F = 30$ mm	50 m	Photoelectric device for automatic exposure calculation. Electric counting device for number of exposures.
Lumoprint M.T. 1 (13)	$1640	35N	—	18 x 24 24 x 36 32 x 45 22.5 x 32	—	164 ft	—
Filmautomat normal (14)	$1000	35p 35up	1:16 or 1:12	24 x 36 18 x 24 32 x 48 32 x 22	$f/5.7$ $F = 60$ mm	60 m	Automatic illumination. Variable exposure times. Automatic focusing. Roll or strip.
Filmautomat technik (14)	$1250	35p 35up	1:20 or 1:24	24 x 36 18 x 24 32 x 45 32 x 22	$F = 60$ or 75 mm	60 m	Two book-holders. Camera revolves 180°. Variable exposure times.
Ultraplex (14)	6,630 DM	100 x 150 or 210 x 300	1:12 1:6	100 x 150 to 210 x 300	$F = 210$ mm	Single sheets	Drawing holders. Used as enlarger.
Microfiche automatique (14)	—	75 x 125 90 x 120 105 x 150	1:21	6 x 9 to 28 x 33	R	Single sheets	Variable exposure times by electric counter.

TABLE I (*Continued*)

West Germany (Continued)

Type	Price	Film, size in mm	Reduction ratio	Image size, mm	Lens	Capacity	Remarks
Mikrophot (14)	$625	35	—	—	—	—	Wt. 105 kg. 130 x 70 x 86 cm. Similar to Griscombe.
Autophotom F (15)	1,891 DM	35p	1:12.5	24 x 36	—	5 m	Larger documents can be supported on the table if an additional supporting rod is fitted.
Autophotom F52 (15)	$856.25	35p	1:125	24 x 36 18 x 24	—	30 m	42 x 60 cm max. With automatic equipment for books with 30 x 42 cm format.
Microprint RO (16)	—	35p or 35up	—	24 x 36 32 x 54	—	—	—
Microprint PL (16)	550 DM	90 x 120	—	18 x 24	—	—	Book copying device now incorporated. Cheapest camera for sheet film.
"Fu T" Automatique (17)	5,900 DM	35up	1:4 1:19	33 x 54	$f/4.5$ $F = 75$ mm	50 m	Var. illum. Book-holder and bookwedge. Camera revolves 180°.
"Fu" Automatique (17)	4,800 DM	35up	1:4 1:10	33 x 54	Xenar $f/4.5$ $F = 75$ mm	50 m	One book-holder and bookwedge.

TABLE I (*Continued*)

Type	Price	Film, size in mm	Reduction ratio	Image size, mm	Lens	Capacity	Remarks
					West Germany (Continued)		
"Fp" (17)	4.200 DM	35p	1:12.5	24 x 36	Tessar $f/4.5$ $F = 50$ mm	50 m	Variable exposure times by exposure counter. One book-holder.
"FKp" Portable (17)	3.200 DM	35p	1:12.5	24 x 36	Tessar $f/4.5$ $F = 50$ mm	50 m	Weight 95 lb.
"Akts" (17)	8.500 DM	90 x 120 180 x 240	1:11– 1:6	90 x 120 to 180 x 240	Tessar or Apo Tessar $F = 210$ mm	Single sheets	For copying drawings. Vertical copy-holder.
Microprint RO (18)	$203.81	35p	1:20 1:10	24 x 36 18 x 24	$F = 50$ mm $f/3.5$	30 m	Semiportable. Daylight loading (cassettes).
Microprint PL (18)	$175.68	35p	1:20 1:10	18 x 24	$F = 50$ mm $f/3.5$	100 ft	Semiportable. Daylight loading (cassettes).
					France		
Soretex portable (19)	151,515 fr	35p	1:10	24 x 36	Boyer $f/4.5$ $F = 40$ mm	30 m	Used as reader, enlarger, projector, film printer. Timing device ½ to 12 seconds.
Appareil de reproduction de radio-graphies (19)	390,000 fr	25p	1:15	24 x 36	Boyer $f/4.5$ $F = 55$ mm	30 m	Opaque documents can be photographed also.

TABLE I (*Continued*)

France (Continued)

Type	Price	Film, size in mm	Reduction ratio	Image size, mm	Lens	Capacity	Remarks
Film automat Normal (20)	565,000 fr	35p 35up	1:4 1:16 1:4 1:12	24 x 36 18 x 24 22 x 32 32 x 45	Olor $F = 60$ mm Olor $F = 75$ mm	60 m	Automatic illumination. Variable exposure times. Automatic focus. Reels or strips.
Film automat Technic (20)	768,400 fr	35p 35up	1:4 1:24 1:4 1:20	24 x 36 18 x 24 22 x 32 32 x 45	Kinoptik $F = 65$ mm Kinoptik $F = 68$ mm	60 m	Two document-holders.
Microfiche (20)	771,200 fr 861,200 fr	75 x 125 90 x 120 105 x 150	1:6– 1:21	27 x 36 27 x 35 28 x 33	Xenar $F = 50$ mm	Single sheets	Electronic exposure counter for 6–170 pages per sheet.
Ultraplex Micronegatif (20)	826,000 fr	100 x 150	1:12	100 x 150	Apographe Berthiot $F = 240$ mm	Single sheets	One upright holder for single sheets.
Microplex A1 fixed (20)	835,000 fr	75 x 125 mm fiche	1:6– 1:24 Title 1:1.4	7.6 x 10.6 to 29 x 37.7	$F = 50$ mm Title $F =$ 100 mm	—	Maximum document 60 x 84 cm. 3–10 images horizontal. 2–7 images vertical.
Microplex A2 semiportable (20)	700,000 fr	75 x 125 mm fiche	1:6– 1:24 Title 1:1.4	7.6 x 10.6 to 29 x 37.7	$F = 50$ mm Title $F =$ 100 mm	—	Maximum document 42 x 60 cm. 3–10 images horizontal. 2–7 images vertical.

TABLE I (Continued)

France (Continued)

Type	Price	Film, size in mm	Reduction ratio	Image size, mm	Lens	Capacity	Remarks
Microjumma (21)	1,069,250 fr	35p	1:25	24 x 36	F = 75 mm	120 m	Rheostat for adjusting illumination. Double cameras make simultaneous exposures on two films. Fixed exposure time.
Microstyle Mural I (21)	299,650 fr	35p	1:12.5 1:10 1:8	24 x 36 18 x 24	Kinoptik F = 75 mm	120 m	Camera revolves 90°. Various exposure times.
Microstyle Mural II (21)	440,050 fr	35p	1:15	24 x 36 18 x 24	Kinoptik F = 75 mm	120 m	Greater reduction possible than for Model I.
Microstyle Mobile (21)	445,250 fr	35p	1:15	24 x 36 18 x 24	Kinoptik F = 75 mm	120 m	Portable model. Weight 70 lb.
Microdoc Normal (22)	1,500,000 fr	150mmp	1:4- 1:18	12 x 17 to 95 x 133	—	30 m	1-64 pages per 105 x 150 mm fiche.
Polydoc (22)		150mmp	1:4.5- 1:18	17 x 24 34 x 48 67 x 48	—	30 m	6 formats. 105 x 150 mm fiche.
Planodoc (e) (22)	900,000 fr	150mmp	1:1- 1:9	95 x 133	—	30 m	May be used as enlarger. Electromagnetic shutter.
Endoc (22)	75,000 fr	35p	—	21 x 30 30 x 42	—	—	—

TABLE I (*Continued*)

France (*Continued*)

Type	Price	Film, size in mm	Reduction ratio	Image size, mm	Lens	Capacity	Remarks
Graphauto Microfiche (23)	250,000 fr	195 x 150	1:15	105 x 150	Apo $F = 175$ mm	Single sheets	For photographing large sheets and maps.
Graphauto Meuble (23)	710,000 fr	35p	1:32	24 x 36	Saphir Apochrome Boyer $F = 75$ mm	30 m	Electronic exposure counter. Automatic focusing and exposure control.
Microfrance MT 2 Portable (24)	247,250 fr	35p	1:11	24 x 36 18 x 24	Olor 5.7 $F = 59$ mm or Saphir B 3.5 $F = 50$ mm	10 and 60 m	Mechanical exposure counter. Adapted for use in tropics. Used as enlarger. Weight approx. 85 lb.
Microfrance A II (24)	322,250 fr	35p	1:18	24 x 36 18 x 24	Olor 5.7 $F = 59$ mm or Saphir B3.5 $F = 50$ mm	10 and 60 m	Can receive a light box for x-ray photographs or an apparatus for photocopy. Variable exposure times.
Microfrance MT 20 (24)	244,000 fr	35	1:3– 1:20	18 x 24 24 x 36	—	10 m	Semifixed.
Microfrance MT 25 (24)	300,000 fr	35	1:3– 1:25	18 x 24 24 x 36	—	10 m	Demountable.

TABLE I (*Continued*)

Type	Price	Film, size in mm	Reduction ratio	Image size, mm	Lens	Capacity	Remarks
				France (*Continued*)			
Microfrance M 2 (24) Automatique Thomson-Houston	785,000 fr	35p	1:25 or 1:35	24 x 36 18 x 24	Berthiot $F = 50$ mm	120 m	Movable camera head view finder lens. Illumination by mirrors. Automatic focusing device.
Microfilm Sertie (25)	264,498 fr	35p	1:16	24 x 36	Tessar 3.5 $F = 50$ mm	5 or 30 m	Uses Exacta Camera.
Microfilm industriel (26)	397,250 fr	35p	1:30	24 x 36	Berthiot 2.8 $F = 50$ mm	120 m	Fixed exposure time and focusing. Film controlled by hand or pedal.
Multiphot Standard (26)	336,000 fr	35p	1:16	24 x 36	Berthiot $F = 50$ mm Boyer $F = 50$ mm	10, 30, 60, 120 m	Book-holder is used for the photocopy.
Multiphot Portatif E (26)	189,700 fr	35p	1:10	24 x 36	Berthiot $F = 50$ mm Boyer $F = 50$ mm	10, 30, 60, 120 m	—
				Japan			
Konica copy attachment (27)	$127.50 incl. camera	35p	—	24 x 36	$F = 50$ mm $f/3.5$		35 mm miniature camera with attachment.

TABLE I (Continued)

Type	Price	Film, size in mm	Reduction ratio	Image size, mm	Lens	Capacity	Remarks
Japan (Continued)							
Lectra C 1 Microfile (28)	—	35up 16up	1:8– 1:18	32 x 22	Toho $F = 63$ mm	100 ft	Portable model.
Great Britain							
Automatic Fixed focus (29)	£1450	16p 16up	1:30 1:18 1:37	13 x 16 8 x 10 6 x 8	R	100 ft	A copy of American "Bell-Howell," at present being manufactured in England.
Microfile A H (30)	£385	35p	1:18	24 x 36 18 x 24	$f/3.5$ $F = 36$ mm Dallmeyer	—	Built-in exposure meter. Camera head rotates 360°.
Statfile Recorder Model 2 (30)	£555	120 x 165	1:7	120 x 165	Apotal Taylor $F = 300$ mm	300 exposures	Camera for use in copying large sheets. Vertical copy holder. Can be used as projector.
Universal (31)	£360	35p	—	25 x 25	$f/3.5$ $F = 36$ mm	21 ft	Desk type.
Netherlands							
Automatic Microfiche (32)	6.950 Fl.	90 x 120 75 x 125	1:14 and 1:25	6 x 9 to 28 x 33	$F = 50$ mm	Single sheets	Automatic movement with winding device to avoid double exposures. Uses cut film.

TABLE I (*Continued*)

Type	Price	Film, size in mm	Image size, mm	Image size, mm	Lens	Capacity	Remarks
Netherlands (Continued)							
NDR Dr. Goebel (32)	—	3 x 5 in. or 9 x 12 cm. sheet	1:12 1:18	9 x 12 or 7.5 x 12.5	f/8	Sheet	Formerly marketed by AEG in Germany.
Sweden							
Dokumat Mod. M (33)	—	35up 16up	1:10– 1:30	33 x 46.5 14 x 19.9	—	100 ft	Camera head turns 90°. Electric counting device for number of exposures.
East Germany							
Reprovit (I) I and II (II) (34)	658 DM 1.333 DM	35p	1:17	24 x 36	Elmar 3.5 F = 50 mm	36 exposures	Uses ordinary Leica camera. Additional extension tubes for small reductions.
Dokumator (35)	—	35p	1:19	18 x 24	Dokumar F = 35 mm		Variable exposure times by electrical exposure counter. Roll or strip. Film take-up regulator.

(1) Burroughs Adding Machine Corp., Detroit 32, Mich.
(2) Diebold, Inc., Canton 2, Ohio.
(3) Eastman Kodak Co., Rochester 4, N. Y.
(4) Film N' File, 330 W. 42nd St., New York 18, N. Y.
(5) Graflex, Inc., Rochester 8, N. Y.
(6) Graphic Microfilm Corp., 112 Liberty St., New York 6, N. Y.
(7) Griscombe Corp., 1228 National Bldg., Newark 2, N. J.
(8) Microtronics Division, Photostat Corp., 303 State St., Rochester 14, N. Y.

TABLE I (*Continued*)

(9) Migel Distributing Co., 14 W. 44 St., New York, N. Y.

(10) Photographic Products, Inc., 6916 Romaine St., Hollywood 38, Calif.

(11) Remington Rand Inc., 315 Fourth Ave., New York 10, N. Y.

(12) Standard Register Co., Dayton 1, Ohio.

* Kenyon Instrument Co., Inc., Depot Road & New York Ave., Huntington Station, Long Island, N. Y.

(13) Dr. Böger, Hallerstrasse 59, Hamburg (13), West Germany.

(14) Fotokopist, Hardenbegrufer 59, Essen-Werden, West Germany.

(15) Foto Clark, Friedrich Grün K. G., 9 Dahlmannstrasse, Bonn-am-Rhein, West Germany.

(16) R. Kabitz, Sprendlingen, Rhein-Hessin, West Germany.

(17) Kontophot-Wedekind, Motzstrasse 64, Berlin W. 30, West Germany.

(18) Dr. Rodehüser, Bergkamen, Westfalia, West Germany.

(19) Alsaphot, 177 Rue de Courcelles, Paris 17, France.

(20) Les Appareils Contrôleurs, 44 Rue Chanzy, Paris 11, France.

(21) Andre DeBrie, 111 Rue St. Maur, Paris 10, France.

(22) Matériel d'Organisation Documentaire, 9 rue Rubens, Paris (G. Cordonnier), France.

(23) Photelec, 27 Rue Costé, Cachan (Seine), France.

(24) Société de construction d'appareils de précision, 69 Cours de la République, Lyon-Villeurbanne, France.

(25) Société d'études et de réalisations industrielles et commerciales, 32 bis, Rue Greuze, Paris 16, France.

(26) Société d'exploitation photographique, 35, bd du Temple, Paris 3, France.

(27) Konishiroku Photo Ind., Tokyo, Japan.

(28) Toho Optical Co., Ltd., 105 I-chome, Shimomeguro, Meguro-ku, Tokyo, Japan.

(29) Burroughs, Avon House, 356 W. Oxford St., London W.1, England.

(30) Kodak Ltd., Adelaide House, London Bridge, London E.C.4, England.

(31) Ruthurstat Ltd, 104 High Holborn, London W.C.1, England.

(32) Nederlands Document Reproductie, Valeriusstraat 28, den Haag (Dr. Goebel), Netherlands.

(33) Dokumat A/B, Nybrokajen 5, Stockholm, Sweden.

(34) Ernst Leitz, Wetzlar, East Germany.

(35) Carl Zeiss, Jena, East Germany.

---

* Products of this manufacturer are not listed in this table.

If records accumulate rapidly yet must be available in live storage and presently occupy more space than can be justified, there is some microrecording equipment and/or service now available that holds the key to the economic solution of the problem. After records have been carefully analyzed by means of a suitable record retention schedule that has been approved by attorneys for its legal suitability, the overall layout of the procurement of services and equipment may be begun. The first step is the filming of the primary microdocument; the format chosen must be compatible with the end-use form desired. In most cases microfilm will be used as the first step; the camera equipment is of interest since its functions must be understood if the proper choice of the first step is to be made.

Bibliography

Military Standard Photographic Lenses, MIL-STD-150, October 23, 1950 (Nomenclature, Definitions and Practices Including Methods of Measurement). Government Printing Office, Washington, D. C. 25c.

Sir Isaac Newton. *Optidks.* Dover Publications, New York, 1952. Reprint of 1730 ed.

Ernst Mach. *The Principles of Physical Optics.* Dover Publications, New York, 1953. Reprint of 1926 English translation.

Donald Jacobs. *Fundamentals of Optical Engineering.* McGraw-Hill, New York, 1943.

L. C. Martin. *Introduction to Applied Optics.* Pitman, London.

Hardy and Perrin. *Principles of Optics.* McGraw-Hill, New York.

A. Conrady. *Applied Optics and Optical Design.* Oxford University Press, London.

C. Deve. *Optical Work Shop Principles.* Adam Hilger, London.

B. Johnson. *Practical Optics.* Hatton Press, London.

F. Twyman. *Prism and Lens Making.* Adam Hilger, London.

B. Johnson. *Optical Design and Lens Computation.* Hatton Press, London.

Drude. *Theory of Optics.* Longmans Green, New York.

R. Wood. *Physical Optics.* Macmillan, New York.

F. Wright. "The Manufacture of Optical Glass and of Optical Systems." Ordnance Department Document 2037, U.S. Army.

THE PRIMARY MICRODOCUMENT

In practice, camera equipment for microfilming varies widely in physical arrangement; this is an outgrowth of adaptation to the specific needs of microfilm users. At the inception of commercial microfilming the possibilities of the process were considered so remarkable that novelty and the mere ability of apparatus to produce a small image that could be enlarged satisfactorily seemed to justify the existence of a commercial design. Today this is not enough; equipment designs are based upon very specific combinations of anticipated operating conditions that reflect plainly both the first cost of the equipment and all its operating costs.

Because of the need for know-how on the part of those responsible for microfilming operations, and because of the high cost of microfilming equipment of high productivity (high document recording rate with low cost per document recorded), microfilming operations were restricted to organizations where savings effected by the use of microrecording would justify the costs of the installation. Since there were many users whose requirements in documents to be recorded per unit time were not large enough to justify owning and operating a microrecording facility, and since such needs were continuous rather than a "one-shot" operation arising from a one-time need (such as a one-time need for duplicate records for dispersal purposes during World War II), manufacturers of microrecording equipment and others started to offer microfilming service on a contract basis.

Users of microdocumentation services have benefited by the keen competition among equipment manufacturers providing this service, through a special department, and through organizations not affiliated with an equipment manufacturer, because the quality of the service furnished has improved markedly and the costs have dropped simultaneously. Marked improvement in the suitability of microfilming equipment designs has also resulted; most equipment not only functions well, but also it is neat and attractive in appearance, relatively easy to operate, reliable in performance, and it causes a minimum of operator fatigue when operated continuously over long time intervals.

The time element in regard to the finished microrecord may create other problems. Operational procedure may require that the microrecording be returned to the original owner within twenty-four hours. This is particularly true in certain types of industry and business such as department stores, hospitals, banks, credit and circulation departments. Newspapers may require a finished micro-record at ten-day intervals. Industrial firms under government contract may need the finished microrecord daily for each day's operations. Often duplicate enlargements of microfilmed blue prints are essential for various departments for the manufacture of a product.

Lack of active filing space may create pressure in firms under contract. Engineering drawings and blue prints that must be kept in active reference file require considerable filing space; such drawings become worn through use or because of improper filing equipment. Often they are handled too frequently merely in the process of locating another drawing. When such drawings are not used daily, and when the rate at which new drawings is produced is quite large, the pressure for space becomes quite apparent. Such drawings may be microfilmed to save space, to provide security controls, and to prevent the loss of pertinent information. The importance of this to a manufacturing organization can be appreciated when it is recognized that a ton or more of blue prints may be required to manufacture a single product.

Although microfilming can lessen the space problem materially, the rapid addition of new drawings to an existing file may make it imperative that the microfilming be completed almost as rapidly as drawings are completed. The time requirement and the volume of material to be microfilmed may involve a higher cost for the user because of the additional labor and the additional equipment required to get the job done within the time limits set by the need. This cost may be partially offset by the increased accessibility and facility of use of the microrecorded material.

MICROFILM

Documents that are to be microfilmed may be photographed and processed at the site of the records if there is reason for doing so. Documents may be photographed on site and processed off site; they may also be both photographed and processed off site. The microfilm service company will indicate the most satisfactory procedure after a complete appraisal of the problem has been made. Factors influencing the choice have been discussed in Chapter III and earlier in this chapter.

The problem may be one of microfilming old or current records and materials or both. The type and size of the original record may indicate whether it is to be photographed in 16, 35, or 70mm microfilm. The end use of the microrecord may also determine microfilm size and type. If the microrecord will be used infrequently, it may be more economical to microfilm it at a higher reduction in 100-foot reels. If the original records are to be destroyed and frequent high definition enlargements must be made from microfilm, it may be preferable to select 35mm instead of 16mm, or 70mm instead of 35mm and to photograph at a lower reduction ratio to obtain suitably high definition in the end-use copy.

When frequent use is made of the microrecord, search time can be reduced by using one of the newer techniques of processing the microfilm in strip or sheet or 70mm form; this has been discussed in Chapter III. In the case of an engineering drawing, one image may appear on a single positive or negative frame or the positive or negative frame may contain a number of related documents pertaining to the same subject matter. In 16mm or 35mm microfilm numerous frames of material on the same subject may be inserted in a protective jacket or card. In 70mm microfilm only a single positive or negative frame is ordinarily inserted in a protective jacket. The purpose of such jackets or cards is to protect the film image against abrasion and handling and to facilitate filing and search. It is possible to insert assorted film sizes in these card jackets and to use punch-card applications for mechanical search. The jackets may have to be used to collate microfilm material on the same or related subject. Microfilming programs may prescribe

that certain records of related subjects be photographed at three
different film sizes, 16, 35, and 70mm. Thus, despite the assortment
of film sizes, search time can be reduced by assembling related
material as a subject matter entity in card jackets. This technique eliminates the necessity of scanning long reels of film to locate
a specific image, but it is not warranted where microfilmed records
have very infrequent use and are microfilmed solely for protective
reasons.

The record owner should have a broad understanding of the
entire procedure of preparation, filming, recording and filing, even
though the process may be undertaken by a microfilming company. However complete technical knowledge of the process,
although desirable, is not essential for the owner of original records.
A great assurance of conformity to established working standards
and appreciably lower cost can be obtained if the record owner
endeavors to learn as much as possible. This knowledge will
enable him to discuss the operation intelligently with the processor's representative. It also acts as a challenge to the microfilm
contract company to maintain established standards and to follow
the most economic and most advanced practices.

General procedural practices are quite similar among microfilm service companies. These practices are based upon the standards that have been formulated through the American Standards
Association; such standardization has become really active only in
the last few years. Unfortunately standards or proposed standards
do not exist for microfilming all current materials; despite this,
several guides do exist for many such practices. The American
Library Association* has issued "A Guide to Microfilming Practices" which was prepared by its Committee on Photoduplication
and Multiple Copying Methods. It is "primarily intended to aid
microfilm laboratories in standardizing their production of permanent record microfilm." It provides the more common operational
details for newspapers, books, pamphlets, serials, manuscripts,
and maps. It is especially useful for areas not covered by standards and for its breadth of scope of subjects.

The January 1954 issue of *National Micro-News*,† the official
publication of the National Microfilm Association, contains an

---

* American Library Association, 50 East Huron Street, Chicago 11, Ill.
† National Microfilm Association, 19 Lafayette Ave., Hingham, Mass.

informal yet useful checklist of "suggested points for consideration in drawing up specifications for Service Contract Microfilming of permanent records."

As a general guide, and especially for newspapers though not
entirely applicable to all forms of records, the proposed standards
for newspapers (which appeared in *American Documentation*,
January 1950), is a good general model to follow because it includes both bibliographical and technical standards. Its revision
was approved by the American Library Association Council in
1953. It was submitted to the American Standards Association
for approval, and present indications are that it will probably be
approved without significant modification in the near future.
ASA standards Z22.36-1944, Z38.3.2-1945, Z38.7.8-1947, and
Z38.7.17-1946, mentioned in the proposed standard, are reproduced
in Appendix B, pages 383 to 384, 374 to 380, 369 to 370, and
386 respectively.

The proposed standard was revised in June 1953. As a result,
the footnote pertaining to Section 3.6f was omitted, and in Sections 5.1 and 5.4 the reduction 1/18 was changed to 1/22. The
proposed standard is reproduced here for reference (Figure 1).

The problems of bibliographic treatment are similar for all
types of records to be microfilmed. Records that are old, rare,
and fragile need greater care in preparing for microfilming than
new or current records and materials do. Normally current records are unmutilated, legible, and complete. The older the records,
the greater is the probability of damage or loss of some portion
of the record and the greater is the necessity of careful handling.
Section III of the Newspaper Standard indicates bibliographical
treatment. One of the principal problems is the repair of damaged
records. They may be stained, creased, folded, ripped; they may
be fragmentary. If duplicate records in good condition are not
available as replacements for the mutilated sections, repair is
essential.

Stains and discolorations on the original records should not
be removed without expert advice. The type of stain should be
ascertained and properly treated. Ink stains may vary greatly.
The composition of old inks is different from that of modern inks;
thus different solvents are needed to produce legibility.

Creases and folds in the original record that impair legibility

A PROPOSED STANDARD
FOR THE MICROPHOTOGRAPHIC
REPRODUCTION OF NEWSPAPERS

In 1947 a Committee on the Photographic Repro-
duction of Research Materials was appointed by
the Association of Research Libraries. The mem-
bership included: Ralph Beals, New York Public
Library, Donald Coney, University of California,
Herman H. Fussler, University of Chicago, Keyes
D. Metcalf, Harvard University, George A.
Schwegmann, Library of Congress and Vernon D.
Tate, Massachusetts Institute of Technology
(Chairman). A primary objective was the study
of problems relating to the microphotographic
reproduction of long runs of material, specifically
newspapers. One phase of the Committee's work
resulted in the compilation and publication of a list
of newspapers on microfilm.[1] Another activity
was the development of a set of bibliographic and
technical standards for the microphotographic
reproduction of newspapers.

A preliminary draft of the standards follows. It
is the product of many hands and has been discussed, reviewed and amended by several operating
laboratories. In its present form the proposed
standard has not yet been adopted by the Association of Research Libraries or any other group and is
reproduced here for information and discussion.
Any comments or opinions sent to the Editor
AMERICAN DOCUMENTATION will be forwarded to
the Committee.

SECTION I. DEFINITIONS

1.1 *Microfilm*. Microfilm shall mean a transparent
flexible material carrying microphotographs
for optical, but not cinematographic projection
or viewing. (A.S.A. Z38.7.8-1947.)[2]

1.2 *Microphotographs*. A microphotograph is a
reduced-size photographic documentary reproduction, generally too small to be read by the

unaided eye. Microphotographs usually are
made from documentary material, such as
texts or drawings, or from physical objects.
(A.S.A. Z38.7.8-1947.)

1.3 *Reduction*. Reduction is the ratio of a linear
dimension of the object to the corresponding
dimension of the image on the film. (A.S.A.
Z38.7.8-1947.) Reduction should be expressed
as fractions, e.g., 1/10, while magnification or
enlargement should be expressed as multiples,
e.g., 10X.

1.4 *Mutilations*. Mutilations shall be defined as
tears, clipped portions, ink stains, and discolorations or other blemishes which remove
the text or make it illegible to an extent which
prevents a reconstruction of it from the
remaining portions.

SECTION II. MATERIALS

2.1 *Film stock*. Newspaper microfilms shall be
intended for permanent preservation and shall
be made on fine-grain, high-contrast, panchromatic, safety film stock meeting the American
Standard Specifications for Films for Permanent Records, Z38.3.2-1945, or the latest
revisions thereof approved by the American
Standards Association. Film stock and processed film shall also meet the standards of the
National Bureau of Standards for permanent
records.[3]

2.2 *Width and Perforations*. Stock 35 mm. wide
must be used for newspaper microfilm and it
shall conform in width and perforations, if the
latter are present, with the American Standards for Cutting and Perforating Dimensions
for 35 mm. Motion Picture, Negative and
Positive Raw Stock, A.S.A. Z22.36-1944, or
the latest revisions thereof approved by the
American Standards Association. An addi-

[1] See section *Shorter Communications, News and Technical Notes* in this issue.
[2] Where reference is made from the text of an American Standards Association standard, the original language has usually been used, though slight changes or deletions have occasionally been made. It is assumed that any subsequent revision of an A.S.A. standard shall apply in lieu of the standard cited.

[3] If in the future standards issued by the American Standards Association and the National Bureau of Standards should come into conflict, National Bureau of Standards standards shall govern.

FIG. 1. Proposed Standard for microphotographic reproduction of newspapers. (Courtesy of *American Documentation*, Vol. I, No. 1, Jan. 1950.)

tional tolerance of $\frac{+0.2}{-1.0}$ per cent may be added to the dimensions specified in the above standards at the time the film is first removed from its original container. Film perforated along one edge, or unperforated, may be used for newspaper reproduction.

2.3 *Film Base Thickness.* The film base used for microfilm should be within the range of 0.11 to 0.17 mm. (0.0045 to 0.0065") in thickness. (A.S.A. Z38.7.8-1947.)

2.4 *Reels.* Reels for processed microfilm shall conform with the American Standard for Reels for Processed Microfilm, Z38.7.17-1946, or the latest revision thereof approved by the American Standards Association.

2.5 *Boxes.* Boxes used for storage shall not exceed 4 x 4 x 1-9/16" in the outside dimensions, and shall be fabricated of cardboard as free of sulphur as possible.

SECTION III. BIBLIOGRAPHICAL TREATMENT, FILM IDENTIFICATION, AND ARRANGEMENT

3.1 *Files to be used.* The best available copy of the file shall be used for reproduction whether in the filming library or secured from other sources. When the principal file is seriously mutilated, it shall be supplemented by additional files if available in order to produce as complete and perfect a microfilm copy as possible.

3.2 *Bindings.* Wherever possible the file being filmed should be removed from its binding and filmed as loose-leaf material.

3.3 *Creases and Folds.* Creases and folds shall be corrected before filming where they impair legibility.

3.4 *Division of Files — Bibliographic.* Files of newspapers, as they shall appear on the film, shall be divided systematically and bibliographically. This division shall be made according to the bulk of the file. Newspapers may be divided, for example, so that one roll will *regularly* accommodate the complete issues for the first ten days, the first fifteen days, a full month, two months, etc., begin-

ning with the first of each month. Arbitrary irregular divisions, e.g., 1-17, 18-29, 30-15, etc. should not occur.

3.5 *Arrangement of Issues and Sections.* All sections and pages of newspaper files shall normally be filmed. The arrangement of issues shall be chronological. Numbered sections shall be filmed in order of numbers, with unnumbered sections placed at the end of the numbered sections for the date in question, except that the principal news section shall always be first without reference to the number of the section.

3.6 *Titles and related information.* Each separate roll of microfilm, in addition to the reproduction of the full text of the newspaper, shall have added at the beginning and at the end of the roll, the information listed in (a)-(i) below. This information may be contained in one, two, or three title frames at the beginning and at the end of each reel of film. The number of frames to be used for this purpose may be determined by the producing laboratory except that START shall appear on the first frame of any roll and END shall appear on the last frame of any roll.

(a) the designation START or END (height of letters as reproduced on the film to be at least 2 mm. (0.08")).

(b) the title, or a condensed version of the title (height of letters as reproduced on the film to be at least 2 mm. (0.08")).

(c) the place of publication (height of letters as reproduced on the film to be at least 2 mm. (0.08")).

(d) the inclusive publication dates of the roll's contents (height of letters as reproduced on the film to be at least 2 mm. (0.08")).

(e) the source of the original.[4]

(f) the name of the organization or institution responsible for the actual filming, together with the name of any sponsoring agency which may have organized the project and

[4] It has been pointed out that in many instances it may be difficult and cumbersome to list all sources in complete detail when scattered issues are gathered from a number of repositories. For such cases a general statement may suffice.

FIG. 1. (*Continued*)

be handling the distribution of copies if different from the filming agency.[5]

(g) an indication of the reduction ratio, which may best be shown by filming, at the reduction ratio used for the roll, a section of an inch and centimeter scale at least 7.5 cm. (3.0″) long.

(h) where it is appropriate (see sections 4.1 and 4.4) the designation FRAGMENTARY.

(i) a list of issues omitted or included (see section 4.5).

SECTION IV. INCOMPLETE AND DAMAGED FILES
(See also Section 3.6)

4.1 *Missing Issues.* When an issue is found to be missing from a file, and cannot be found elsewhere, a space of one frame or at least 1¼″ shall be made on the film. A very fragmentary file, so identified on the title frame, may have such spaces omitted in filming.

4.2 *Filming of Mutilated Pages.* Pages mutilated by the loss of a portion of the page shall have the lost portion revealed by backing the page with a sheet of white paper, held flat during filming.

4.3 *Illegibility of Original Text.* Where the original text is illegible as a result of insufficient inking or because of a double impression, and no substitute text can be located, a note stating the fact of original illegibility shall be prepared for filming as a marginal note within the area of the frame concerned. Any other illegibility in the original *which could not be distinguished from a failure in copying technique* on the finished microfilm shall be similarly identified.

4.4 *Title Frame — Designation of Fragmentary Files.* Fragmentary and badly broken files should be clearly designated as such on the title frames by a suitable legend on the same line with or immediately below the line carrying the inclusive dates.

4.5 *Listing of Omissions.* A list of all omitted issues shall be prepared for each portion of the

[5] This provision has been criticized on the ground that it may be difficult to keep large projects current as a project may be started by a small group and concluded by a larger one.

file appearing on one roll of film. In the case of a fragmentary or badly broken file, a list of issues filmed, instead of a list of missing issues, may be substituted at the discretion of the producing laboratory. The list, of either type, shall appear with the other titling information at the beginning and at the end of each roll of film, in the frame just preceding and just following the newspaper text.

SECTION V. CAMERA ADJUSTMENTS

5.1 *Arrangement of Images and Reduction.* The images on the film for general library use should be arranged, when possible, as shown in Fig. 1A (A.S.A. Z38.7.8-1947-3.3).

The arrangement designated, "I," is the normal standard.

The arrangement designated, "III," may be used under the conditions described in Section 3.5, or in those cases where the double spread of the paper does not result in a reduction in excess of 1/18.

The arrangement designated "IIA," with the lines of print parallel to the long axis of the film, shall be permissible provided the paper height is not such as to require a reduction in excess of 1/18.

5.2 *Width of Image.* The width of the image on 35 mm. film shall not exceed 28.6 mm. (1.126″) on film perforated along one edge; and 31.75 mm. (1.250″) on unperforated film (A.S.A. Z38.7.8-1947-3.1.1). The image width of newspapers shall not be less than 24.0 mm. (0.945″) if the reduction ratio is 12 or more diameters.

5.3 *Separation of Images.* When framing in the reader is important, successive images should be separated by at least 0.5 mm. (0.02″), and on strips or rolls 3 m. (10′) or longer, the separation should approach this value to conserve film and storage space (A.S.A. Z38.7.8-1947-3.2).

5.4 *Filming of Small Sections.* If possible, within the limits of reduction 1/18 (see Section 5.1), small sections may be filmed two pages to a frame with the lines of print at right angles to the edges of the film. When the framing

FIG. 1. (*Continued*)

device for the camera is adjustable, the small sections shall be properly framed as to the length of film exposed. A change of reduction for this purpose need not be indicated except at the option of the producing laboratory. Laboratories are urged to show the reduction changes for non-syndicated sections and special supplements — particularly those of historic importance — or, preferably, leave the reduction unchanged for such items.

5.5 *Sequence of Pages.* The sequence of pages on microfilms of newpapers should be such that the first line of the following page is nearest to the last line of the preceding page when the filming is done with one page to the frame and the lines of print are at right angles to the long axis of the film (see Section 5.1).

be measured by the American Standard for Diffuse Transmission Density (A.S.A. Z38.2.5-1946).

6.3 *Density Variation within Frames.* The variation of background density permissible on a single frame shall not exceed ±2.5 per cent of the average density for that frame, except where the variation is caused by stains, discolorations, or other physical characteristics in the original, beyond control by normal photographic means.

6.4 *Density Variation within Rolls.* The variation of background density within any one roll shall not exceed ±15 per cent of the most common background density.

6.5 *Resolution — Negatives.* The resolution of the camera and the film used for making micro-

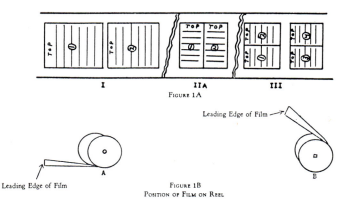

FIGURE 1A

Leading Edge of Film ↗

Leading Edge of Film

FIGURE 1B
POSITION OF FILM ON REEL

SECTION VI. PHOTOGRAPHIC, TECHNICAL

6.1 *Processing.* Films shall be processed according to the National Bureau of Standards standards for films for permanent records.

6.2 *Density.* The background transmission density on a negative film shall have an acceptable range if it lies between 1.2 and 1.9. A higher range (up to 2.5) will be acceptable if the print areas in the negative do not show fog or noticeable loss of finer details. Density may

photographic negatives of newspapers shall show at least 80.0 lines per millimeter in the center of the film, while corner values of a newspaper frame should show a resolution of not less than 70.0 lines per millimeter, as a result of the usual exposure and processing routines as tested with the National Bureau of Standards or Eastman Kodak Company resolution test charts. Higher resolutions are regarded as desirable.

FIG. 1. (*Continued*)

6.6 *Resolution — Positives.* Positive copies made from negatives shall have a resolution equal to at least 75 per cent of the minimum negative resolution.

SECTION VII. ASSEMBLY AND FILING

7.1 *Use of reels.* Microfilms 7.6 m. (25') long or longer should be wound on standard reels (see Section 2.4). Normally, film rolls of newspapers should not be less than 50', and should not exceed 110'.

7.2 *Winding of Film on Reels.* Processed microfilm prints normally are wound with the emulsion out for negatives and with emulsion in for positives. If the supply reel of processed film has a round spindle hole, the film should unwind downward from the right-hand side when the round hole is toward the observer (see Fig. 2A), (A.S.A. Z38.7.8-1947-2.3).

7.3 *Leader and Trailer.* When the film is long enough to be stored on reels, a leader and a trailer of at least 45 cm. (18") each should be provided (A.S.A. Z38.7.8-1947-4.1).

7.4 *Splices.* Splices shall be 5/32" in width where splices occur on negative film. There shall be a space of not less than ⅜" between the last frame of the first strip and the splice, and not less than ⅜" space between the splice and the first frame of the following strip. All splices must be firmly cemented. The emulsion of the film area covered by the splice must be removed from the film base before splicing. Approved butt-welded splices are equally satisfactory and if used, regulations governing cemented splices above shall not apply.

7.5 *Filing.* (a) When filed, the standard boxes containing the finished film shall be in an upright position with the reel of film on edge, and labeled as to contents on one visible edge. (b) (Archival storage) when filed the standard boxes containing the finished film shall be in a horizontal position with the reel of film resting on the horizontal base of its circumference and labeled as to the contents on one visible edge.

FIG. 1. (*Continued*)

can be removed sometimes by steaming the crease or fold, experimenting with a steam iron, or placing the entire record containing the crease or fold in slightly warmed water. If the record is fragile, it can be removed from a water bath by adhesion through the insertion of a stiff but flexible piece of manila or blotting paper. The crease or fold can then be removed from the record by passing it through heated rollers in a photographic dryer or by ironing out, using a *slightly* warmed hand iron. If this procedure is not advisable because of the nature or age of the record, the crease or fold can be flattened by using No. 810 Scotch permanent mending tape, made by the Minnesota Mining and Manufacturing Co., or similar acetate tapes. These tapes do not shrink or discolor on aging and show little contrast when photographed. Ordinary cellulose tape has a tendency to discolor and obscure the original record after a long period of time. It also has a tendency to shrink which will cause an adhesion of original records to each other. For this reason, when original records are to be retained for future reference, a suitable acetate tape should be used for repairs.

Tears or rips in original documents need repair before microfilming. The procedure varies with the type and value of the original document. It is probable that repair may have been attempted long before it was determined to microfilm, as in the case of rare, one-of-a-kind documents. Prior repairs to such documents may create an additional problem. Although such repairs may have prevented further deterioration, they may also have obscured a portion of the record to such a degree that it becomes illegible when microfilmed. This necessitates the removal of the original patch under expert guidance and the making of a new repair to permit the record to be microfilmed. If removal of the original repair is not feasible, the record is photographed "as is." Rips and tears can be reinforced by a sufficiently wide strip of acetate tape. Preferably, the tape should be used on the side of the document that is not photographed.

Segments of records can be carefully matched and pieced to a document; the acetate tape serves for this purpose also. Where duplicate records exist and both document and duplicate are in poor condition, it is sometimes possible to make one acceptable page by taping the best portions of each together. When this is not feasible and a portion of the record is lost, the lost portion should be indicated by backing the page with a sheet of white paper held flat during filming.

Titles and related information should be prepared with the original material and inserted in correct sequence. Titling procedure varies with the nature of the records microfilmed and the problems involved in locating material on such microfilmed records. The record owner may prepare titles unless the entire preparation operation is undertaken for him by the microfilming company. It is usual for the individual or firm that photographs the original material to prepare the titles.

In Section 3.6 of the Newspaper Standard are the standards for titles and related information. This section indicates that the minimum height for letters, dates, and other information is 2mm (0.08 inch). Titles can be written, typed, or printed on white paper. Titles that are too long may have to be reduced photographically to keep within specified limits. This is particularly important in the case of Microcards, Readex Microprint, and sheet film, and yet the reduction cannot be too great, as the titles should be readable with the naked eye.

University Microfilms of Ann Arbor, Michigan, used "menu

boards'' with movable letters or hand lettering for setting up titles
(Figure 2). This method was used so the titles could be read with

FIG. 2. Title prepared from menu
board. Courtesy of University Microfilms.)

the unaided eye for rapid identification of the film. This technique
gave satisfactory results on the film but was discarded because of
the length of time involved in preparation. A more rapid method
uses an IBM electric typewriter. Titles are set up on 3 by 5 cards
(Figure 3). The titles are photographed separately at a very low
reduction (approximately 1:8) so that they may be read with the
naked eye. Titles are photographed on positive raw stock as it
has high contrast; the image to be produced is either black or
white with no intermediate shades. To have white letters on a
black background in the title, a title card such as that shown
in Fig. 3 is photographed. To have black letters on a white
background, just as the title appears in the title card, would
require that either (1) a print of the title film be made or (2) that
the title card itself have white letters on a black background.

If complete information relating to omissions, illegibility, or
damage of the original documents is not included in the microfilm,
the user may mistrust the microfilm record. Certain omissions could
make some microfilm records valueless.

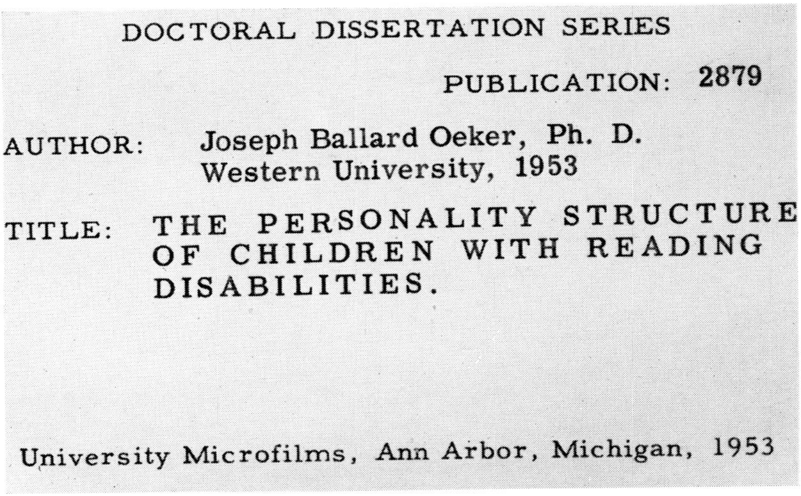

DOCTORAL DISSERTATION SERIES

PUBLICATION: 2879

AUTHOR: Joseph Ballard Oeker, Ph. D.
Western University, 1953

TITLE: THE PERSONALITY STRUCTURE
OF CHILDREN WITH READING
DISABILITIES.

University Microfilms, Ann Arbor, Michigan, 1953

FIG. 3. Title prepared using IBM electric typewriter. (Courtesy of University Microfilms.)

The arrangement of material for microfilming is dependent on the type of record and its use. Chronological arrangement is used for books, periodicals, and newspapers. Records classified in a particular manner are photographed according to that classification. The arrangement of material for photographing may also be affected by the arrangement and reduction of the record on the microfilm image, as illustrated in Figure 1A in the Newspaper Standard. When one image appears on one frame of microfilm, laying out the material for photographing is a simple task; a check must be made to make sure that the originals are in the desired order. Mounting or layouts are usually not necessary when material is photographed by a rotary camera. Where several images appear on one frame or on a single positive or negative, as in 70mm microfilm, it may become necessary to employ a layout before photographing. Records should be mounted on black mounting paper. The paper size will vary with the reduction and the size of microfilm employed. This, and the appropriate margin to be left on the mounting paper, will be indicated by the microfilming company. Usually, original records should be attached to the mounting paper with the acetate tape so that they will read from left to right in rows (Figure 4). This tape should be applied so

FIG. 4. Mounting clippings for 70mm. film. (Courtesy New York *Times.*)

that records will lie flat when being photographed and thus avoid distortion. Additional aid may be obtained by photographing the mounting under glass. If records of irregular size are to be mounted (newspaper clippings for example), time should not be consumed in fitting such material together on the mounting sheet to eliminate waste space. The labor and time involved in such an attempt will far exceed the cost of microfilming. Illegible dates or notations stamped on printed material should be repeated elsewhere on the same document with a marking medium, such as dark blue ink, that will provide sufficient legibility when photographed.

Even if the 70mm positive or negative is self-indexing because of the subject matter, it is advisable to mount an accession number in the same place on each layout sheet. The preparation of titles for each 70mm layout is time-consuming. (Accession numbers are discussed in Chapter IX.)

Section IV of the Newspaper Standard deals with incomplete and damaged records. A portion of this section deals with omissions. It is possible that omissions may occur in photographing; these may be inadvertent or they may be the result of the carelessness of the operator. For this reason the original record should not be destroyed until the microfilmed record and the original have been compared in order to verify that there are no omissions. If this check is not made, the omission may be discovered after the original records have been destroyed; then there is no possibility of completing the record. Reliable microfilming companies utilize such checking methods as routine procedure. When an omission is discovered, it can be photographed and spliced in its proper place in the original record or added as an appendix.

MICROPRINT AND MICROCARDS

Generally the same procedure is followed to prepare material for Readex Microprint or for Microcards, if microfilm has been employed first to record the image. For both purposes material is laid out so that it is photographed to read from left to right. For Readex Microprint, where the decimal arrangement is used for 100 pages, it is necessary to lay out the material in 10 rows of 10 images each in correct sequence.

The page size of such material used for Readex Microprint must be reduced to 4/10 by 7/10 inch. When it cannot be reduced to this size, the decimal arrangement cannot be used. The reduction of such material varies between 12 and 20 diameters, depending on the size of the original material.

Microcards are prepared from microfilm. In preparation, the original material is all faced at right angles to the film. If the printing being copied is no smaller than 10 point, 16mm film can be used. If the print on the original material is unusually small or the documentation is extra large, 35mm film may be used.

TECHNICAL PROBLEMS

The technical problems involved in microfilming appear in Sections II, V, and VI of the Newspaper Standard. Little attention need be given to the film stock, mentioned in Section II, as the microfilming company probably uses safety film stock meeting current standards. The reduction ratios of the microfilm are determined by the size and type of the original material as well as the end use of the microrecord. Some records, blue prints or engineering drawings for instance, may require a reduction that will project an image the same size as the original. Such a reduction permits copies to be traced directly from an image projected onto tracing paper. The reduction is also governed by the projection of the microfilm in a reader. For reasons of economy, greater reductions may be employed at a sacrifice of some quality in the projected image. This may not be important with certain types of records. With others it may create difficulty in ascertaining the exact context of original material, either in a microfilm reader or in an enlargement made from the microfilm. If there is doubt about the legibility of a portion of the original document, it could make a difference in litigation or in proving certain facts when required.

Microfilming companies adhere to self-imposed standards in microrecording. Variations in quality, both technical and bibliographic, do occur from company to company, and from time to time within a particular company. While one company may turn out a product that is barely within the acceptable quality range, another may operate well within the desired range. Such variations are due to know-how as well as to procedure, equipment, and personnel. All factors are reflected in the quality norm of the product and in the day-to-day variations from that norm.

Bibliography

"Quality Loss in Newspaper Microfilm." *Amer. Documentation*, Vol. 2, No. 2, pp. 112-113.

"A Proposed Standard for the Microphotographic Reproduction of Newspapers" *Amer. Documentation*, Vol. 1, No. 1 (Jan. 1950).

L. J. v.d. Wolk and J. C. Tonnon. "The Microcopy on Flat Film as an Aid in Documentation." *Rev. Documentation*, Vol. 17, 1950, fasc 5, 8.

E. N. Jenks. "Micro-Editions of Newspapers: A Survey of Developments." *Journalism Quarterly*, Vol. 27, No. 4, pp. 391-398.

"A Program for the Microfilming of Newspaper Files." Micro-Photo Service Bureau, Cleveland 3, Ohio.

"A Comment on the Proposed Standard for the Microphotographic Reproduction of Newspapers." *Amer. Documentation*, Vol. 1, No. 2, p. 121.

"Microfilming with Kodagraph Micro-File Equipment and Materials." Eastman Kodak Company Co., Rochester 4, N. Y.

"Preserving Your Newspaper for Posterity." University Microfilms, Ann Arbor, Michigan.

American Standards Association Z38.3.2-1945. Specifications for Films for Permanent Records.

"Recommendation Regarding Maximum 'Hypo' Content of Archival Film." Natl. Bureau of Standards, Sept. 14, 1938.

"Standard for Permanent Record Photograph Microcopying Film." Natl. Bureau of Standards, Sept. 14, 1943.

Wm. H. Offenhauser, Jr. "Preservation by Microfilm." *Special Libraries,* pp. 369-373, 397-400, Dec. 1951.

"A Guide to Microfilming Practices." Prepared by the American Library Association. *National Micro-News,* No. 10, March 1955. National Microfilm Association, 19 Lafayette Ave., Hingham, Mass.

Clapp, Henshaw, and Holmes. "Are Your Microfilms Deteriorating Acceptably?" *Library J.,* pp. 589-595, March 15, 1955.

Casey and Perry. *Punched Cards.* Reinhold, New York, 1951.

COPIES AND COPYING.
PROCESSING. ENLARGEMENT

COPYING

Between the microrecord facsimile original and the end-use copy is a series of steps that may be broadly called copying. As mentioned earlier, the end-use copy may be required in any of a wide variety of forms:

(1) It may be a transparency or an opaque.
(2) It may have any size relationship desired relative to the original document.
(3) It may have any desired end-use form.
(4) It may have any desired quality.

The difference between the form and format of the microrecord facsimile original and of the end-use copy must be effected in the processing of the materials between the two terminal steps of the process. Thus, if the original is recorded on 16mm microfilm which is to be used for producing Microcards, the spacing of the images on the original film must conform to the ultimate requirement; in addition, after the original facsimile has been processed, the edges must be slit away and the 14mm film that results must be cut up into appropriate lengths so that the format requirements of the Microcard may be met. Also, the quality of the end-use copy depends upon the number of process generations between the original microrecord and the end-use copy, as well as upon the quality with which each individual step has actually been accomplished. Each process step is responsible for a significant and measurable quality loss; the end product *must* limit in a practical way the losses that can be tolerated at each step if the end-use copy is to be reasonably certain to meet the requirements of the user.

The quality desired of the end-use copy may be high—suitable for publication as an enlargement in a high quality textbook; it may be a fair copy suitable for work material, for example, as source material to a reporter seeking to write a story for his paper. The end-use copy may be a transparency contact positive print of 1:1 size compared with the microfilm negative; the user may merely wish to view the text in a reader. In a properly designed and controlled process there should be no question that the end-use objective for each desired use can be readily realized at the lowest practicable cost.

Since microrecording must be employed by a large number of small users as well as by a small number of large users if it is to grow rapidly commercially, it should be apparent that small users must have available to them facilities for performing all the required steps at a cost that is reasonable. The availability of such services on a competitive basis in the United States through the specialist companies performing such work on a contract basis for users has brought about a wide use of microfilming in business in this country that has not occurred in Europe. If, for example, the microrecord facsimile original is made as a 16mm negative microfilm, there is an important stage of preparation of the microfilm in a form suitable for photoprinting on a Microcard if that is to be the desired end-use form. To a considerable extent such preparation is relatively costly because it is time-consuming and because it requires specialized methods and apparatus; such Microcard preparation is performed by microrecording operating companies rather than by those concerned with the end-use itself. In the United States more often than not, even the microfilm original itself is developed by microrecording operating companies remote from the user's premises; in fact, only large volume users attempt such processing. As is customary in most commercial matters, the choice between methods is based upon the quality and the price of the service offered. European practice, on the other hand, has involved relatively little contract operation; a user who photographs his microrecording facsimile originals more often than not develops them. Such differences in marketing procedures result in marked differences in the nature and complexity of the equipment offered for sale, both for developing the original microrecords and for producing the desired end-use copies in the desired forms.

The most common width of microfilm in both Europe and the United States is 35mm. In the United States 16mm microfilm is widely used, especially for photographing bank checks as well as ordinary commercial correspondence. Since the size of the individual image on 16mm and 35mm microfilm is quite small, more often than not, these films, especially original facsimile negatives, are stored in roll form; and they are usually processed in roll form. In the United States, 70mm film also is usually processed in roll form; after processing, it may be stored in roll form or it may be cut into individual frames or strips. To some extent 150mm film is used in European-made equipment; although placed in the photographing camera in roll form, it is usually cut into strips or frames before processing and handled subsequently as sheet film.

Automatic high speed developing machines are in rather wide use for motion picture and television purposes for processing 16mm and 35mm film. They run at speeds as high as 250 feet and more per minute; such machines are often 100 feet long or more. In these machines exposed film is placed in the feed-in chamber and emerges at the tail-end fully processed. The total amount of microfilm used in the United States, although very large compared with any other country, is still very small compared with the total amount of motion picture and television film processed. In practice, when automatic processing machines are desired, the big problem commercially is to find a sufficiently automatic machine small enough and cheap enough to be fitted economically to the need at hand; this is especially true for the large number of small users upon whom a major part of the microfilm business must rest in the United States. In Table I is listed a commercial processing machine offered for sale that has an operating speed of less than 1 foot per minute; the largest machine offered by the same manufacturer, as shown in the table, runs at a speed of only 7 feet per minute. In the same table is listed European-made equipment which involves racks or frames around which films are wound or to which sheet films are attached before being plunged into a series of tanks containing the appropriate series of chemical solutions. This equipment requires considerable hand labor and especially manual transport of the film and its rack; considerable manual effort and dexterity and exacting timing of all operations performed are required at all times. Such equipment can hope to find little or no application in the American market where wages are relatively very high and electric power costs relatively very low. Such operations, similar to those performed in a very small processing plant for still pictures, may possibly find application outside the U.S.A. where wages are relatively low and electric power costs relatively high. Despite the very adverse economic considerations affecting rack-and-tank processing in a high-wage-level area such as the United States, there is little doubt that intelligent and inquisitive individuals who have actually processed film by such rack-and-tank methods understand and appreciate the performance criteria applicable to the developing machine as few others really do.

PROCESSING

A common type of processing equipment is that required for microfilm. Such equipment is designed to be capable of developing either negative or positive film; ordinarily it is not designed to process reversal film because extra processing baths are required. The processing equipment causes sensitized material such as microfilm or sheet film to be transported through several chemical and physical operations, either by hand or by mechanical transport or a combination thereof, to produce a visible image from the latent image impressed upon the film by the camera. The negative microfilm exposed in the cameras described in Chapter V is usually developed in such equipment.

Negative and positive processing are alike except for the baths used and their processing times. For negative developing, the film must pass through the following baths for a specified length of time depending upon the exposure of the film and its recommended development;

1. A developer bath in which the film is developed and the exposed emulsion "develops up," becoming dark in the process. Since development is more uniform and the development rate is more rapid with a high degree of agitation (stirring), various arrangements are used to provide satisfactory agitation. Temperature has a very important effect; the more nearly constant the temperature can be maintained, the better is the control. In commercial machines control of temperature to plus or minus one-fourth degree Fahrenheit is common.

2. A wash bath to remove traces of developer before the film enters the fixing bath.

3. The fixing bath, which "clears" unexposed emulsion. This bath usually has formaldehyde or other chemical hardener in it to harden the emulsion.

4. A final wash bath to remove traces of hypo from the fixing bath so that the film can meet archival requirements for hypo content. Washing must be sufficiently thorough to assure that traces of hypo present shall under no circumstances exceed the maximum permissible for archival film.

5. Drying (to dry the film). The right amount of moisture must be removed in the right amount of time so that the film will be ready for use when dried or as soon thereafter as practicable.

Drying is very important; it is not uncommon for microfilms to be improperly dried. A common error in drying is to apply air and/or infrared heating that is too hot for too short a time, leaving the surface of the film excessively dried and the body of the film with an excessive moisture content. After such a film is removed from the developing machine, the internal moisture in the base of the film diffuses to the surface and into the emulsion of the film, making it sticky. Such a film is known as a "green film." "Green film" has a soft emulsion; the slightest abrasion will cause a scratch. The scratches widen as the gelatin dries; in really bad cases, the film appears "rainy."

"Green film" is too often explained away rather than investigated and corrected. It can be avoided by proper drying. Frequently "film-preservative processes" are offered as a means of correcting "green" film; although such processes have their proper place, they are not in any sense a substitute for proper drying. Proper drying effects the removal of precisely the correct amount of moisture from the film being dried.

If copies of an original microfilm are being made, it is obvious that the original film will acquire slight superficial scratches on both of its surfaces as a result of handling. If some form of protective coating is applied to the original, the scratches resulting from normally careful handling can be restricted to the protective coating. When that coating has been damaged to the point where it begins to interfere with the high quality desired on the copy, the protective coating should be removed and a new coating applied.

To protect an end-use copy of a microfilm against gross carelessness in handling, another form of protective coating may be applied. Such a coating should be physically hard after it is applied; if it is, it will usually be impractical to remove it. A coating of this kind is sold through the Peerless Film Processing Corp. of New York and Hollywood; it has been widely used for prints of 16mm motion pictures. The use of hardening agents in the fixing bath, a common practice for decades, is often sufficient protection for end-use films without any "preservative" processes. Such coating processes provide suitable protection against gross carelessness and improper use.

The manipulation of films, papers, and other photosensitive materials of microrecording in photographic processing represents a high order of technological development in the chemical industry. The standards of purity for chemicals for photographic purposes are very explicit; a series of chemicals of photographic grade, for example, has been standardized through the American Standards Association. Since these and related standards are far too voluminous to be reproduced, they are listed in the appendix to this chapter.

Because film and paper development is a chemical process that requires accurate controls, the process requirements must be fully understood and rigidly adhered to. The American Standard Practice for Photographic Processing Manipulation of Films and Plates, ASA Z38.8.3-1947, and American Standard Practice for Photographic Processing Manipulation of Paper, ASA Z38.8.6-1949, define the terms applicable to processing and specify how the processing is to be accomplished in a standard manner. Papers may be tested by the American Standard Method for Determining Residual Thiosulfate and Tetrathionate in Processed Photographic Papers, ASA Z38.8.25-1950. Films may be tested in accordance with the requirements of "Standard for Permanent Record Photographic Microcopying Film," published by the National Bureau of Standards, Washington, D. C., in 1943. The Bureau also published "Recommendations Regarding Maximum 'Hypo' Content of Archival Film" in 1938.

Another hypo test that deserves mention is the Kodak Hypo Estimator (for Films). This is described in the Kodak Photographic Notebook published by the Eastman Kodak Company of Rochester, New York, in 1954. In all tests it is necessary to determine that the hypo content does not exceed 0.005 mg per square inch of film. The Kodak Hypo Estimator is a simple method to use; unfortunately it cannot be used on the exposed portions of the film under test and must be used only on the clear areas of processed film. For precise determinations such as those to be made by the commercial testing laboratory, the Crabtree-Ross Test* is more suitable.

It is possible that in the future diazo sensitized films and papers may enter the market as copy materials; such materials are marketed under the Ozalid trade name and are a product of the Ansco Division of General Aniline and Film Corp. of Binghamton, New York. The resolving power values of many of the newer dyes are even higher than the silver films of highest commercial ratings; since the sensitized material can be dispersed in the base material of the film or paper, surface abrasion does not obliterate the image. Such diazo materials are "developed" in ammonia gas, usually put into the machine as an aqueous solution of ammonia. The image appears in positive form when copied from a positive original; such duplication eliminates one additional processing operation, the making of an intermediate negative.

The price of equipment for developing microfilm and sheet film varies with its performance and the degree to which it is automatic; the same may be said of equipment for developing enlarged paper prints and enlarged transparencies. Much of the processing equipment sold is a design offshoot of equipment manufactured for still picture or motion picture purposes. The simplest equipment consists of developer trays where the film is developed, washed, and fixed by hand manipulation and where the film is dried on drying drums about as it was 50 years ago. Some machine processors offered for sale are highly automatic for developing and drying and show considerable ingenuity; the objective of designers is a machine that can be operated readily by an unskilled operator such as a file clerk.

The term processing usually includes both the wet stages of development, in which the latent image becomes a visible image as a result of the action of the chemicals used, and the subsequent drying of the developed light-sensitive material to a point where it

---

* "A Method of Testing for the Presence of Sodium Thiosulfate in Motion Picture Films," *J. Soc. Motion Picture Engrs.*, Vol. 14, p. 419 (April 1930).

is suitable for further use. In the simplest nonautomatic arrangements, the wet stages and the drying are two separate and distinct
functions, as development involves the immersion of the sensitized
material in suitable solutions for proper periods of time at suitable
temperatures with suitable solution agitation, whereas drying involves the removal of surplus water moisture acquired primarily
as a result of final washing occurring in processing.

A wide variety of apparatus can be used to accomplish these
purposes, the choice depending upon the degree to which the functions are made automatic. Motor-driven film and paper processors
often include not only the functions of transport and immersion
of the light-sensitive materials into and through the appropriate
baths, including the wash baths with suitable control of solution
temperatures, agitation and circulation and the like, but also the
drying of the material in similarly automatic manner. In the
simplest form of processing equipment the wet stages of processing
are separate from the drying stage; the wet stages involve hand
transport and manipulation of the microfilm, sheet film and/or
sensitized paper, and include hand agitation of solutions as well as
little or no control of processing solution temperatures other than
the use of an ambient room temperature approximately equal to
the desired processing temperature. Flowing water from a tap is
frequently used for washing with such equipment. Since in the
simplest case processing equipment may involve merely developing
trays and the like, no attempt to list the sources of such items will
be made since the number and variety of sources are so large.
Suitable data can be obtained locally from the representative of
the manufacturers of the sensitized film and paper products used.

Figure 1 is a photograph of the Burroughs 16mm microfilm
processor made for Burroughs by Bell & Howell; the price is about
$4310. One processing machine, the Aiglonne, made by Andre
DeBrie of Paris in 35mm and 16mm models, is especially worthy
of close study because of its daring and unique design. Since its
solutions are circulated with extreme rapidity and are accurately
metered for use, and since exhausted solution is not mixed with
fresh solution but is emptied to waste, this machine should be capable of furnishing processing of the finest quality at a low first cost
and at a low operating cost compared with other machines. Continuous processors for paper in rolls, such as that manufactured by

Diebold, Inc., are available; numerous similar machines are available from Eastman Kodak, Ansco, and other manufacturers. Table I lists processing equipment for film, paper, and the like; machines for processing sheet film are available through the photographic trade from suppliers of machines for processing paper.

FIG. 1. Burroughs processor. (Courtesy of Burroughs Corp.)

CONTACT PRINTERS

A printer is a machine that forms a latent image in the photographic emulsion of raw film with light modulated by the image of image-bearing preprint material. In the simplest case, a contact printer is a machine quite similar to a printing frame for photoprinting still pictures. A simple yet effective contact printer of this type that is suitable for small quantity operations is the Ilford Film Strip Printer shown on page 70; it is used for making 35mm positive prints from 35mm negative. The price of this printer is £13 (about $36). A typical continuous contact printer is the Microtronics (division of Photostat Corp.), which is capable

TABLE I. Processing Apparatus

p = perforated
up = unperforated
DM = German marks
$ = Dollars (U.S.)
fr = French francs
Fl = Dutch florins

Name	Price	Material, size in mm	Capacity, ft	Speed, ft/hr	Thermostat control	Reservoir capacity	Remarks
				United States			
Microfilm Processor (1)	$4305	16	100	600	yes	3 gal	Daylight op. Auto stop. Cont. auto. Dev. w. and dry 100 ft in 10 min. Infrared dry. Electric drive.
Flo-Film Processor 9107 (2)	$2795	35/16	100	250	yes		Daylight op. Auto stop. Cont. auto. Electric drive.
Paper Processor 9140 (2)		paper	14 in. x 350		no	2½ gal	Motor driven.
Recordak Railroad Developer (3)							Simple small developer operating at room temperature.
Film tank (4)	$348	16p/up 35p/up 70p/up	100	200	no	1 qt	Uses no electricity; powered entirely by water pressure. All operation performed in the same tank. Drying with other apparatus.
Continuous roll tank (4)	$1162	75 to 450 width	400	800	no	1 gal	Processes rolls of paper or film. Powered by water. Portable drying rack dries film by air and infrared radiation.

TABLE I. (*Continued*)

Name	Price	Material, size in mm	Capacity, ft	Speed, ft/hr	Thermostat control	Reservoir capacity	Remarks
United States (Continued)							
Continuous Daylight Processor (5)	$3800	16up	200	600	yes		Stainless steel and plastic. Cont. auto. Electric.
West Germany							
FEM (6)	952.38 DM	35p/up	100		no	2 qt	Small portable processing apparatus. Functions in dark room.
Film Developprint (7)	700 DM						For hand processing.
Paper Developprint (7)	855 DM						For hand processing.
France							
N 4 (8)	132,270 fr	16p/up 35p/up	210 100		no	4 qt	Functions in dark room. Develops 8mm and 9.5mm film sizes.
PR 2 (8)	136,620 fr	16p/up 35p/up	220 105		no	8 qt	Type more important than N 4.
Aiglonne (9)	990,000 fr	35p/up	Unlimited 215 m/h		yes	10 qt	Complete operation in 3 min 15 sec. Functions in daylight.

TABLE I. (Continued)

France (Continued)

Name	Price	Material, size in mm	Capacity, ft	Speed, ft/hr	Thermostat control	Reservoir capacity	Remarks
Aiglonne (9)		16p/up					
K D B (10)	150.000 fr	35p/up	33		yes	12 qt	3 tanks and 1 frame manual processing. Solutions are thermostatically controlled.
Microfiches (11)	14.000 fr	75 x 125 90 x 120 105 x 150	30, 18, or 12 sheets				Special tanks and frames for processing microfiche.

Netherlands

Name	Price	Material, size in mm	Capacity, ft	Speed, ft/hr	Thermostat control	Reservoir capacity	Remarks
KT 15 (12)	1350 Fl	35p	200	50	no		Darkroom. Variable speed.
KT 16 (12)					yes		Same as KT 15 with thermostatic control.
KT 19 (12)		35p		65			Darkroom. Variable speed.
KT 60 (12)	4675 Fl	35p 16p	200	200 160	yes		Darkroom. Processing speed variable, 3–15 min.
KT 61 (12)	5725 Fl	35p 16p	400	200 160	yes	10 gal	Darkroom. Automatic pump.
KT 136 (12)	2850 Fl	35p 16p	200	200 160	no	3 qt	Darkroom. Variable speed.
KT 612 (12)		35p 16p		400 320	yes	20 gal	Darkroom. Variable speed. Twice output of KT 61.
Kiton		35up	65	65	no	2 qt	Darkroom. Variable speed.

* Ansco Division, General Aniline and Film Corp. Binghamton, N. Y.

(1) Burroughs Adding Machine Corp., Detroit 32, Mich.

(2) Diebold, Inc., Canton 2, Ohio.

(3) Eastman Kodak Company (Recordak Division), Rochester 4, N. Y.

(4) Microtronics Division, Photostat Corp., 303 State Street, Rochester 14, N. Y.

(5) Remington-Rand, Inc., 315 Fourth Ave., New York 10, N. Y.

(6) Dr. Böger, Hallestrasse 59, Hamburg 13 (Lumoprint), West Germany.

(7) Kontophot-Wedekind, Metzstrasse 64, Berlin W30, West Germany.

(8) Microfilmex, 75 rue St. Lazare, Paris 9, France.

* Jean Arhuero, Joué-les-Tours, Indre et Loire, France.

(9) Andre DeBrie, 111 Rue St. Maur, Paris 11, France.

(10) Kolen et Delhumean, 7 Rue d'Hautpol, Paris 19, France.

(11) Les Appareils Controleurs (LAC), 44 Rue de Chanzy, Paris 11, France.

* Besancenot et Cie. (Luminox), 83 Rue du Faubourg St. Martin, Paris 10, France.

(12) N. V. Kinotechnik, Prisengracht 530, Amsterdam, Netherlands.

* Great Britain: Puthurstat, 104 High Holborn, London W. C. 1, England.

* Products of these manufacturers are not listed in this table.

of printing 16, 35, or 70mm film; this printer is shown in
Figure 2; its price is about $1380. A still larger printer capable

FIG. 2. 16/35/70mm. positive printer. (Courtesy of
Microtronics Division of Photostat Corp.)

of printing up to 1200 feet in a single roll is the Carlson-Craft
Depue No. PL 1635 microfilm printer, which can print 35mm film
and, by the substitution of a few parts furnished, 16mm microfilm.
The price of this machine is $2400; its printing speed is rated at 94
feet per minute for slow speed, fine-grain film. The printing speed
for a microfilm positive type of film will probably be somewhat
slower than the value mentioned; it is presumed that the film
referred to is motion picture fine-grain positive film rather than
microfilm positive.

TABLE II. Contact Printing Equipment

p = perforated   S = strip   DM = German marks   Lit = Italian lire
up = unperforated   V = volt $ = Dollars (U.S.)   (in thousands)
C = continuous   A = ampere   fr = French francs   Fl = Dutch florins

Type	Price	Film, mm	Continuous or strip	Speed	Capacity	Remarks
United States						
Depue printer No. PL 1635 (1)	$2400	16/35 p/up	C	1800 m/h	360 m	Vary illumination by means of an adjustable aperture.
Contact #94-05 Flo-film (2)		35up	C	5½ ft/min	100 ft	Both raw film and negative on daylight loading spools.
Continuous printer (3)	$1380	16/35/70 p/up	C	900 m/h	5-360 m	Light tight compartment for positive film. Various illumination possible after notching negative film.
France						
Soretex (4)		35p				Combination camera contact printer, projection printer, viewer, and projector.
RBS-A (5)	300.000 fr	16/35 p/up	C,S	1200 m/h	300 m	Rheostat for adjusting illumination. Variable speed. Delivered with support.
RBS-B (5)	192.000 fr	16/35 p/up	C,S	600 m/h	120 m	Rheostat for adjusting illumination. Table model.
RBS-C (5)	150.000 fr	16/35 p/up	C,S	300 m/h	300 m	Rheostat for lamp on request.

TABLE II. (*Continued*)

Type	Price	Film, mm	Continuous or strip	Speed	Capacity	Remarks
France (Continued)						
Bicontact 24 x 36 (6)	18,000 fr	35p	S		1.80 m	Small manual printer. Low voltage lamp 7 V., 0.3 A. Rheostat. Frame 24 x 36 mm.
Planodoc (7)		150up				Used interchangeably as a camera or enlarger.
Netherlands						
Goebel (8)	767 Fl	75 x 125 90 x 120	C; Single sheets			Automatic microfiche printer. The positive microfiche is cut in dimensions before printing. Holds 100 unexposed microfiches.
Micop (9)		35p	C,S	1500 ft/hr	400 ft(A) 1000 ft(C)	Vary illumination by rheostat and diaphragm. Possibility of film-strip production.
Micop (9)		16p			1000 ft(E)	
Coton (9)		35up	C	600 ft/hr	100 ft	Vary illumination by rheostat and diaphragm.

TABLE II. (Continued)

Italy

Type	Price	Film, mm	Continuous or strip	Speed	Capacity	Remarks
Stampatrice Rotativa Automatica (10)	225 Lit	35p	C	480 m/h	120 m	Automatic printer. Illumination controlled by rheostat.
Bromographo (10)	26 Lit	35p/up	C,S		1.50 m	Nonautomatic printer. No film holder.

* Ansco Division, General Aniline and Film Corp., Binghamton, N. Y.

(1) Oscar F. Carlson Co., 2600 West Irving Park Blvd., Chicago 18, Ill.

(2) Diebold, Inc., Canton 2, Ohio.

* Eastman Kodak Company, Rochester 4, N. Y.

(3) Microtronics Division, Photostat Corp., 303 State St., Rochester 14, N. Y.

(4) Alsaphot, 177 Rue de Courcelles, Paris 17, France.

(5) Société d'exploitation photographique, 6 Rue du Tunnel, Paris 19, France.

(6) Etablissements Volomat, 25 Rue d'Hauteville, Paris 10, France.

(7) Material d'Organisation Documentaire (MOD), 9 Rue Rubens, Paris (G. Cordonnier), France.

(8) Nederlandse Dokument Reproductie N. V., Valeriusstraat 28, The Hague, Netherlands.

(9) N. V. Kinotechniek, Prinsengracht 530, Amsterdam MKOP, Netherlands.

(10) Fotorex, Viale Corsica 85, Milano, Italy.

* Germany: Apparate-und Kamerabau G.m.b.H., Friedrichshafen/Bodensee.
Arnold & Richter K. G., Muenchen 13, Tuerkenstrasse 89 (Fabrik kinotechnischer Apparate).
Gesellschaft fuer Andre-Debrie-Geraete, Ernst Linke OHG, Remagen/Rhein, Berstrasse 38.

* Products of these manufacturers are not listed in this table.

Table II lists film printers; the products vary widely in the extent to which they are automatic. The prospective user should study equipment offered for sale in detail, as manufacturers' published data are seldom sufficiently complete to permit him to determine whether the equipment under consideration is suitable for his purpose.

The scope and purpose, size accommodation, and other data are given in American Standard Specifications for Contact Printers, ASA PH3.8-1953.* In a contact printer, the exposure of the raw stock is made in a printing frame. A printing frame is the holder used to keep the emulsion of the raw stock to be exposed in contact, during the exposure interval, with the image to be copied. Specifications for printing frames are given in American Standard Specifications for Printing Frames, ASA PH3.15-1944.* Standard methods of testing printing and projection equipment are outlined in American Standard Methods of Testing Printing and Projection Equipment, ASA Z38.7.5-1948.* When negatives are contact-printed from sheet film and the like, such as the microfiche, separate masks are often required to limit the image; this is shown in American Standard Specifications for Masks (Separate) for Use in Photographic Contact Printing of Roll Film Negatives, ASA PH3.9-1953.*

PROJECTION PRINTERS AND ENLARGERS

When an image is to be printed at a size different from the size of the negative or preprint material to be used, some form of projection optical system is required to effect the size change. A projection printer may be designed to reduce the image size, it may copy with an image of about 1:1 in size by projection printing, or it may enlarge image size; it capability depends upon its design.

Quite apart from the first cost and the operating cost of a projection printer, its all-important characteristic is how well it does its job. To a considerable extent how well the image is transferred from the preprint material to the print depends upon the lenses used, and especially upon how well they are made, and upon the ability of the machine to hold the films in the correct

---

* Reproduced in Appendix D, pages 409 to 412.

plane or planes during the exposure interval. Some theoretical discussion of the relationships among the lenses required for the various purposes will clarify the requirements for differing quality levels.

It is reasonable to believe that camera equipment should and may be quite costly compared with a reader. The lens of the reader can not be expected to give the same high grade performance as the lens of a camera. Readers are made in quantity and at a reasonable price; cameras are made in a small fraction of the quantity of readers and their performance must be much better. If one reader is better than another and detail that can be seen with one reader is not seen with another, potential buyers will purchase the good reader, especially if it is sold at the same or a similar price. Similar considerations govern the price and performance of enlargers, printers, and all other apparatus for copying and duplicating.

LENS PERFORMANCE IN ENLARGERS AND PRINTERS

A summary of the differences in performance among the different kinds of lenses classified by types according to purpose has been published in "Military Standard Photographic Lenses MIL-STD-150, 23 October 1950."* This booklet is an excellent source of fundamental definitions and of test methods for photographic lenses of all types. Section 1.2 lists 13 types of lenses; the distinctions, while purely arbitrary, are consistent with commercial practice and aid in clarifying thinking about the fundamental distinctions. Types IV, VI, VII, XII, and XIII are of especial interest and are given here:

Microphotographic-type XIII lens shall be suitable for microfilming and microcopying. It is corrected primarily to provide acceptable photographic performance over a designated small image area. It is generally used at magnification between 0.1 and 0.024.

Projection-type VII lens shall be suitable for use as an objective lens in opaque, slide, film strip projectors. It is corrected primarily to provide acceptable photographic projection performance over a designated field of view. It will be used at finite magnifications and will have a flat field. This

---

* Published by the Department of Defense, U.S.A. (sold by the Superintendent of Documents of the U. S. Government Printing Office, Washington 25, D. C., at 25 cents).

type of lens differs from a type-VI lens in that it is faster, covers a smaller field of view and has less correction of aberrations.

Enlarger-type VI lens shall be suitable for use in photographic enlargers. It is corrected primarily to provide acceptable photographic projection performance over a designated range of image areas. It will be used at finite magnifications, will usually have low color aberrations and in certain applications distortion characteristics will be designated and controlled to within precise limits.

Process-type IV lens shall be suitable for use in photolithography, process work, and precise reproduction from flat copy. It is corrected primarily to provide acceptable photographic performance over a designated image area. It will be used at or near unity magnification. In this type of lens lateral and longitudinal chromatic aberration, secondary spectrum, and distortion are corrected to a high degree.

Copying-type XII lens shall be suitable for use in reproduction from flat copy. It is corrected primarily to provide acceptable photographic performance over a designated area. It will be used at or near unity magnification. It usually differs from type IV lens in that it has greater lens speed and less correction of aberrations.

Unfortunately manufacturers' literature has not always been precise in describing the performance of equipment offered for sale; one important reason is that explicit nomenclature, such as that just given as descriptions of the performance characteristic of different types of lenses, has not yet been standardized nationally. Despite this, however, standard methods have been worked out to test photographic enlargers; the methods are quite explicit, for example, American Standard Methods for Testing Photographic Enlargers, ASA Z38.7.6-1950.* As with processing equipment, the trends in the United States and Europe are different, apparatus used in Europe requiring considerable hand manipulation and American apparatus tending to be automatic. The SCAP Microfrance enlarger is similar functionally to American enlargers such as the Simmon Brothers, the Eastman Kodak, and the Federal enlargers. Figure 3 is a Microtronics automatic enlarger for enlarging 16, 35, and 70mm microfilm to photosensitive paper; its price is about $5300. Some of the simplest enlargers, which use the lens from a camera, are little more than a light source and mounting for the film to be enlarged; these often cost less than $50. Conventional photographic enlarger types often start at about $40 in price, automatic operation becoming common and fairly com-

---

* Reproduced in Appendix D, pages 413 to 416.

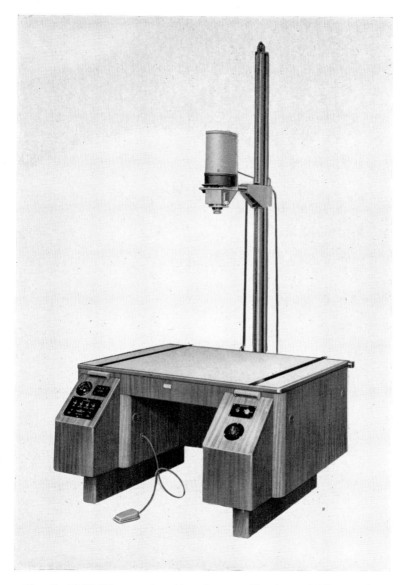

F<small>IG</small>. 3. 16/35/70mm. automatic enlarger. (Courtesy of Microtronics
Division of Photostat Corp.)

TABLE III. Enlargers

p = perforated   A = Automatic   DM = German marks   fr = French francs

up = unperforated   F = Fixed $ = dollars (U.S.)   ∞ = infinity

Type	Price	Film, size in mm	Degree of enlargement	Maximum size, mm	Lens	Focusing	Remarks
United States							
Auxiliary enlarger Model 90-47 (1)	$750	16/35 p/up	× 11 × 24	18 x ∞ 36 x ∞		F	Enlarger is an auxiliary furnished for the No. 90-46 camera for converting it to an enlarger.
Kodagraph enlarger Model A (2)	$498	16/35 p/up	× 30	94 x 132	Kodak Microfile Ektar 4.5		Will accommodate 100 ft. of film.
70mm Precision enlarger (3)	$2540	70 35	× 14 × 14	92 x 112 43 x 60	Wollensak Microraptar $f/12.5$ $F = 115$	A	Special frames for 70 mm or 35 mm. Micro-meter focusing control.
West Germany							
MT. 2/36 (4)	3880 DM	35p/up	× 17.5 × 13	40 x 62	Zeiss Tessar $f/4.5$ $F = 75$	A	Same apparatus used for recording. See Chapter IV.
Vu (5)	1050 DM	35up	× 13	40 x 62	Schneider Xenar $f/4.5$ $F = 75$	A	Separate table available for each model. Price 140 DM.
Vp (5)	980 DM	35p	× 10	24 x 36	Zeiss Tessar $f/4.5$ $F = 50$	A	Illumination controlled by pedal.

TABLE III. (*Continued*)

Type	Price	Film, size in mm	Degree of enlargement	Maximum size, mm	Lens	Focusing	Remarks
				France			
Agrandisseur automatique (6)	59,650 fr	35up	× 13	30 x 30	Angénieux	A	Low voltage lamp 6 V 10 A.
V.30 (7)	295,000 fr	35p/up	× 35	84 x 126	Obj. $F = 75$ mm	A	Frame 24 x 36 mm or 32 x 45 mm. Pinpointed light source. Low voltage. Focusing controlled from base of apparatus.
Micrographe 50 (8)	340,000 fr	35p	× 32	76 x 115	Obj. $F = 50$ mm	A	Frame 24 x 36 mm. Pinpointed light source. Automatic focusing.
Micrographe 49 (8)	300,000 fr	35p	× 32	76 x 115	Obj. $F = 50$ mm	A	Similar to Micrograph 50, but a mural model.
Graphauto Microfiche (8)	300,000 fr	105 x 150	× 15	142.5 x 210	Saphir Boyer $f/4.5$ $F = 170$ mm	A	Pinpointed light source. Lamp 6 V, 5 A. Rheostat 8 V, 5 A. One adjustment possible to lamp.
				Italy			
Normali Ducati OE 6202 (9)		35up	× 10	24 x 32			Frame 24 x 36 mm. Larger enlargements by wall projection.
Normali Ducati OE 6201 (9)		35up	× 5	9 x 12		F	Frame 18 x 24 mm. One degree of enlargement. Fixed focus.

(1) Diebold Inc., Canton 2, Ohio.

(2) Eastman Kodak Co., Rochester 4, N. Y.

  * Federal Mfg. and Eng. Corp., Brooklyn 5, N. Y.

(3) Microtronics Division, Photostat Corp., 303 State St., Rochester 14, N. Y.

  * Simmon Brothers Inc., 30-28 Starr Ave., Long Island City, N. Y.

(4) Dr. Böger K. G., Hallerstrasse 59, Hamburg 13 (Lumoprint), West Germany.

(5) Kontophot-Wedekind, Moltzstrasse 64, Berlin W. 30, West Germany.

(6) Alsaphot, 177 Rue de Courcelles, Paris 17 (Soretex), France.

  * Besancenot et Cie. (Luminox), 83 Rue du Faubourg St. Martin, Paris 10, France.

  * Société de Construction d'Appareils de Précision (SCAP), 69 Cours de la République, Lyon-Villeurbanne, France.

  * Matériel d'Organization Documentaire (G. Cordomier), 9 Rue Rubens, Paris, France.

(7) Microfilmex, 75 Rue Saint-Lazare, Paris 8, France.

(8) Photolee, 27 Rue Couste, Cachan (Seine), France.

(9) Ducata, Borgo Panigale, Bologna, Italy.

  * East Germany: Ernst Leitz, Wetzlar.

* Products of these manufacturers are not listed in this table.

plete when the price reaches thousands of dollars. Table III lists a
few commercially available enlargers. Among the many makes and
models sold to the photographic trade will be found quite a number
that are suitable for microfilm or microfiche enlargement purposes
if manual operation of the enlarging equipment is desired. As in
the case of rack-and-tank development, considerable hand labor
and manual dexterity and exacting timing of operations are
required.

A consideration of the broad requirements of microrecording
and the wide variety of possible needs in end-use copies shows that
so-called direct-copying processes and materials find a very important place in the scheme of things for providing end-use copies
from microrecordings just as they would in providing end-use
copies from original documents. For this reason the latter part of
this chapter is devoted to several processes, all unique, which bid
fair to improve the quality of end-use copies in approximately 1:1
size and to reduce the costs of them. Such developments bring
home the fact that one portion of the microdocumentation field
cannot be arbitrarily separated from another, or that one form
of duplication such as stencils, for example, cannot be entirely
ignored in the consideration of microrecording and microdocumentation.

An important area yet to be thoroughly explored in the microdocumentation field is the making of intermediate microrecord
duplicates. In general, the photographic characteristics of this
portion of the process are developing along the lines previously
laid down in motion picture and still photography practice.
Special materials and special methods will be used just as they
have been in the motion picture and still picture fields; no doubt
duplicating films quite like those for motion pictures but designed
with better sharpness and resolving power are certain to be produced as the need becomes more apparent.

VAPORIZED INK ENLARGEMENTS

Certain types of industrial and government operations gradu-
ally increase their volume of material in microrecord form to meet
established objectives. Conservation of record space may be one
objective indicated by contractual completion or a change in the

product manufactured, when future reference to technical data and voluminous blue prints may occur infrequently or not at all. Such space reduction can be achieved by microrecording the documents concerned. Readers or viewers will provide access to any portion of the material, and enlargements may be required of one or more sections for reference. Conventional enlarging techniques may or may not be adequate. For example, an automobile or aeronautical company may have an urgent demand for enlargements of all microfilmed data pertaining to a specific product. The enlargements may be required in large volume for reference in readable form. Facsimiles or paper prints can be provided by present enlarging processes, but new ways of resolving such demands are being investigated with the objective of producing copies in volume more rapidly and more economically. The Standard Register Co. of Ohio is one of the companies engaging in such research.* One of their prototype devices, a "smoke printer" or Photronic Reproducer, is an ingenious means of printing microfilm enlargements utilizing vaporized ink (see Figure 4). It will probably be some time before either the reproducer or their other development, a "Vertical Step and Repeat Microfilming Camera," is commercially available. At present no technical data, advertising literature, or prices are available for either machine. The description and objectives of this research are summarized in a communication from Mr. K. P. Morse, Executive Vice-President and General Manager of Standard Register, who states:

Generally speaking, it has been brought to our attention that present day microfilming methods have two main objections which have prevented more expanded use of microfilming in the field of record keeping. The first of these objections seems to be that the conventional method of microfilming, that is, to produce the images on large rolls of films which causes considerable difficulty and expense to properly index individual frames on the film so that they can be found quickly and easily if at any time in the future reference must be made to the individual frame.

The Vertical Step and Repeat Microfilming Camera is designed to eliminate that objection as it produces microfilm images on flat film and the particular machine which we have built, and is now in a customers office for field tests, has the ability to produce approximately sixty such images on a negative the size of a 3 x 5 card. Many presently known methods of indexing

---

* The story of their developments was told in the February 27, 1954, issue of *Business Week* Magazine.

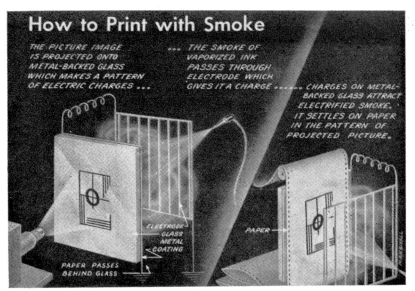

How to Print with Smoke

THE PICTURE IMAGE
IS PROJECTED ONTO
METAL-BACKED GLASS
WHICH MAKES A PATTERN
OF ELECTRIC CHARGES ...

... THE SMOKE OF
VAPORIZED INK
PASSES THROUGH
ELECTRODE WHICH
GIVES IT A CHARGE ...

... CHARGES ON METAL-
BACKED GLASS ATTRACT
ELECTRIFIED SMOKE.
IT SETTLES ON PAPER
IN THE PATTERN OF
PROJECTED PICTURE.

ELECTRODE
GLASS
METAL
COATING

PAPER

PAPER PASSES
BEHIND GLASS

FIG. 4. Photronic reproduction. (Courtesy of *Business Week* Magazine.)

and selection seem to be available for this type of microfilming which are not available when the image is on microfilm on a large roll. Also the transportation and utilization of a flat film seems to have many advantages over the roll of film in certain applications..

The second main objection that we have heard to present day microfilm equipment is that reproductions from a microfilm are quite expensive to make and there has been no quick and economical methods yet offered commercially for reproducing from the microfilm negatives. The Photronic Reproducer we believe eliminates this objection inasmuch as it can reproduce from microfilm, either in rolls or in flat negative form quickly and inexpensively. The microfilm image is projected on a plate which has the ability to transform light energy into electrical energy thereby producing electrical pattern of the image on the opposite side of the plate. Paper is introduced by the machine on the side of the plate on which the electrical image has been set up and is also enclosed in an atmosphere of mist or smoke containing the pigment from which the reproduction image is made. A stream of electrons passing through the smoke or mist compartments therefore cause the pigment in the smoke or mist to be deposited on the paper to conform to the electrical pattern set up on the plate. Under these circumstances no specially treated paper is necessary nor is any subsequent reproduction of the plate required. Reproduction images can be made at the rate of sixty per minute under this system thereby providing an economical and easy way of reproducing images previously photographed on a microfilm.

ENLARGING BY XEROGRAPHY

Xerography is a dry electrical copying process that does not require a negative. It copies drawings and handwritten or typed material in sizes up to 8½ by 13 inches and produces a duplicate in less than 2 minutes. The original may be duplicated on offset paper masters and run off on duplicating machines. By the addition of an ordinary photographic enlarger it is possible to produce microfilm enlargements. The Xerography equipment includes three pieces, a XeroX fuser, copier, and camera, which can be bought outright or rented. (See Figure 5.)

The steps for making direct copies are:

1. Material to be copied is placed face down on the plate glass top of the XeroX camera.

2. A metal plate kept in a holder is sensitized with a coating so that it is light-sensitive. This is done by charging it in the copier unit.

3. The light-sensitive plate is then placed in the XeroX camera where light is reflected from the original copy onto the sensitized plate through the camera lens. The image can be varied in size if an enlarging-reducing camera is used.

4. After a few seconds' exposure the projected image is fixed on the sensitized plate; then a negative charged powder is sprinkled over the plate and a black deposit is left on places on the plate where light has not been reflected.

5. A sheet of paper, or a paper master, is placed over the plate.

6. Both are placed in the XeroX fuser, where the heat fuses the black particles into the paper. (See Figure 6.) This process makes a permanent print. The result is a single reproduction; if a paper master is used, multiple reproductions can then be run off. This is the normal use of Xerography.

It is possible to enlarge microfilm using Xerography through a modification of the XeroX copying unit and the addition of a photographic enlarger. A light box is built between the lens and the copy board of the enlarger to permit daylight operation. The procedure is as follows:

1. The microfilm is placed in the enlarger.

2. Xerographic plate is charged in the copier.

FIG. 5. Xerography equipment: fuser, copier, and camera.
(Courtesy of The Haloid Co.)

HOW XEROGRAPHY WORKS—

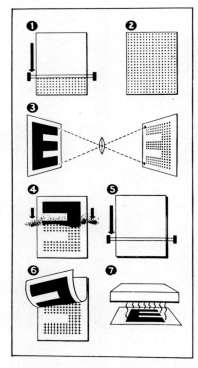

1 SURFACE OF SPECIALLY COATED PLATE IS BEING ELECTRICALLY CHARGED AS IT PASSES UNDER THE WIRES.

2 SHOWS COATING OF PLATE CHARGED WITH POSITIVE ELECTRICITY.

3 COPY E IS PROJECTED THROUGH LENS IN CAMERA. PLUS MARKS SHOW PROJECTED IMAGE WITH POSITIVE CHARGES. POSITIVE CHARGES DISAPPEAR IN AREAS EXPOSED TO LIGHT AS SHOWN BY WHITE SPACE.

4 A NEGATIVELY CHARGED POWDER ADHERES TO POSITIVELY CHARGED IMAGE.

5 AFTER POWDER TREATMENT FIG. 4 A SHEET OF PAPER IS PLACED OVER PLATES AND RECEIVES POSITIVE CHARGE.

6 POSITIVELY CHARGED PAPER ATTRACTS POWDER FROM PLATE FORMING DIRECT POSITIVE IMAGE.

7 PRINT IS HEATED FOR A FEW SECONDS TO FUSE POWDER AND FORM PERMANENT PRINT.

FIG. 6. How Xerography works. (Courtesy of The Haloid Co.)

3. The charged plate is placed in the enlarger and exposed to microfilm for about 10 seconds.
4. The dry powder is cascaded over the plate to make the image visible.
5. The image is then transferred to a single sheet of paper or to an offset paper master.
6. The finished copy is permanized by heating for a few seconds in the XeroX Fuser. Direct positive copies can be

made through Xerography from either positive or negative microfilm originals.

7. The rental cost of this equipment would preclude its use solely for microfilm enlargements unless there was sufficient volume to justify such an expenditure. The same is true when Xerography is used for other purposes.

Continuous Xerographic Microfilm Enlarging

Recently the field of Xerography has been particularly fertile. A new technique has been introduced whereby up to 10 copies of a document can be made on XeroX equipment without exposing and developing more than once. Another involves the use of a refined system of development which makes for relatively good lithographic quality from inexpensive offset paper mats. Field tests are being conducted on a means of making hectograph masters by Xerography.

A continuous Xerographic microfilm enlarger was perfected by The Haloid Co. as the solution of the records-handling problem brought to the Company by the Navy Department. A means was sought to get the content of microfilm speedily back into working paper form again for the required distribution of copies or abstracts of the huge volume of correspondence that constantly flows into the Navy's Records Management Center. The equipment developed has won endorsement by its users on counts of speed, economy, and other points of superiority over other microfilm print-producing equipment.

The major features of the Xerographic enlarger are:

1. Permanent, accurate, positive paper prints are produced from either 16 or 35mm microfilm at the rate of 20 feet a minute.

2. Either negative or positive microfilm may be used to make positive black on white copies.

3. The enlarger will accommodate ordinary, unsensitized, roll paper of standard weights in widths of from 5 to 10 inches.

4. The paper magazine handles stock ranging up to 2000-foot rolls thus the content of an entire roll of microfilm can be printed without interruption for reloading.

5. Finished prints begin moving from the machine to the take-up roll within 5 seconds after controls of the apparatus are turned on.

6. Since the Xerographic process does not call for the use of sensitized paper or other materials that would be affected by radiation, it has minimum vulnerability to radioactivity.

7. It can be operated in a lighted room and functions on ordinary 110-volt current without special power sources or plumbing connections.

The heart of the machine is a cylindrical, metal drum with a photoconductive coating on its surface similar to Xerographic plates used in the manually operated Xerographic copying units. As the drum turns clockwise in the machine, it passes various sections of a housing wherein the steps in the Xerographic process occur. The only material added to the machine is the dry, resinous Xerographic developer powder which ultimately prints the image of the original on the copy paper and is fused into it to become as permanent as the paper itself.

Mail reproduction with the machine already has reached a volume exceeding 50,000 linear feet of 5-inch paper monthly. It has been used to reproduce health records of Navy personnel and as a replacement for photocopy methods in supplying prints of microfilmed records of various Navy offices. Undoubtedly, the Enlarger will find applications in other Government agencies and industries which have voluminous records on microfilm.

Xeroradiography

Recently xerography has been developed to include xeroradiography,[*] the making of X-ray pictures without film. In this joint development of The Haloid Co. and the General Electric Co., the amount of discharge depends upon the opacity of the object that is X-rayed. When the charged plate is sprayed, the powder gathers more thickly in the highly charged areas (just as in conventional xerography) revealing the image.

---

* The New York *Times*, Jan. 29, 1956, Sec. IV, p. 19.

ENLARGEMENTS MADE WITH READERS

The loss of quality (detail) in copying may be as much as 30 per cent in a single copy step from any record. Enlargements made from the next-generation microfilm copy will have still poorer definition than an enlargement made from the original record. When possible, original records should be retained unless readable enlargements made from the microrecord are adequate to serve the user's purpose. Microfilm enlargements made from 70mm will give better definition than those made from 35mm film. When frequent enlargement of the microfilm record is necessary, it may be preferable to photograph the originals in the 35mm instead of the 16mm size, 70mm instead of 35mm size.

A user with an inquiring mind may ask: "Why can't I put my microfilm negative in my microfilm reader, and, when I have just the image I want, turn off all the lights—those of the reader and those in the room—place photosensitive paper on top of the reflective screen of my reader, turn on the reader lamp for an appropriate length of time, and, after shutting off the lamp, develop the photosensitive paper. Won't that give me the enlargement I want without buying an expensive enlarger?" If the microfilm reader provides a sharp image, the answer is "Yes." Ordinarily enlargers provide brighter and sharper images than readers because their lenses are usually better. However, some of the newest readers, which have excellent lens systems, can be used as suggested here to produce copies as satisfactory for ordinary purposes as enlargers. Such readers show little, if any, trace of fuzziness of image anywhere within the projected field, even if the microfilm remains stationary for many minutes. The way to find out whether this will work is to try it.

Enlargements of the microrecord can always be made with photographic enlargers. Some microrecord readers come equipped to make enlargements by exposing sensitized paper in the reader and processing it in the conventional manner. Such processing is time-consuming compared to relatively new direct copying developments.

Within the past few years several types of direct copying equipment have appeared on the market, both in the United States and in Europe. The function of such equipment is to produce excellent readable copies made from originals *in less than a minute.*

This equipment is not designed for large-size copy duplication. It will produce copies of originals up to a maximum of about 18 by 24 inches. Most of these units are combinations which contain developing and printing equipment or, if preferred, separate developing and printing units (see Figure 7). It is feasible to

Fig. 7. Remington Rand Portagraph and single unit Transcopy.
(Courtesy of Remington Rand, Inc.)

make readable enlargements of microrecords using the individual units of this equipment. The purpose in using such equipment for making microrecord enlargements is to produce a *readable* copy in a very short time for reference purposes. This readable copy is adequate for most industrial or library uses. When it is not adequate, photographic means will produce copies with better definition.

The basic advantage of such equipment, whether for making direct or microrecord copies, is the enormous saving in time, and elimination of installation cost, operation labor, and fuss required with conventional processing. No special plumbing or wiring is needed. The units are compact and fit anywhere in office or library. As they can be operated in subdued light, and some in full light, no dark room is necessary. The copies produced are sharp black on a clear white background. If desired, double-sided copies can be made, or transparencies for blue prints and diazo prints. If separate printing and developing units are used, copies may be made directly from books and ledgers. Cormac Industries Inc., for instance, has developed a printer specifically for books that will not damage the binding. The single combined units will not accommodate originals of such thickness unless the page is removed from the book or ledger. The printers vary in construction, and several are so devised that it is possible to copy pages of thick books without loss of margin. In order to utilize some printers it is necessary to press the ledger or book firmly against the glass in the printer in order to prevent loss of margin particularly if the spine of the book is not flexible. Copies may be reproduced from an original that is on lightweight, heavyweight, air mail or transparent paper. The finished copy lasts indefinitely. The print emerges from the processing unit almost dry. It is a clean operation eliminating the need for the usual numerous large chemical trays. The principal American manufacturers or distributors, equipment and costs are given in Table IV. European and American contact copying equipment is also listed and described in the "Manual on Document Reproduction and Selection."*

The normal procedure for using this duplicating equipment is as follows:

1. Negative or light-sensitive paper is exposed to the original copy in the printer in the combined or separate unit. (Uniform contact is necessary during exposure.)

2. A second sheet (positive paper) is placed face to face against the exposed sheet of negative paper which is then run through the developing unit. The developing unit contains a finishing solution which both develops and fixes at the same time, transferring the image from the negative to the positive paper. Both sheets are separated by feeds or guides as they are moved through the developing solution and proceed through rollers which press the two papers firmly together and remove excess solution.

3. The papers are removed from the roller and separated after approximately 15 seconds, and the negative sheet is thrown away

---

* Available from the International Federation for Documentation, The Hague, Netherlands, $7.50, Parts I and II.

TABLE IV. Equipment and Material
(Courtesy *Library Journal*, June

Cormac Industries, Inc.[a] "Cormac" [k,l]	Duplomat Co. of America [b] "Duplomat" [k,m]	Copease Co.[c] "Copease" [k,m]	Copycraft, Inc.[d] "Photo-rapid" [k,m]	F. G. Ludwig, Inc.[e] "Contoura," "Constat" [k,l]
		Simplex Units—Exposing Devices (with Automatic		
Maximum size of copy, in.				
8½ x 14	8½ x 14	8½ x 14	8½ x 14	8 x 10
Price				
$143	$59–67	$119.50	$150	$39
Maximum size of copy, in.				
14 x 17	18 x 24	14 x 17	13 x 17	8½ x 14 *
Price				
$172	$107–115	$199.50	$175	$59
			Simplex Units—Processing	
Construction				
Plexiglas and nylon; rubber rollers	Plastic; rubber rollers	Plastic and nylon; rubber rollers	Plastic; rubber rollers	Stainless steel, plastic; rubber rollers
Maximum width of copy, in.				
9	9	8½	8½	9
Price				
Elec ° : $196	Hand: $80 Elec: $145	Hand: $96.50 Elec: $212.50	Elec: $205	Hand: $55
Maximum width of copy, in.				
14	12	14	13	—
Price				
Elec: $227	Hand: $105 Elec: $170	Hand: $119.50 Elec: $249.50	Elec: $230	—
Maximum width of copy, in.				
—	17	—	—	—
Price				
—	Hand: $185 Elec: $250	—	—	—

for the Diffusion Transfer Process
15, 1954, and William R. Hawken)

General Photo Products, Inc.[f] "Exact-Phote Copy" [k]	Remington-Rand, Inc.[g] "Transcopy" [k,m]	Hunter Photo-Copyist, Inc.[h] "Heccokwik" [k,l]	Peerless Photo Products, Inc. [i] Dri-Stat" [k,l]	Amer. Photocopy Equipment Co.[j] "Autostat" [k,l]
Exposure Timer unless Indicated by *)				
8½ x 14 [l]	9½ x 15	14 x 19	8½ x 14	11 x 17
$67	$171.50	$105	$149	$88.95
18 x 24 [l]	20 x 24	16 x 20	—	—
$115	$245.25	$170	—	—
Devices				
Stainless steel; rubber rollers	Stainless steel, plastic; rubber rollers	Stainless steel; rubber rollers	Stainless steel; rubber rollers	Stainless steel, nylon; neoprene rollers
12 [l]	9	—	12	11
Hand: $105 Elec: $175	Elec: $185	—	Elec: $175–185	Elec: $189.50
14 [m]	14½	14	—	—
Hand: $125 Elec: $235	Elec: $245	Elec: $185	—	—
18 [l]	—	—	18	—
Hand: $185 Elec: $255	—	—	$255	—

TABLE IV.

Cormac Industries, Inc.[a] "Cormac" [k,l]	Duplomat Co. of America [b] "Duplomat" [k,m]	Copease Co.[c] "Copease" [k,m]	Copycraft, Inc.[d] "Photo-rapid" [k,m]	F. G. Ludwig, Inc.[e] "Contoura," "Constat" [k,l]

Duplex Units [p,q]

Maximum width of copy, in.

9	9	—	—	—

Price

$359	$265	—	—	—

Maximum width of copy, in.

—	14	14	—	—

Price

—	$350	$434	—	—

Positive Paper Stocks [r,s]

Cut sizes available, in.

8½ x 11 to 14 x 17 [m]	6 x 8 to 16½ x 23½ [m]	8½ x 11 to 14 x 17 [m]	8½ x 11 to 13 x 17 [m]	8 x 10 to 8½ x 11 [m]

Regular wt.

$8.00	$8.00	$8.25	$8.00	$8.00

Duplex

$14.75	$15.00	$15.25	$16.00	—

Card stock

$12.95	—	$12.55	$13.00	—

Transparent

$13.10	$14.45	$12.70	$14.00	$14.35

Tissue

$12.00	$11.75	$11.65	$12.00	—

[a] 80 Fifth Ave., New York 11, N. Y.
[b] 2 Stone St., New York 4, N. Y.
[c] 270 Park Ave., New York 17, N. Y.
[d] 105 Chambers St., New York 7, N. Y.
[e] Box 1091, Deep River, Conn.
[f] General Photo Bldg., Chatham, N. J.
[g] 315 Fourth Ave., New York 10, N. Y.
[h] Syracuse 4, N. Y.
[i] Shoreham, Long Island, N. Y.
[j] 2849 No. Clark St., Chicago 14, Ill.
[k] Trade name.
[l] Domestic.

(Continued)

General Photo Products, Inc.[f] "Exact-Phote Copy"[k]	Remington-Rand, Inc.[g] "Transcopy"[k,m]	Hunter Photo-Copyist, Inc.[h] "Heccokwik"[k,l]	Peerless Photo Products, Inc.[i] Dri-Stat"[k,l]	Amer. Photocopy Equipment Co.[j] "Autostat"[k,l]

Duplex Units [p,q]

12 [l]	9	—	12	11
$375	$410	—	$395	$370
14 [m]	14½	14	—	—
$450	$575	$395	—	—

Positive Paper Stocks [r,s]

8½ x 11 to 18 x 24 [l,m]	8½ x 11 to 14 x 17 [l,m]	6 x 9 to 12 x 18 [l]	[t]	5½ x 8½ to 11 x 17 [l]
$8.00	$8.50	$8.40	$7.98	$8.50
$16.00	$16.59	$16.80	[t]	$16.02
$12.00	$11.52	—	—	—
$15.00	$12.59	$14.00 [u]	—	$13.10
—	—	—	[t]	—

[m] Imported.

[n] Most prices shown are f.o.b. eastern distribution points.

[o] All electrically operated powered units operate on 110 volt 60 cycle alternating current.

[p] Construction of Duplex same as shown for Simplex processing units.

[q] All Duplex units have electric motor drive.

[r] Available paper stocks are those regularly listed.

[s] Prices shown are for 100 sets, negative and positive. Duplex sets include 2 negative sheets.

[t] Price quotation not received at time of publication.

[u] Translucent.

leaving the permanent positive copy. The positive copy is slightly damp from chemical contact, and it is laid on a flat surface for a few minutes before use. This helps retard curling and permits the finished positive to dry. The drying can be accelerated by the use of a small hand dryer or a small rotary-type dryer. Normally a dryer is not necessary but may be useful when a large quantity of material is copied.

The complete printing process can be accomplished in less than 1 minute. Learning to operate this equipment is a matter of a few minutes' instruction. Operational skill is developed through constant use. Copies that are overexposed have a tendency to be light, and copies underexposed tend to be grayish or dark. Consequently an adjustment in the amount of exposure or exposure time or perhaps a fresh processing solution is required.

The solutions are prepared from a liquid or powder concentrate and require only the addition of water in correct proportions. Dye can be added to the processing solution so that the finished positive is colored. By using a series of dyes in different developing units it is possible to "color-code" copies for file purposes or to meet other individual needs. If the original concentrate is in the form of a solution, it should be thoroughly shaken before the addition of water. After water is added to the solution, it should be thoroughly shaken again in order to combine the mixture thoroughly, but, once the solution is combined with water, mixed, and placed in the developing unit, it should never be deliberately shaken if stored for future use. The use of a siphon in storing the solution will reduce agitation. After numerous copies have been developed and fixed in a solution, an additional adjustment of the exposure time may be required to compensate for an older or used solution. Solutions have a tendency to oxidize if exposed to air for prolonged periods.

If the equipment contains metal feeds or guides, it is best to remove the solution from the tray at the end of each day, without undue shaking, and place it in a tightly capped bottle. The rollers, feeds, and tray that come in contact with the solution should be thoroughly washed with water daily. After washing, the rollers and feeds can be reinserted in the tray and the tray filled with water and left standing until the equipment is reused.

Even plastic feeds and rollers should be thoroughly washed with water occasionally for efficient operation.

The manufacturer of the Photorapid equipment claims that the solution can be kept in his developing box or processor until it is too weak for further use because it is equipped with a cover that retards oxidation of the solution and is manufactured with plastic feeds or guides. The solution for all types of equipment can be used until it becomes too weak to produce copies rapidly or legibly.

The waste of full-sized sheets of positive and negative paper which may result from use of old solutions or improper exposure adjustments can be eliminated by cutting small test strips of both positive and negative paper. These test strips can be processed initially and adjustments made when necessary in exposure or solution before employing full-sized sheets.

Basically, this equipment was designed for direct copying, but it can be utilized to make readable enlargements from some microrecord projectors. The process is much the same except for the time and method of exposure, which depend upon the type of microrecord reader utilized for making the enlargements. Enlargements made by utilizing an inexpensive photographic enlarger will give results superior to those made by using microrecord projectors.

Microrecord readers have two types of projection:

(1) direct projection, where the image is projected directly onto an opaque surface;

(2) indirect projection, where the image is projected onto a mirror and reflected through translucent glass or onto an opaque surface.

Normally microrecords are made in positive form. Enlargements made from positive microfilm require the following procedure:

1. The desired image is located on the microfilm reader.

2. The film containing the image is reversed in the microfilm reader. This is accomplished by removing a short section of the film from between the pressure plates and inserting it back in the reader, thus projecting the desired image in reverse. This reversing of the image is less awkward with sheet film than with long runs of film on rolls. Before exposure the reader focus control

should be checked to ascertain that all parts of the projection are legible and not fuzzy.

3. In subdued light the negative paper is placed (under glass* to hold it flat) in such a position that the desired image is projected to the coated or glossy side of the paper. Any movement of the paper, projection, or reader during exposure will result in a fuzzy copy. It is processed in the same manner as direct copies.

Aside from the type of paper used, the exposure time varies according to the type of reader projection. Exposure time is usually less in readers using direct projection. The exposure time in a Recordak MPE or American Optical Company reader is approximately 15 seconds. (See Figure 8; and also Figure 3 of Chapter IV on page 72.) In some other readers exposure time has taken 90 seconds or longer. This time also varies according to the size of the screen area and the distribution of illumination on the screen. The "hot spot" or area of greater brilliance in the center of the reader screen may be more noticeable on some readers than on others. This contrasting brilliance can be reduced in the finished enlargement by using a translucent masking in the area on the glass that is used to hold the negative paper flat or by waving an opaque sheet of paper back and forth in this area during exposure. Some experimenting is necessary to find the correct exposure for the particular type of reader and paper used. A readable copy can be made from a projected microfilm image, on the average, in about 2 minutes.

It is also possible to make a duplicate from a microfilm projection by the following procedure:

1. The desired image is located on the reader (if possible, away from the "hot spot").

2. The negative paper is laid so that the uncoated side is exposed to the image and the image is "burned" through or projected through the paper. This requires a longer exposure time, and the enlargement is not apt to be as well defined.

The procedure for making duplicates from the projected image of micro-opaques is the same as that outlined for microfilm. However, results vary with the model and type of reader used. If the reader has very uneven or poor illumination, this method

---

* Any sheet of clear flat glass of adequate size to cover the negative paper.

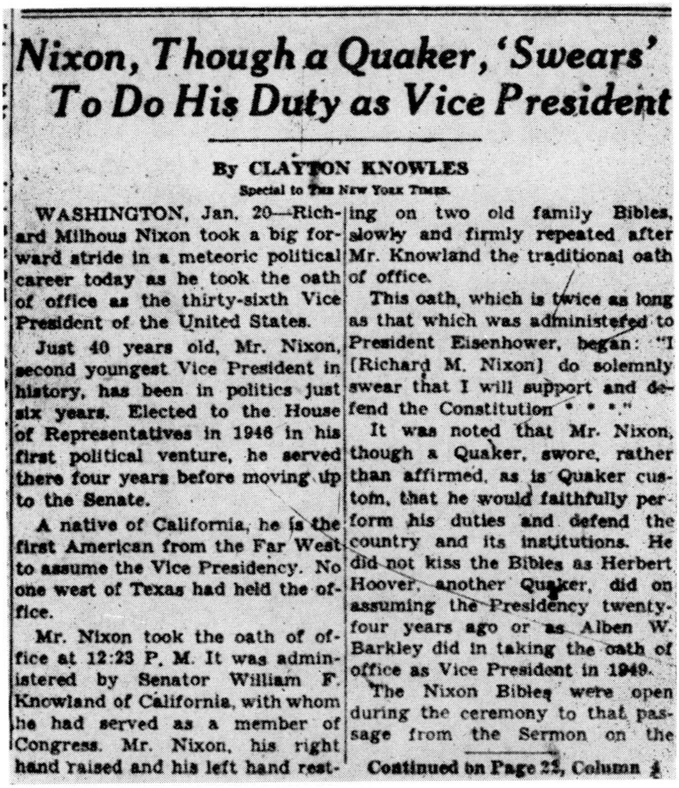

Nixon, Though a Quaker, 'Swears' To Do His Duty as Vice President

By CLAYTON KNOWLES
Special to The New York Times.

WASHINGTON, Jan. 20—Richard Milhous Nixon took a big forward stride in a meteoric political career today as he took the oath of office as the thirty-sixth Vice President of the United States.

Just 40 years old, Mr. Nixon, second youngest Vice President in history, has been in politics just six years. Elected to the House of Representatives in 1946 in his first political venture, he served there four years before moving up to the Senate.

A native of California, he is the first American from the Far West to assume the Vice Presidency. No one west of Texas had held the office.

Mr. Nixon took the oath of office at 12:23 P. M. It was administered by Senator William F. Knowland of California, with whom he had served as a member of Congress. Mr. Nixon, his right hand raised and his left hand resting on two old family Bibles, slowly and firmly repeated after Mr. Knowland the traditional oath of office.

This oath, which is twice as long as that which was administered to President Eisenhower, began: "I [Richard M. Nixon] do solemnly swear that I will support and defend the Constitution * * *."

It was noted that Mr. Nixon, though a Quaker, swore, rather than affirmed, as is Quaker custom, that he would faithfully perform his duties and defend the country and its institutions. He did not kiss the Bibles as Herbert Hoover, another Quaker, did on assuming the Presidency twenty-four years ago or as Alben W. Barkley did in taking the oath of office as Vice President in 1949.

The Nixon Bibles were open during the ceremony to that passage from the Sermon on the

Continued on Page 22, Column 4

FIG. 8. Copy of enlargement of 35mm microfilm projected in MPE Recordak reader. (Courtesy of New York *Times*.)

of copying should not be attempted. The objective in using any of these copying methods in conjunction with microrecord readers is the rapidity, as compared with conventional methods with which enlargements can be made for reference purposes.

Recordak Co. has recently introduced a "Rapid Facsimile Kit" ($35), which utilizes a contact paper and squeegee method for making readable copies directly from the projected image in microrecord readers.

The next several years may produce several inexpensive, rapid copying techniques specifically designed for making enlargements from microfilm projections. These enlargements may have better than readable quality produced at the same low cost. This will be due to the increased use of microrecordings and the competition (that has been created already) among the manufacturers of microfilm and copying equipment. It will be the result of an increasing users' demand and the manufacturers' desire to create quality products with greater versatility at a lower price for the purpose of gaining wider markets.

SOME OTHER COMMERCIAL PROCESSES

Electrofax (RCA)

On February 14, 1956, RCA released data on Electrofax, a high-speed enlarger-printer of the dry-process type reported to be capable of reproducing fifteen engineering drawings (17 by 22 inches) per minute from 35mm microfilm positive. The price is $85,000.

The Electrofax enlarger-printer will be combined with Filmsort equipment (Dexter Folder Co.) and other processing equipment by the Bureau of Aeronautics at the Naval Air Station at Alameda, California, to provide an "integrated system for low-cost storage and high-speed processing of engineering drawings essential for the maintenance and modification of naval aircraft.

"The system will introduce at the Alameda repair center important savings in the cost of handling and reproducing engineering drawings, and in the space required for their storage. The high-speed selection and reproduction system will make possible rapid, push button availability of filed drawings." The estimates of direct savings to Naval aviation exceed one million dollars annually in procurement, reproduction, and storage costs.

The machine can be loaded with up to 500 Filmsort cards or with a 100-foot reel of 35mm microfilm positive. It uses an electrically sensitive printing paper and a "brush." The paper, which is claimed to be several thousand times faster than blue print paper, runs at a linear speed of 23 feet per minute. When the charged paper is exposed to light, the areas affected by the light are discharged, leaving a latent image in the unexposed or lightly exposed areas. "Brushing" with a resin powder causes the positively charged particles of the powder to adhere to the negatively charged areas of the paper. Subsequent heating causes the pigmented resin powder to set in the paper, producing a permanent image.

Kalfax

Another process for providing dry prints is being marketed by Kalfax, Inc., 714 Gerard Street, New Orleans, Louisiana. Here again the paper used employs the principle of physical fusion of the image-producing material by heat. In this process there are two steps:

  (1) Impregnated paper is placed in contact with a photographic negative and exposed to light (3 to 5 seconds exposure).
  (2) The paper is put through a heat roller (160 to 250° F.), which simultaneosuly removes the unexposed substance.

An enlargement of 14 to 20 times can be made in about 30 seconds directly on a single sheet of Kalfax paper from a microfilm. A contact printer is sold for $425. The enlargement printer for microfilm costs $2800. The cost of Kalplastic paper is 7 cents per square foot; 100 sheets of 8½ by 11 inch paper cost $7.

As for other processes, it is difficult to judge the quality attainable in copies without suitable tests. Possible difficulties with Kalfax copies are low contrast, and fog in image areas that are supposed to be white. Because the process is a diffusion process rather than an absorption one, a direct positive is produced when viewed by reflected light, but it appears as a negative when viewed by transmitted light. Photographic speed is comparable with usual blue print papers.

The contact printer will handle up to 11 by 17 inches. The enlarger will handle up to 8½ by 14 inches.

An unexposed sheet is dark—black or dark colored. The exposed areas appear white because the light is diffused. Full data will become available when the patents covering the process have been issued.

LAWS GOVERNING COPYING

Rapid copying equipment is low cost, simple to use, and effective in making reproductions. Anything that is written or printed can be reproduced by utilizing one of these techniques. More attention is being given to means of reproducing original-size photo-copies from microrecords and the projected images of microrecords in the refinement of copying equipment. Books and periodicals can be easily copied in part, or in toto, to meet various needs. Such material is protected by copyright law, and unpublished material by common law. Other laws prohibit photographing, photocopying, or making enlargements of certain types of documents, certificates, stamps, licenses, and currency. These are listed in Appendix A, pages 352 to 354.

Exceptions to these laws may be made from time to time under very specific conditions by authors, publishers, or the authorities concerned. For example, "hot" or filmed money that is unmarked is proving an effective deterrent in bank robberies and in running down bank robbers and establishing their guilt. Part 404, Chapter IV, Title 31, of the Code of Federal Regulations dated February 11, 1946, amended January 1951, sets forth this authority and the limitations under which it may be undertaken. Such film records are maintained as confidential, and no prints, enlargements, or other reproductions of the film records may be made except with the permission of the proper authorities.

The avoidance of infringement and the protection of the author become a broader problem and a graver responsibility for more people because of the rapid market expansion of copying equipment. Large libraries and corporations, probably, are more cognizant of these problems than the new owner of such devices, who may not be aware of all laws governing copying, or who incorrectly interprets such laws without legal counsel. Copyright law is involved and subject to various interpretations by both lawyers and the courts.

The basic approach is to list every known need in each individual operation for making copies, and present it to a lawyer for his advice. He should be apprised of each departure from this basic list or of new needs as they arise. Changes in the law or its interpretation necessitate periodic reviews.

In some respects common law protects the author to a greater degree than the statutory rights. Generally, common law rights endure as long as the work remains unpublished. Also there is the doctrine of "Fair Use" that generally, in the United States, applies only to published literary works. In addition, a so-called "Gentleman's Agreement" was arrived at among certain, but not all, publishers, that permits copying of single copies of portions of a book or magazine under certain conditions. The full text of this agreement was published in the *Journal of Documentary Reproduction,* March 1939.

An excellent analysis of the multiple problems involved, and the needs for making photocopies, was written in two parts by Louis Charles Smith, Senior Attorney of the Copyright Offices, Library of Congress, for the August 1953, and August 1954, *Law Library Journal,* published by the American Association of Law Libraries. The article was entitled "The Copying of Literary Property in Library Collections." The first part reviews the needs, laws, and past efforts to solve the problem.

The second part explores the possibilities for meeting copying needs without infringing upon authors' rights. He suggests a set of conditions upon which endorsement might be sought by various parties involved in such problems. These suggestions "have not yet been given the express sanction of law. Whether the courts would agree that the present law permits photocopying under those or any other conditions is a matter of conjecture." They do provide a guide in photocopying operations by a library for the use of a scholar. The conditions are:

1. The scholar would be required to give some assurance (a) that the photocopy requested by him is desired for the sole purpose of his private study and (b) that he will not reproduce or distribute the photocopy, or copy any substantial part of it in his own work without the permission of the copyright owner.

2. Not more than one photocopy would be made for any one scholar.

3. Each photocopy would bear notations showing the source of the material and stating that it is copyrighted.

4. The scholar would be required to pay the full cost of making the photocopy in any event. Where the work to be photocopied is believed to be available for purchase from trade sources, the charge for the photocopy should be greater than the price of a trade copy.

Mr. Smith states that, "In view of the uncertain status of the present law, and in the absence of judicial decisions on the basic questions involved, perhaps the ultimate solution of the problem would be legislation permitting libraries to make photocopies under specified conditions." This is a challenge for library and research groups to resolve.

Copies of ASA Specifications can be obtained from:

The American Standards Association, Inc.
70 East 45th Street
New York 17, New York

A complete list of ASA Standards offered for sale may be obtained free of charge by writing to the Association.

Appendix
Printing Paper

PH1.11	-1953	Photographic Paper Rolls, Dimensions for
PH1.12	-1953	Inch Size Photographic Papers, Dimensions for
PHI.1	-1953	Thickness of Photographic Paper, Designation for
PH1.13	-1953	Moulded Type Cores for Photographic Film and Paper Rolls, Dimensions for

Sheet Film

PH1.15	-1953	Industrial X-ray Sheet Film (Inch Sizes), Dimensions for
PH1.16	-1953	Graphic Arts Sheet Film (Inch Sizes), Dimensions for
PH1.17	-1953	Medical X-ray Sheet Film (Inch and Centimeter Sizes), Dimensions for
PH1.18	-1953	Professional Portrait and Commercial Sheet Film (Inch Sizes), Dimensions for
Z38.1.29	-1949	Professional Portrait and Commercial Sheet Film (Centi-
PH1.19	-1944	Emulsion Side of Photographic Sheet Films, Designation of meter Sizes), Dimensions for
Z38.1.30	-1951	Photographic Dry Plates (Inch Sizes), Dimensions for
Z38.1.31	-1944	Photographic Dry Plates (Centimeter Sizes), Dimensions for

Film Spool

Z38.1.49	-1951	35-Millimeter Magazine Film (for Miniature Cameras), Dimensions for
Z38.1.52	-1951	16-Millimeter 100-Foot Film Spool for Recording Instruments and Still Picture Cameras, Dimensions for
Z38.1.53	-1951	16-Millimeter 200-Foot Film Spool for Recording Instruments and Still Picture Cameras, Dimensions for
Z38.1.54	-1951	35-Millimeter 100-Foot Film Spool for Recording Instruments and Still Picture Cameras, Dimensions for
Z38.1.55	-1951	70-Millimeter 100-Foot Film Spool for Recording Instruments and Still Picture Cameras, Dimensions for

Measurement

PH.2.2	-1953	Sensitometry and Grading of Photographic Papers (Revision of Z38.2.3-1947)
PH2.5	-1954	Photographic Speed and Exposure Index, Method for Determining

PH4.4   -1952   Channel-Type Photographic Hangers, Plates and Sheet Film,
                      Specifications for
Z38.8.1   -1944   Temperature of Processing Solutions, Practice for
     R1948
Z38.8.2   -1945   Conversion of Weights and Measures for Photographic Use,
                      Practice for
Z38.8.3   -1947   Photographic Processing Manipulation of Films and Plates,
                      Practice for
Z38.8.4   -1945   Bite of Film Clips, Dimensions for
Z38.8.6   -1949   Photographic Processing Manipulation of Paper, Practice for
Z38.8.7   -1946   Radiographic Film Processing Tanks, Internal Dimensions for
Z38.8.8   -1946   Deep Tanks for Commercial Photofinishing, Internal Di-
                      mensions for
Z38.8.9   -1946   Scales, Graduates, and Thermometers for Use in Photog-
                      raphy, Accuracy of
Z38.8.11 -1948   Photographic Thermometers
Z38.8.12 -1948   Photographic Graduates
Z38.8.13 -1950   Safety-Time of Photographic Darkroom Illumination, Pro-
                      cedure for Determining the
Z38.8.14 -1950   Photographic Wetting Agents, Requirements for
Z38.8.18 -1948   Chromium-Plated Surfaces for Ferrotyping
Z38.8.19 -1948   Maximum Safe Temperatures for Photographic Processing
                      Solutions, Method for Determining
Z38.8.20 -1948   Melting Point of the Photographic Layer of Films, Plates,
                      and Papers, Method for Determining the
Z38.8.23 -1949   X-Ray Sheet Film Hangers (Clip-Type)
Z38.8.25 -1950   Residual Thiosulfate and Tetrathionate in Processed Photo-
                      graphic Papers, Methods for Determining

SPECIFICATIONS FOR PHOTOGRAPHIC GRADE CHEMICALS

Acids

Z38.8.100-1949   Acetic Acid, Glacial
Z38.8.101-1949   Sulfuric Acid
Z38.8.102-1949   Citric Acid
Z38.8.103-1949   Boric Acid, Crystalline
Z38.8.104-1949   Hydrochloric Acid
PH4.105-1952   Photographic Grade Sodium Acid Sulfate, Fused ($NaHSO_4$)
                      (Sodium Bisulfate, Fused; Niter Cake), Specification for
Z38.8.106-1949   Acetic Acid, 28 Per cent

Developing Agents

Z38.8.125-1948   Mono-Methyl-Para-Aminophenol   Sulfate   (Armol,   Elon,
                      Genol, Graphol, Metol, Photol, Pictol, Rhodol, Veritol)
PH4.126-1955   Hydroquinone   (Para-Dihydroxybenzene,   Quinol,   Hydro-
                      chinone, Hydroquinol)

Z38.8.127-1948 2,4-Diaminophenol Hydrochloride (Acrol, Amidol, Dianol, Dolmi)

Z38.8.128-1949 Para-Hydroxyphenylglycin (Athenon, Glycin, Iconyl, Monazol)

Z38.8.129-1948 Para-Aminophenol Hydrochloride (Kodelon, P.A.P.)

Z38.8.130-1948 Pyrogallic Acid (1,2,3-Trihydroxybenzene, Pyro, Pyro gallol)

Z38.8.131-1948 Catechol (Ortho-Dihydroxybenzene, Pyrocatechin, Pyrocathechol)

Z38.8.132-1948 Para-Phenylenediamine (1,4-Diaminobenzene)

Z38.8.133-1948 Para-Phenylenediamine Dihydrochloride (1,4-Diaminobenzene Dihydrochloride)

Z38.8.134-1948 Chlorhydroquinone (2-Chlor-1,4-Dihydroxybenzene, Adurol, C.H.Q.)

PH4.135-1954 Mono-Benzyl-Para-Aminophenol Hydrochloride (N-Benzyl-p-Aminophenol Hydrochloride, p-Benzyl-Aminophenol Hydrochloride)

Hardeners

Z38.8.150-1949 Aluminum Potassium Sulfate, Crystalline
Z38.8.151-1949 Chromium Potassium Sulfate, Crystalline
Z38.8.152-1949 Formaldehyde Solution
Z38.8.153-1949 Paraformaldehyde

Miscellaneous

Z38.8.175-1949 Sodium Sulfate, Anhydrous
Z38.8.176-1949 Sodium Acetate, Anhydrous
Z38.8.177-1949 Potassium Dichromate
Z38.8.178-1949 Potassium Permanganate
Z38.8.179-1949 Potassium Ferricyanide
Z38.8.180-1949 Copper Sulfate
Z38.8.181-1949 Potassium Persulfate
Z38.8.182-1949 Sodium Sulfide, Fused
PH4.183-1953 Photographic Grade Ammonium Chloride, Specification for (NH_4Cl)
PH4.184-1953 Photographic Grade Ammonium Sulfate, Specification for ($(NH_4)_2SO_4$)
PH4.178-1954 Photographic Grade Isopropylamine, 50 Per Cent Aqueous Solution (Monoisopropylamine)
PH4.181-1954 Photographic Grade Benzyl Alcohol

Restrainers and Antifoggants

PH4.200-1955 Potassium Bromide
Z38.8.201-1948 Potassium Iodide
Z38.8.202-1948 Potassium Chloride
Z38.8.203-1948 Sodium Chloride
PH4.204-1955 Benzotriazole

Z38.8.205-1948   5-Methylbenzotriazole
Z38.8.206-1948   Nitrobenzimidazole

Alkalies

Z38.8.225-1948   Sodium Hydroxide
Z38.8.226-1948   Potassium Hydroxide
PH4.227-1954   Sodium Carbonate, Monohydrate
PH4.228-1954   Sodium Carbonate, Anhydrous
Z38.8.229-1948   Potassium Carbonate
PH4.230-1954   Sodium Tetraborate, Decahydrate (Borax)
Z38.8.231-1948   Sodium Metaborate
Z38.8.232-1948   Ammonium Hydroxide

Fixing Agents

PH4.250-1953   Sodium Thiosulfate, Anhydrous
PH4.251-1953   Sodium Thiosulfate, Crystalline
PH4.252-1953   Photographic Grade Ammonium Thiosulfate, 60 Per Cent
                Solution, $(NH_4)_2S_2O_3$, (Ammonium Hypo Solution), Spe-
                cification for
PH4.253-1953   Photographic Grade Ammonium Thiosulfate, $(NH_4)_2S_2O_3$,
                (Ammonium Hypo), Specification for

Sulfites

PH4.275-1952   Photographic Grade Sodium Sulfite (Na_2SO_3), Specification

Miscellaneous

PH1.11 -1953   Photographic Paper Rolls, Dimensions for (Revision of
                 Z38.1.5-1943 and Partial Revision of Z38.1.6-1943)
PH1.12 -1953   Photographic Paper Sheets, Dimensions for (Revision of
                 Z38.1.43-1947 and Partial Revision of Z38.1.6-1943)
PH22.53 -1953   Method of Determining Resolving Power of 16mm Mo-
                 tion-Picture Projector Lenses
PH22.86 -1953   Dimensions for 200-Mil Magnetic Sound Tracks on 35mm
                 17½mm Motion-Picture Film
PH22.87 -1953   Dimensions for 100-Mil Magnetic Coating on Single-Per-
                 forated 16mm Motion-Picture Film
Z38.7.4 -1944   Projectors for Opaque Materials for Use in Small Audi-
                 toriums, Specifications for
Z38.7.9 -1946   Microfilm Readers, Specifications for

Other ASA Standards that are of interest are to be found in the following
standards groups:

PH 1   Photographic Films, Plates and Papers
PH 2   Photographic Sensitometry
PH 3   Photographic Apparatus

PH 4   Photographic Processing
PH 5   Photographic Reproduction of Documents
PH 22   Motion Pictures

Bibliography

"Lensless Copying with Sensitized Papers." Frank Smith, Photographic Dept., General Motors Corp. Paper presented at American Chem. Society Symposium, September 9, 1953.

Ivan G. Grimshaw. "Contoura Printing Saves Day at Beloit College Libraries." *Library J.*, Vol. 65, No. 6, pp. 546-548 (1951).

"The Copy Rapid Process Camera (Lucerne)." *Agfa*, Vol. 29, pp. 376-377, 392 (1950).

P. M. Van Alphen and C. J. Dippel. "New Technical Possibilities in the Micro-reproduction and Multiplication of Documents." Rapports 17th Conf., FID, 1947, pp. 75-78.

Chester Lewis. "Rapid Copying Equipment." *Library J.*, Vol. 78, No. 16, pp. 1508-1509 (Sept. 15, 1953).

William R. Hawken. "New Methods for Photocopying." *Library J.*, pp. 1115-1124, June 15, 1954.

"Standard Register's Electronic Find." *Business Week*, Feb. 27, 1954, pp. 41-43.

Haloid Company, 48th Annual Report.

Haloid Company Release of March 22, 1954, on the Continuous Xerographic Microfilm Enlarger.

"The Use of Xerography in Libraries." James G. Hodgson, Colorado A & M College Library, Fort Collins, Colo., Oct. 1952.

Chester Lewis. "Library Use of Xerography." *Library J.*, Vol. 78, No. 12, June 15, 1953, pp. 1095-1096, 1098.

W. D. Oliphant. "Xerography: A Non-Chemical Photographic Process." *Discovery*, Vol. 14, No. 6, pp. 175-179 (1953).

"X-ray Pictures Made with Film (Xeroradiography)." *New York Times*, Jan. 29, 1956, Sec. IV, p. 9, columns 7 and 8.

W. C. Huebner. "The Photronic Reproducer." *Amer. Documentation*, Vol. II, No. 4, pp. 238-240 (Oct. 1951).

Walter Clark. "Document Reproduction by Photography in the United States." *Phot. Sci. Tech.*, Tech 1, Ser. 2, No. 2, pp. 31-37 (May 1954).

Frank E. Smith. "Lensless Copying with Sensitized Papers." *J. Chem. Education*, Vol. 31, pp. 351-353 (1954).

"Hot Money For Bad Boys." Protective Bulletin of the American Bankers Association, March 1953, pp. 1-2.

Donald H. Niven. "New Photostat Apparatus To Enlarge and Process From Microfilm." *Proceedings of the National Microfilm Association*,* 1954, pp. 11-15.

* National Microfilm Association, 19 Lafayette Ave., Hingham, Mass.

George H. Hamp. "Microfilm Enlarging via Xerography." *Proceedings of the National Microfilm Association,** 1954, pp. 47-50.

Charles H. Benbrook. "Diazotype Duplication of Microfilm." *Proceedings of the National Microfilm Association,** 1954, pp. 79-89.

Kenneth P. Morse. "A New Approach to Some Microfilm Problems." *Proceedings of the National Microfilm Association,** 1954, pp. 90-97.

* National Microfilm Association, 19 Lafayette Ave., Hingham, Mass.

VIII

READERS

Microrecord readers are of two basic types: those for the projection of opaque materials such as Microcards and Readex Microprint, and those for the projection of transparencies such as microfilm or sheet film. Although a small hand magnifier is frequently useful in viewing small portions of a microrecord, it is not considered a microrecord reader.

The performance, construction, operation, and cost of microrecord readers vary widely from manufacturer to manufacturer and for a particular manufacturer they vary significantly from one type or grade to another. Because of variations in performance and in operating characteristics per unit cost, there is now a strong urge in the United States toward standardization of the microrecord itself and of the equipment employed to project it. Since a microrecord may take any of several formats and forms, according to its manner of storage and use, standardization implies detailed specifications for those forms and formats and the equipment for viewing them that have acquired commercial acceptance or bid fair to acquire such acceptance. Broadly speaking, in the United States microfilm has been used almost to the exclusion of sheet film; recently more attention has been paid to sheet film and it seems probable that it will be marketed much more widely in this country in the near future. Since sheet film has not yet found wide usage, opaque materials printed from sheet film have not appeared in an important degree. Microcards and Readex Microprint have been used to a considerable extent.

Standards for microfilm already exist, other standards are being prepared, and older standards are being revised. There will be some standardization of sizes; it is hoped that this will encourage the refinement in design of readers capable of being used for microopaques. At present most readers are limited to a single size; this is an understandable result of the desire of each manufacturer to furnish equipment useful only for his specific proprietary form of microtext. The cost, to the consumer, of reading facilities would be reduced materially and other advantages would be gained if multi-purpose readers were offered for sale which were suitable for all the forms the user might reasonably wish to employ. Through organizations like the National Microfilm Association, the American Standards Association, and the International Standards Organization, manufacturer and consumer work together for a solution of such problems. For example, as a result of such cooperation a revision of American Standard Specifications for Microfilm Readers for 16 and 35mm Film on Reels (ASA PH5.1)* is being undertaken.

Manufacturers find it difficult to determine precisely what a consumer wants in his apparatus; frequently he is not certain himself. Furthermore, consumer preferences for micro-recording programs vary. If such preferences can be determined, fewer varieties of apparatus will be manufactured, the cost will be less, and apparatus performance will improve. This will be no less true of microrecording equipment than it has been of automobiles, radio, television, and all other quantity-produced American products.

The Documents Research Unit of the Navy Research Section of the Library of Congress undertook a survey in 1951 to enable them to prepare specifications for a "universal reader" which could be used for all existing forms of microrecords, whether opaque or transparent, in rolls or in strips. Inquiries were mailed to 2227 present or potential users of microrecords in all fields. Replies were received from 34.5% of those solicited; they came from forty-one states, Alaska, Hawaii, and three Canadian provinces. The preliminary results of the survey indicated that:

84% preferred a single reader for all forms. 49% were willing to pay $200 for such a reader. 78% wanted a portable reader. 71% wanted a projected image on the reader screen. 67% wanted an image 10 by 12 inches. 81% wanted a full page presented at a time.

The survey also indicated that, of the readers in use:

79% were for microfilm. 30% were for opaque microrecord. 4% were for transparent microrecord.

These preferences are significant because they indicate that users want a single universal reader. It is extremely doubtful that an excellent reader incorporating all the desired features could be produced for as little as $200.00. The more complex the reader, the

---

* Reproduced in Appendix E, pages 417 and 418.

higher the cost; and certainly such a multiple-use reader would, of necessity, be complex in order to accommodate all forms of micro-records.

The performance of a reader depends upon its construction, and its construction depends upon its use. In order to facilitate reading, the projected image should be larger than that of the original record. This will reduce unnecessary searching. The projected image should have excellent definition.

Direct projection upon an opaque reflective matte white surface will give the best viewing for microfilm and other transparencies. The screen should be sufficiently large to project the whole of one image, whether it is a book or newspaper page or an engineering drawing. The texture of the screen should be such that light from stray sources, such as light fixtures in the room and from windows, is minimized when such light cannot be completely excluded; images from protected screens are suited to prolonged viewing. "Hot spots" in the projected image must be avoided through good optical design embracing suitable lamps, reflectors, objective, and condenser lenses. The intensity of the light source in the reader should be adjustable to provide the individual user with precisely the proper brightness, neither too bright nor too dim. The definition of the image in the corners should be good and sharp; it should not be expected to be quite as good as the image sharpness accomplished by a microfilm camera. The illumination of the image at the corners should be sufficiently high to meet the requirements of Section 4.1 of Proposed American Standard PH5.1/12 or the latest revision thereof.

The heat generated by the light source should be controlled in such manner as to prevent damage to the microtext. Proposed Standard ASA PH5.1/12 specifies that: "The temperature of the film should not exceed 75°C (167°F) when measured by the testing method specified in American Standard Methods of Testing Printing and Projection Equipment Z38.7.5-1948,* or the latest revision thereof [approved by the American Standards Association]."

Some readers utilize lamps with a prefocused base; prefocusing usually eliminates fussy adjustments when a lamp is replaced. The lamp should be simple to remove and replace. Bulbs that are

---

* Reproduced in Appendix D, page 411.

insufficiently cooled or improperly made or both have a tendency to "balloon" when the lamp burns out, separating or breaking from the base and making removal difficult and dangerous. Proper lamps sufficiently cooled eliminate this safety hazard and nuisance.

The screen should be tilted so that the viewer can read the entire image comfortably. The tilt of the screen should permit the user to view the image without blocking the projected light beam and also permit him to copy any image portion conveniently.

The controls of microtext readers should be readily accessible to the user and designed to permit ease of loading and handling. Preferably the movement of the image should be that of conventional reading. The image should remain in focus during movement and not require refocusing, yet focus controls should be provided when adjustment is necessary.

In the case of microfilm in reel form, the film may be transported or moved through the reader by hand or motor. Motor-driven readers are convenient when the primary use is that of scanning long lengths of film; such readers are usually more expensive than hand-driven ones. Hand-driven readers are adequate for most purposes and should be constructed so that the "drive" will stand hard use. Links in some chain drives loosen, or, if a cable is used instead of a chain-drive, it may have a tendency to go out of order when turned too fast. Controls should permit rewinding the film at faster speeds than those used for scanning.

The loading or feed mechanism should not cause damage, curvature, or abrasion to the microrecord. This part of the reader assembly should be accessible for cleaning purposes so that it can be kept free from dust or other foreign particles.

All readers should, if possible, provide means for rapid facsimile production of copies from the projected images of the reader. Some readers accomplish this by conventional processing methods for the copy produced; a few employ direct positive or rapid copying techniques. Facsimile production is rapidly becoming a required feature of a reader; the need becomes greater as more and more material is stored in microtext form.

The reader should be light; its cabinet or case should be made of light weight yet sturdy material for portability, a highly desirable feature. Such a case should withstand wear and tear without warping or breakage in normal use.

Operation and maintenance should be simple enough so that a user will not need lengthy involved technical instruction, either verbal or written.

All these properties are desirable, but unfortunately it is not feasible at present to incorporate them all in one low-cost reader. To permit proper projection of all sizes of transparencies and opaque materials in a single instrument would require a reader so complex that it would be very costly. Practical readers, as now manufactured and sold, may possess most of these properties in a particular size and type of microrecord or in a very small number of closely related sizes; no commercial reader possesses them for even the small number of different forms, both opaque and transparency, in widest use. Ordinarily a particular make and model of reader can project images of only one projected image size from one form and size of microtext. Although theoretically the adaptation to another size or form or both may not be a difficult matter, in practice such adaptation would be tantamount to a complete redesign of the instrument in question. For this reason a user should study carefully the specifications of readers he is considering purchasing. These are listed in Table I, page 260.

AMERICAN READERS

Microfilm Readers

Probably the greatest variety in reader design is found in the United States. Equipment varies from a simple hand magnifying glass viewer costing as little as $2.00 to readers that cost $2500 or more. Most American readers are made to accommodate roll film in either the 16mm or the 35mm size; a few are being made for 70mm and for sheet film (microfiche). The number and types of readers for micro-opaques are increasing. A number of readers are made for a single size of microtext. Some readers are portable; some are light enough to be picked up easily and moved about from location to location, others are moved about on their casters.

American microfilm readers are made in a variety of optical system types. Some use a straight-line optical system in which the projected image appears on an opaque white matte reflecting surface. Others use folded optical systems with a reflecting or mir-

ror surface relaying the image to the projection screen at an angle
with respect to the angle at which the light beam approaches the
relaying reflecting surface from the projection objective lens. A
translucent screen, used in some readers, is viewed from one side
and the image from the microfilm is projected on the other side.
There is apt to be greater eyestrain with this type than with the
opaque white matte reflecting surface unless very special precautions are taken to exclude or otherwise control the stray light incident on the viewed screen. Such control is often accomplished by
the use of a tinted or light-absorbent screen; the stray light
reflected by the screen must be absorbed upon entering the translucent screen and again when it emerges after reflection inside the
reader toward the outside surface again. Since light from the
microfilm image also is absorbed by the partial absorption of the
screen, the amount of light delivered by the optical system must
be increased to allow for such absorption of the screen. This is the
principle used in the "black-daylight" television tubes currently
provided by some manufacturers in television sets.

Uneven illumination found in some readers may be due to the
optical system used or to an inappropriate texture of the screen
surface; since low illumination is a common defect in readers,
some designs utilize translucent screens that are quite directive in
their characteristics. Such screens are quite bright when viewed
head on but become progressively dimmer rapidly as the viewer
moves off to the side. If the stray light that hits such a screen approaches it from the side, the amount of stray light reflected from
the surface of the screen is appreciably smaller than the amount
reflected when the stray light source is "head on" to the screen.
Because of these limitations, the translucent screen reader, in comparison with matte reflecting screen readers, often produces excessive fatigue under ordinary operating conditions. Since translucent screen readers are usually much more costly than matte reflecting screen readers of equivalent performance, there is a growing
trend toward the use of the matte reflecting screen type.

There still exists a psychological block on the part of some
users to the prolonged use of microrecord readers because of eye
fatigue or strain. This may have been true to some extent in early
readers. But present image quality and reader performance negate
this premise. A technical treatise written by Carmichael and Dear-

born* measured visual fatigue through the measurement of eye movements in reading. A base period of six hours reading was used, and the authors state that "the form of reproduction of reading material, book or microfilm, was not clearly differentiated in producing fatigue."

Because microfilm when properly exposed and processed has appreciably higher image contrast than the average original document from which it is photographed, it should be easier to read than the original document. Since it is not always properly exposed and processed, the end-use image may be poorer in quality. Poorer quality in the micro-image is a serious handicap to the use of micro-text in preference to original material.

The microrecord is usually fed into the reader at a point directly in front of the user, at the base or the top of the reader. Focusing and magnification controls are usually located with the feed assembly. Scanning controls for moving the image are contained with the feed assembly or as separate units on the side of the reader.

Some readers are manufactured with a fixed magnification or enlargement, and others permit some variation in magnification. The average range of magnification seems to be from 18 to 23×. Although magnification may be as low as 10×, it is usually not higher than 40×.

Some readers remain in constant sharp focus even when the image is moved. The Burroughs Microfilm Reader, the Griscombe Portable, and the Recordak Model MPE (see Figure 3 of Chapter IV, page 72) and Model C are notable in this respect. This is one of the features that account for their wide use and popularity. Some types distort the image when it is moved for scanning. Less eye strain is encountered during prolonged periods of use if the image stays in sharp focus at all times.

Most American readers are manually operated. Some companies such as Diebold, Recordak, and Burroughs sell both motorized and manually operated readers.

Notable among the new readers are those designed for holding microfilm inserted in either protective jackets or cards. Filmsort

---

* "Reading and Visual Fatigue," by Leonard Carmichael and Walter F. Dearborn, Houghton Mifflin Co., N. Y., 1947, pp. 359-360.

markets four basic models, the "Inspector," the "Inspector 200," the "Reviewer," and the "Surveyor." All four accommodate roll film as well as film in jackets. The "Inspector," designed for desktop use, is portable. It weighs less than 20 pounds, has a translucent screen 11 inches square and is available in two models with a magnification of either 16× or 22×. The "Inspector 200" (Figure 1), also a desk-top model, is available in three magnifications of

FIG. 1. Filmsort Inspector 200. (Courtesy of Filmsort Division of Dexter Folder Co.)

16×, 24×, and 30×. (An extra accessory, not necessary for normal operation, is the Auto-Scan. This device holds jacket cards in position for automatic scanning.) The "Reviewer" offers a 17-inch square screen of the reflective type; using transfer print processes, it can make photographic prints of screen size or smaller in less than one minute per copy (see Figure 2). The "Surveyor" is de-

Fig. 2. Film-a-Record Reviewer. (Courtesy of Remington Rand, Inc.)

signed for reading large-sized copy in 35mm. It is available in two
screen sizes: 24 by 18 inches or 36 by 24 inches, both translucent.
This reader is useful for viewing engineering drawings, maps,
bound books, or any other material required to be viewed in full.
At present the "Surveyor" (Figure 3) has the largest screen of any
35mm reader made in the United States.

Other readers made for holding cards or jackets are the Rem-
ington-Rand Kard-a-Film Reader F-71 and the readers made by
Griscombe Products Inc., of New York City, and Erban Products,
Inc.

The student or researcher can own an inexpensive microfilm
viewer devised by Mr. Atherton Seidell that is useful for reading
short lengths of 35mm microfilm. It has a magnification of about
10× and sells for $2.00 (see Figure 4). This is a hand magnifying
glass viewer.

FIG. 3. Film-a-Record Surveyor. (Courtesy of Remington Rand, Inc.)

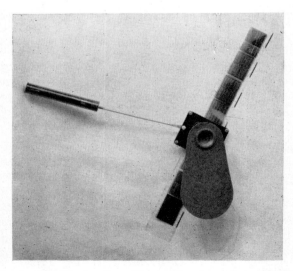

FIG. 4. Seidell microfilm viewer. (Courtesy of A. Seidell.)

Microfilm service companies are photographing newspapers at reductions ranging from 1 :16 to 1 :19. Often, when the larger reduction is used, on 35mm microfilm the image is arranged at right angles to the film and not with the length of the film. A small saving results because of the reduction permitted with less film waste, but it presents a problem for the viewer if the newspaper is not tabloid size. When a full-sized newspaper has been filmed in this manner, the user must make more reader adjustments to view the page. No reader has been specifically designed to solve this problem, but the Recordak Film Reader Model C is the best available commercially for this use. It accommodates either 16 or 35mm microfilm with a screen size of 18 by 18 inches and its magnification can be adjusted from 12 to 23× by a movable screen. A full-sized newspaper page can be projected for scanning purposes at the lower magnifications, but newspaper pages photographed at reductions of about 1 :16 cannot be viewed at the largest magnification available on this reader (23×) without using the scanning lever.

The image in a reader is usually viewed by one person at a time. Readers that project an image onto a translucent screen at high magnification can be viewed by several persons simultaneously. The number depends to a degree upon the reduction at which the image occurs on the end-use copy. Although so used occasionally, translucent screen readers were not intended for audience viewing. The readers developed for 16 and 35mm microfilm by the American Measuring Instrument Corporation and Griscombe Products, Inc. (Portable Reader) can project an image on wall or screen for group observation and discussion. The side panels on the Filmsort "Reviewer" may be removed for "conference" viewing. The Federal Manufacturing & Engineering Corp. manufactures a portable microfilm reader-projector for 16 and 35mm microfilm. It has a magnification ranging from 6× (at approximately 22 inches from the screen) to a maximum of 30 diameters with ordinary room illumination; it may be used up to 60 diameters and more in a darkened room. This reader gives a sharp image from microfilm at more than 24 times film size and requires a projection throw of as little as 3 feet. Although not specifically designed for photographic enlargement work, it may be used for such purpose if a suitable photo-enlarger bulb is substituted.

The Recordak Corporation also markets a portable projector, their Model A, that accommodates either 16 or 35mm microfilm. It has a magnification ranging from 10 to 100 diameters at projection distances of 2 to 20 feet; with such image sizes, the image may be viewed by individuals or groups. Mobility is often a prime requirement of use. An excellent reader for 16mm microfilm is made by the American Optical Co. and sold exclusively through Rem-

FIG. 5. Griscombe portable microfilm reader. (Courtesy of Remington-Rand, Inc.)

ington-Rand, Inc. It provides excellent image quality and it may be rolled about on its casters from place to place, as needed. The Filmsort Reviewer is another high-quality reader that may be moved about on casters. Since mobility is frequently a desirable characteristic of readers, it is well to remember that any table model reader may be set up on a table so that it may be moved about in the manner of a typewriter table.

Readers that weigh up to about 20 pounds may be considered portable. Typical readers of this kind include the Filmsort "Inspector," the American Measuring Instrument Company Reader, the Diebold 16mm Reader, and the readers manufactured by Erban Products, Inc. The Griscombe portable reader (Figure 5) was devised with portability in mind. It weighs only 17 pounds with its carrying case, which contains space for screen, extra lamp and lens

and reels of microfilm. Its "fold-away" mechanism makes it especially useful for carrying and storage. Its modest price ($150)
makes microfilm available to many who cannot afford the more
expensive readers.

Facsimile photocopies can be made in the readers marketed by
Filmsort, Burroughs Corp., Diebold, Inc., Griscombe Products, Inc.,
Recordak Corp., and Remington-Rand. Originally most readers
equipped to make facsimiles used conventional photoprocessing
techniques. When there is sufficient image brightness, rapid copying methods, described in Chapter VII can be used. The Filmsort
Reviewer features this method of furnishing facsimile copies.

Very few readers have been designed for the projection of
sheet film in the United States. Griscombe Products, Inc. has designed portable and desk readers with a 9-inch throat to accommodate microfilm transparencies in strip, card, or sheet form. Erban
Products also has a microfilm reader that can be used for sheet
film. The Erban Model 1612-5 and Model 910-5 accommodate 35
and 16mm film in roll or strip form and sheet film up to 75mm.
The Standard Register Co. is experimenting with sheet film that
will record 60 microfilm images on a negative the size of a 3 by 5
card. They will probably develop a reader for their product.

70mm microfilm is another form that is coming into wider use
for specialized applications in the United States. High-definition
readers that project the whole of a low-reduction 70mm positive or
negative are costly. They are designed for a specific critical purpose
which requires the use of expensive parts; they may cost $2200 or
more. Microtronics Division of the Photostat Corp., in conjunction
with Eugene Power, president of University Microfilms, designed
for the New York *Times* a 70mm reader with a folded optical system
projecting transparencies on an opaque screen. It was designed
especially for 70mm positives of newspaper clipping files* (Figure
6). It can be operated conveniently, and it projects the whole of
a 70mm frame area, 2⅞ by 3½ inches, at one time on a large
opaque screen 36 by 48 inches. "The opaque screen type of reader
was preferable to the glass or translucent screen from two basic
points of view, the projected image is sharper since it does not have
to pass through the diffusion layer which is necessary with the glass

---

* Special Libraries Bulletin, March 1954, pp. 111-114.

FIG. 6. Microtronics 70 mm library reader. (Courtesy of Microtronics
Division of Photostat Corp.)

screen type. Further, there is an absence of the eyestrain in this
type compared with the glass screen reader, where the user must
look directly into the light.'' The projected image has to be sharp
because much of the original copy is old or poorly printed. This
requires a source of light of sufficient brightness; a 500-watt bulb
was used. A blower and infrared absorbing filters are used to
keep the temperatures to specified low values. Material is photographed at a reduction of 1:10 and is projected in the reader at an
enlargement of 14×. An excellent, easily read image is projected.
Each 70mm positive contains all the clippings from small files or
from portions of larger ones. The Microtronics Division also produces a 70mm engineering reader with a fixed magnification of
12×. The image is viewed on a sheet of translucent drafting paper
which may be drawn upon and removed. The screen surface can

be renewed quickly by pulling new paper across the 30 by 40 inch
plate glass support from a large dispensing roll (Figure 7).

Fig. 7. 70mm. microfilm reader. (Courtesy of
Microtronics Division of Photostat Corp.)

The Graphic Microfilm Corp. distributes another type of 70mm
engineering reader.

A portable 70mm reader mounted on casters is built by the
Precision Microfilm Corp. of Detroit. It has a 14 by 18 inch screen
with magnification of 5 or $9\frac{1}{4}\times$ for any section of the image.

Graphic Microfilm also markets a 70mm projector that sells for
approximately $367. This includes the projection screen.

Readers designed by Griscombe Products, Inc. and Erban

Products for sheet film project portions of the 70mm image and are less expensive than the larger specially designed 70mm readers.

American Opaque Projection Readers

Eastman Kodak has made a notable step in developing the Kodagraph Microprint Reader Model A (Figure 8) designed to

FIG. 8. Kodagraph microprint reader, Model A. (Courtesy of Eastman Kodak Co.)

take any size of opaque microtext from 8½ by 14 inches down, projecting it on a translucent screen. Its accommodation of a wide range of sizes involves no commitment to any one size. It has a screen size of 8¾ by 10½ inches, and it accommodates Microstrip and Microtape that do not exceed the specified size, and Microcards, Microlex, Readex Microprint, or any other type of micro-opaque. The enlargement is 22×. The opaque print is fed into the reader by means of a typewriter-like roller that carries the card. This reader is an approach to "universal" reader, at least for opaque materials. The current price is $300.

Readex Microprint Corp. has introduced a new reader, the Readex Microprint Reader Model B (Figure 9). It has a magni-

FIG. 9. Readex Microprint reader. (Courtesy of Readex Microprint Corp.)

fication of 20× and a screen size of 8¾ by 11½ inches. It was designed for Readex Microprint, which is 6 by 9 inches in size. Other opaque microtext up to this size can be viewed on it as well. The feed consists of flat pressure plates that prevent abrasion to or curvature of the Microprint. The cost of the reader is $175 f.o.b. Atlanta, Georgia; it is one of the lowest-priced opaque readers in the field at the present time.

Microlex has a low-cost reader designed for its product that is priced at about $142.50 f.o.b. Rochester, New York.

Erban Products, Inc. has two types of opaque readers. Model 3-P (Figure 10) is made for opaque microtext up to 6 by 9 inches in size, although larger sizes up to 8½ by 11 inches are available on special order. It weighs less than 12 pounds, it has a screen size of 9 by 10 inches, and the magnification is 25×. The resolution is 105 to 120 lines per millimeter with the unaided eye at the center of the screen. It is also available with a "Kinoptic" screen that gives center resolutions (with the unaided eye) ranging from 120

Fig. 10. Erban micro paper reader, Model
3-P. (Courtesy of Erban Products Inc.)

to 135 lines per millimeter and, with a 10× magnifier, resolutions
as high as 190 to 210 lines per millimeter. The reader with the
standard screen is priced at $350.

The second Erban reader was built for the American Foundation for the Blind. It enlarges images from any opaque text at 25
or 12×. It was designed to aid individuals who have extreme
difficulties in reading because of defects in vision. Any type of book
or opaque material can be placed on the support of this "Megascope
Projection Reader" (Figure 11) and moved, by means of a scanning arm, for reading. A person with normal vision can read a
number projected from a telephone book with ease at a distance
of 25 feet.

Sometimes it is difficult to foresee what the advances will be
in applications of microtext and in the design of its equipment.
New readers are introduced quite often to accommodate existing or
new applications of microrecords. They find a ready market if they
are superior to available equipment; if they are not, manufacture

Fig. 11. Megascope projection reader. (Courtesy of Erban Products Inc.)

is discontinued. Students of the art prophesy (and perhaps rightly)
a future in which all knowledge will be recorded and stored on a
permanent metallic tape, and so coded that it will become available
in a matter of moments in response to push-button inquiry.

Current developments in data handling include electrostatic
storage tubes, the magnetic core memory, and "video tape recording." There are problems and relative advantages in the use of
punched cards, magnetic tape, disk and drum methods, and in the
various photographic and microphotographic techniques. Some of
the problems may be resolved with refinements in equipment design
and application. One of the newest information-handling systems
is the Minicard that is being developed by Eastman Kodak Co. This
portends one type of development for the immediate future. It is
described in Chapter IX.

Microrecorded information may become as commonplace in the
home as television. At the convention of the National Microfilm
Association one of the speakers described the "kitchen of tomorrow"
exhibited at the Waldorf-Astoria in New York. It featured a kitchen
range with a built-in projector and screen that enabled the house-
wife to consult any of a voluminous file of recipes. The speaker
also visualized a vest pocket encyclopedia and matching pocket

reading machine in the not too far distant future. Applications of this kind are merely a matter of time.

EUROPEAN READERS AND PROJECTORS

Outside the United States, Europe is the major producer of microtext readers. Activity is centered chiefly in Western Europe in France, Germany, Great Britain, Italy, Norway, Switzerland, and the Netherlands.

Although greater use is made in Europe of perforated film and of sheet film and film strips, at present some interest in microcards is developing there as a result of the increasing use of microcards in the United States. The new Eastman Kodak (Rochester, New York) Microprint Reader for opaques is versatile with respect to the size of the microtext it can accommodate. For this reason it may accelerate the use of all types of opaque microtext in Europe, particularly for material of a technical or scholarly nature or rare works that are not available for general distribution in original or reprint form.

The major European objective has been to reduce search time by employing types of microrecords that can be indexed and stored readily; this objective is now gaining overdue recognition in the United States.

Compared with Americans, Europeans use very little microtext; the percentage of all documents microrecorded is significantly smaller than in the United States. European reader design has stressed compactness and portability. There is a noteworthy and commendable trend in the design of a variety of types of light, inexpensive, portable readers, no one of which is being made in large quantities at present. Possibly the absence of more elaborate readers results from the fact that industrial applications in private business are few and of minor importance.

Reader design in Europe, as in the United States, is in a state of flux; fortunately there is a strong desire on the part of the United States and the western European nations to exchange data and to cooperate actively in the field of microphotography through the International Standards Organization and the American Standards Association in formulating suitable standards for microrecords and readers.

For example, the Readex Microprint Corp. of New York offers for sale without restriction such scarce and expensive source materials as the *Evans Chronological Dictionary*, of all books, etc., printed in the United States from 1639 to 1799; Sessional papers of the House of Commons, Great Britain, 1731 to 1800; three centuries of English and American plays of the period 1500 to 1800 with approximately 5000 plays; Proceedings of the Society of Experimental Biology and Medicine, Volumes 1 to 4 (1903 to 1949); Debates of the House of Commons, Great Britain, from 1066 to 1918; and the complete United Nations Documents and Publications since 1946. The availability of such items as these to the individual student wherever he may be in the Western World opens a vista for study never before experienced in the history of the world. Items in the field of all the arts and sciences are likewise available. The cultural and scientific exchange is effective only when all who withdraw from the pool of common knowledge contribute generously to it; such a pool can never run dry. A bright future is in store, since better readers are now increasing the availability of recorded knowledge for selection for study by the individual in Western Europe and the Americas who seeks that knowledge.

French Readers. Les Appareils Controleurs, under the trade name Microplex, distribute a reading apparatus for 35mm microfilm that also accommodates microfiches (sheet film) 75 by 125, or 105 by 150mm.

Microdoc distributes two readers; a pocket reader for microfiches for which no lamp is needed; and a reader, also sheet film, that can be used as an enlarger, a projector, and for tracing, depending upon the attachments used. Mr. G. Cordonnier, chief of the Technical Service of the Navy Document Center, was responsible for these designs.

The Microdiascope 35 sold by Microfilmex is a reader designed for 35mm microfilm in strip or reel form. It has a translucent screen, a control for variable illumination, and an enlargement of 10✕ with a screen 40 by 40 cm in size.

The Lectra by Sermex can be used as a wall projector and enlarger as well as a reader for microfilm and microfiche. The basic apparatus is utilized with three different heads: type A is for 35mm film with an enlargement of 10✕, type B is for 16mm film with an enlargement of 25×; type C accommodates both 35mm film and microfiche 105 by 150mm.

Soretex is the trade name of the equipment designed for 35mm film and distributed by the Société Alsacienne d'Optique et de Photographie. It is unique in that at the present time it is the only multiple use unit on the market. In one single apparatus is offered: (1) a copying camera for all documents up to size 22 by 32cm (about 9 by 13 inches); (2) a projection printer for printing on sensitized material up to original size, or smaller scale if desired; (3) a positive printer for making positive copies on film of original negatives; (4) a viewer (enlargement 10×) for reading negatives or positives; (5) a projector for viewing up to about 18 feet away. Included is a frame counter for keeping track and checking footage.

Société de Construction d'Appareils de Précision manufactures and distributes several readers under the trade name Microfrance. Reader models L-201 and L-202 are both designed for 35mm perforated and nonperforated film. The latter model is for alternating current only. Both models are for table or wall projection, weigh about 6 pounds, and have enlargements ranging from 12 to 50×. Three other types of Microfrance readers are of the cabinet style, designed for microfiches 105 by 148mm, and two of them accommodate both 16 and 35mm strip film in addition to the microfiches; the third reader is made for 35mm film strip and microfiches. Screen size or magnification can be varied on each of these readers. They can also be used for wall projection.

Société Générale d'Optique markets the portable Huet reader for 35mm film and perforated film (18mm by 24mm) with enlargements of 10 and 16×. It can also be used as a table or wall projector.

Other readers made by French concerns are similar in design and performance to the types mentioned above.

German Readers. In West Germany microfilm is stored partially in short reels, film strips and sheet film. Business applications such as microfilming checks, bills, and other business documents are not common because West German law still requires that the original documents be maintained for 10 years. The expected revision of this law will permit wider use of microrecords. Drawings are generally photographed on 35mm nonperforated film, and 70mm film is coming into use.

West German readers are made for both perforated and non-perforated film in reel and strip form as well as microfiches. The majority are designed with interchangeable parts to accommodate the various types of microtext. The Microvist manufactured by Dr. Rodehüser is a good example of adaptability of a reader (Figure 12). Interchangeable optics and adapters permit it to be

FIG. 12. Microvist reader. (Courtesy of Rodehüser.)

used for film in strip, reel, and sheet form. The reader is portable, and the mounting permits it to project on table, wall, or ceiling.

The Dokumator reader made by Optik Carl Zeiss (East Zone) is noteworthy. It utilizes a hood which completely excludes light (Figure 13). Interchangeable parts permit it to be used for sheet film, film strips, and 35mm film in roll form up to about 100 feet in length. The hood can be lifted to enable several persons to view the image simultaneously, or, with the use of an auxiliary mirror, it can be used for wall projections. Copies of the projected image can be made, on Agfa-Copyrapid paper, in a darkened room with the hood lifted.

Great Britain. Readers are made in Great Britain to hold

Fig. 13. Dokumator reader. (Courtesy of Carl Zeiss, Jena.)

100-foot lengths of perforated and unperforated 35 and 16mm film. Some of them, the Ediswan readers for example, are designed to hold film strips also. Kodak Ltd. sells a 35mm reader for reel film and a 16mm combination reader and camera. Ruthurstat has two 35mm readers with enlargements of 18×. Both are floor models mounted on casters and they have glass screens. The screen of the Ruthurstat Universal Model is 27⅞ by 23 inches. This model is unique in that it is designed to project a full-sized newspaper page (Figure 14). At present it is the only European reader that gives this size projection.

Portable readers as well as projectors for film strips and 35mm microfilm are also available in England. The Pilgrim reader was specifically designed for hospitals, and libraries for the ceiling projection of books in microfilm form. This reader can also be adapted for film strips and transparencies in the form of slides 2 by 2 inches in size.

Other European Readers. Sweden produces a 35mm desk model reader for unperforated film with an enlargement of 12× and a screen 52 by 52 cm. Other 35mm readers are made in Czecho-slovakia, Switzerland, Italy, and the Netherlands. Some of these

Fig. 14. Ruthurstat Universal Model
reader. (Courtesy of Ruthurstat Ltd.)

readers are designed for perforated or unperforated film or both.
Others are made specifically for film strips, short rolls of film,
microfiches, or combinations of these film types.

TABLE I. Microrecord Readers

$	= U. S. dollars		RO	= head rotates 360° or sufficient to permit vertical or horizontal images
DM	= German marks			
fr	= French francs			
Kr	= Swedish crowns			
£	= English pounds		SH	= short reels 50 ft or under
Lit	= Italian lire		ST	= film strips
Su	= Swiss francs		Tr	= translucent screen
Y	= Japanese yen		v	= volts
			w	= watts
AC	= alternating current			
cm	= centimeters			
DC	= direct current			
FAC	= facsimile reproduction			
p	= perforated film			
up	= unperforated film			
Op	= opaque screen			
r	= rolls of 100 ft. length			Prices stated are approximate as of 1954-55.

Type	Price	Film (card) size in mm	Enlargement	Screen size in inches, and type	Light source	Remarks
United States						
Amic reader (1)						
Model A	$465	35p/up, r	14×	12 x 12 Tr	100 w, 120 v, AC, DC	RO. Also wall projection to 60×.
Model B	$465	16p/up, r	30×	12 x 12 Tr	100 w, 120 v, AC, DC	As above.
Spencer microfilm reader (2)						
3400	$87	35p/up, ST, SH	15×	14 x 15 Op	100 w, 115 v, AC, DC	RO. Also 230 v model. 100 ft. roll attach. +$27.
3400A	$99	16p/up, ST, SH	23×	14 x 15 Op	100 w, 115 v, AC, DC	RO. Also 230 v. model. 100 ft. roll attach. +$31.

TABLE I. (Continued)

Type	Price	Film (card) size in mm	Enlargement	Screen size in inches, and type	Light source	Remarks
				United States (Continued)		
Bell & Howell reader (3)						
BH289A	$630	16p/up, r	18×, 39× 37×, 49×	14 x 15½ Tr	300 w, 100-125 v, AC, DC	RO. One of one x—either 18×, 30×, or 37×, 49× extra cost. FAC. Hand operated. Elec. drive $760.
Micro-Twin	$1575	16p/up, r	1:1	8 x 11 Tr	200 w, 115 v, AC	Reductions of either 37:1 or 24:1. FAC. Combination camera-reader.
Diebold						
Flofilm (4) Portable	$250	16p/up, r	24×	11½ x 11½ Tr	100 w, 110 v, AC, DC	RO. Weight 19 lb.
Universal (Model 92-02)	$725	16-35p/up, r	18× to 36×	14 x 14 Tr	200 w, 110-120 v, AC	RO. FAC. Elec. drive.
Kodagraph Microprint Reader (5)						
Model A	$300	Micro-opaques to 8½ x 14 in.	22×	8¾ x 10½ Tr	115 v, AC	Accepts all of present sizes of micro-opaques. Feed like typewriter.
Model C	$875	16-35p/up, r	12× to 36×	18 x 18 Tr	250 w, 110-125 v, AC, DO	RO. Variable enlargement.

TABLE I. (*Continued*)

United States (*Continued*)

Type	Price	Film (card) size in mm	Enlargement	Screen size in inches, and type	Light source	Remarks
(Kodagraph) MPE	$350 AC $390 DC	16–35p/up, r	19×	20 x 20 Op	150 w, 100–125 v, AC, DC	RO.
Erban (6) Megascope Reader	$255	Books to 9 x 15	25×	9 x 10 Tr	150 w, 120 v, AC, DC	RO. Enlargements of 12× and 15× available. Books cannot exceed 12 lb.
Microfilm (1612-5)	$650	16–35 p/up, r, ST	15× to 23×	12¾ x 16 Tr	100 w, 120 v, AC, DC	RO. Takes sheet film to 75 mm. Weight 21 lb.
Micro-Paper (3P)	$350	Micro-opaques to 6 x 9	25×	9 x 10 Tr	150 w, 120 v, AC, DC	RO. Also available for micro-opaques to 8½ x 11 in. Weight 12 lb.
Portable (910-5)	$498	16–35 p/up, r, ST	12× to 18×	9 x 10 Tr	100 w, 120 v, AC, DC	RO. Takes sheet film to 75 mm. Weight 11 lb.
Federal (7) Portable Projector (701)	$123.00	16–35 p/up, r, ST	6× to 60×	—	150 w, 100–125 v, AC, DC	RO. Weight 10 lb. Also used as enlarger.
Filmsort (8) Inspector (F600.1)	$285	16–35 mm. jacket or aperture cards—5 in. deep any length	16×	11 x 11 Tr	100 w, 110–115 v, AC, DC	Wall projection. Roll attachments extra.

TABLE I. (*Continued*)

United States (*Continued*)

Type	Price	Film (card) size in mm	Enlarge-ment	Screen size in inches, and type	Light source	Remarks
(Filmsort)						
Inspector (600)	$285	As above	22×	11 x 11 Tr	100 w, 110–115 v, AC, DC	Wall projection. Roll attachments extra.
Inspector 200 (600.6)	$340	35 r; 8 x 8 jacket or aperture cards	16×	11 x 11 Tr	200 w, AC	Auto-Scan for automatic scanning of jacket cards, $100 extra. Weight 65 lb. FAC.
Inspector 200 (600.4)	$340	As above	24×	11 x 11 Tr	200 w, AC	As above. Lens interchangeable with 600.5.
Inspector 200 (600.5)	$340	As above	30×	11 x 11 Tr	200 w, AC	As above, but lens interchangeable with 600.4.
Reviewer (F601)	$875	16–35 mm jacket or aperture cards. 11 in. deep x 8½ in. wide	22×	17 x 17 Op	500 w, 110 v, AC	FAC. Wall projection. Roll attachments extra. Conference viewing.
Reviewer (F601.1)	$875	16–35 mm jacket or aperture cards. 5 in. deep any length	16×	17 x 17 Op	500 w, 110 v, AC	As above.

TABLE I. (*Continued*)

United States (Continued)

Type	Price	Film (card) size in mm	Enlargement	Screen size in inches, and type	Light source	Remarks
(Filmsort) Reviewer (F601.2)	$875	As above	12×	17 x 17 Op	500 w, 110 v, AC	As above.
Surveyor (F602)	$1595	Jacket or aperture cards, 16 mm, 3¾ up to 12 in. 35 mm, 3¾ up to 12 in.	11× to 22×	18 x 24 Tr	300 w, 110 v, AC	FAC. Wall projection. Roll attachments extra.
Surveyor (F602.1)	$1745	As above	11× to 22×	24 x 36 Tr	300 w, 110 v, AC	As above.
Executive Reader	$120	Aperture cards, 16 or 35mm	12×	6 x 8 Tr	110 v, AC (DC special order)	Portable designed for desk use. Projects full 16mm frame, but only portion of 35mm frame.
Graphic 35-70mm (9) Projector (BB Model 2)	$367.50	35p/up, r 70p/up,r, SH	Variable according to reduction	—	750 w, 110–115 v, AC	Price includes screen and attachments.

TABLE I. (*Continued*)

United States (*Continued*)

Type	Price	Film (card) size in mm	Enlargement	Screen size in inches, and type	Light source	Remarks
Griscombe (10) Library Reader (Model 18F)	$415	16–35p/up, r	17× to 25×	18 x 18 Op	50 candlepower, 110 v, AC	RO. FAC. Constant focus.
Portable Reader (Model PA)	$165	16–35p/up, r	23×	14 x 14 Op	50 candlepower, 115 v, AC	RO. FAC. Table or wall projection. Weight 17 lb. Also 17×, $175.
Filmcard Reader (Model KA)	$150	16–35 mm jacket or aperture cards. 5 in. deep, unlimited length.	23×	14 x 14 Op	100–120 AC, 100 w	16 lb. with case. 17× $165. 30× $170.
Filmcard Reader (Model KB)	$250	16–35 mm jacket or aperture cards. 9 in. deep unlimited length.	24× or 17×	10 x 12 Tr	150 w, 115 v, AC, DC	FAC.
Microcard Reader (11) Model 5	$155	Micro-opaques to 3 x 5	26×	9 x 10 Tr	150 w, 110 v, AC, DC	Weight 15 lb. Fresnel screen early model.

TABLE I. (*Continued*)

United States (*Continued*)

Type	Price	Film (card) size in mm	Enlargement	Screen size in inches, and type	Light source	Remarks
(Microcard) Model 5A	$165	Micro-opaques to 3 x 5	—	—	—	Wide angle screen. Early model.
Model 6	$245	Micro-opaques to 3 x 5	26X	10 x 10 Tr	150 w, 110 v, AC, DC	Weight 21 lb. Fresnel Screen. Card-moving mechanism.
Model 6A	$255	Micro-opaques to 3 x 5	26X	10 x 10 Tr	150 w, 110 v, AC, DC	Weight 21 lb. Wide angle screen. Card moving mechanism. $195 without latter.
Model 6B	$255	Micro-opaques to 3 x 5	23X	9½ x 10⅞ Tr	150 w, 110–120 v, AC, DC	Weight 20 lb. Improved image sharpness. Card-moving mechanism.
Pocket Reader	$25	Micro-opaques to 6½ x 8½	12X			Battery and 110 v Handviewer — designed basically for Microcards.
Microlex Reader (12)	$142.50	Micro-opaques to 6½ x 8½	22X	6¾ x 7-1/6 Tr	25 w, 115 v, AC	DC models available.

TABLE I. (*Continued*)

United States (*Continued*)

Type	Price	Film (card) size in mm	Enlargement	Screen size in inches, and type	Light source	Remarks
Microskaner (13)	$12.95	—	20×	—	—	Handviewer. Intended for microfilm and micro-opaques. Illumination provided by batteries. 6¾ in. long. Weight with batteries 2¾ oz. Field of view 5/16 in.
Beattie (14) Projector Viewer (Series 13000)	$2995	35-70p/up, r	—	18 x 18 Tr	75 w, 117 v, AC	Electric drive. Takes 70mm sheet film.
Varifile Viewer (Model B)	$975	35-70p/up, r	—	18 x 18 Tr	75 w, 117 v, AC	Hand operated. Takes 70mm sheet film.
Microtronics (15) Engineering Reader	$2000	70mm sheet film	12×	30 x 40 clear	150 w, 110 v, AC	Image projected through clear glass and translucent drafting paper for tracing.
Library Reader	$2200	70mm sheet film	14×	36 x 48 Op	500 w, 110-115 v, AC	Sharp, low reduction images (10× to 14×) projected in their entirety.
E-Z-Vue-70mm Reader (16)		70mm sheet film	5×, 9¼×	14 x 18 Tr	—	Portable (casters).

TABLE I. (*Continued*)

United States (Continued)

Type	Price	Film (card) size in mm	Enlargement	Screen size in inches, and type	Light source	Remarks
Readex Microprint Reader (17)	$175	Microopaques to 6 x 9	20×	8¾ x 11 Tr	200 w, 115 v, AC, DC	—
Recordak (18)						
JA	$550	16p/up, r	23×	14-11/32 x 14⅛ Op	45 v, 100–125 v, AC, DC	RO. Reconditioned.
JB	$550	16p/up, r	23×	14-11/32 x 14⅛ Op	45 v, 100–125 v, AC, DC	RO. For DC only. Reconditioned.
JC	$600	16p/up, r	23×	14-11/32 x 14⅛ Op	45 v, 100–125 v, AC, DC	RO. Reconditioned.
JD	$975	16p/up, r	34×	13 x 13 Op	450 w, 100–125 v, AC	RO. Recorder-reader. Also DC model.
P-10 (PD)	$190	16p/up, r	23×	14 x 15½ Tr	200 w, 100–125 v, AC, DC	RO. Constant focus—31× available reconditioned (PD-250w).
P-40	$390AC $430DC	16p/up, r	40×	15 x 15 Op	150 w, 100–125 v, AC, DC	RO.
P-F	$190	16p/up, r	31×	14 x 15½ Tr	250 w, 100–125 v, AC, DC	RO. Reconditioned.
P-H	$265	16p/up, r	31×	14 x 15½ Tr	250 w, 100–125 v, AC, DC	RO. Reconditioned.

TABLE I. (*Continued*)

Type	Price	Film (card) size in mm	Enlarge-ment	Screen size in inches, and type	Light source	Remarks
United States (Continued)						
(Recordak) PM	$900	16p/up, r	23×, 30×, or 40×	11½ x 11½ Tr	32 v, 100–125 v, AC	Only 1 lens assembly included in price. FAC. Elec. driva.
Film-A-Record (19) Electronic AC Reader	$625	16p/up, r	20×, 24× or 35×	12¼ x 12¼ Tr	10 v, 200 w, 115 v, AC	RO. Only 1 lens assembly included in price. FAC. Elec. drive. Portable (casters).
Table Reader (Model 9)	$425	16–35p/up, r	24× to 43×	14 x 14 Tr	50 candlepower, 110 v, AC	RO. FAC. Constant focus. (30×, $180.)
Kard-A-Film Reader (F 71)	$325	16-35mm jacket or aperture cards. 8½ in. deep. Un-limited length	23×	14½ x 14½ Op	50 candlepower, 110 v, AC	
Microfilm Viewer (20)	$2.00	35, ST, SH	10×	—	—	Portable hand viewer.
France						
Microlecteur (10x SGM) (21)	3,750 fr	35p, ST, SH	10×	—	—	Hand viewer. Weight 10 oz.

TABLE I. *(Continued)*

France *(Continued)*

Type	Price	Film (card) size in mm	Enlargement	Screen size in inches, and type	Light source	Remarks
Lecteur Damblanc (22)						
No. 1	47,800 fr	35p/up	10×, 12×	Variable	100 w	Wall or table projection. Weight 10 lb.
No. 2	56,500 fr	35p/up	10×, 12×	Variable	—	Has film-winding device.
No. 3	72,000 fr	16up	20×	Variable	—	Will take reels.
No. 4	75,000 fr	Sheet film 100 x 150	12×	Variable	—	—
Automatique	190,000 fr	35p/up	10×, 15×	Variable	—	RO. Elec. drive. 2 speeds.
Episcopique Microcartes	85,000 fr	100 x 150	15×	4 x 4 cm	—	For reading microcards.
Microfiscope (23)	6,500 fr	Sheet film, 100 x 150	—	105 x 105 mm	—	Handviewer for sheet film.
Microliseuse	75,000 fr	35p and sheet film 35 x 150	10.5×, 15×, 21×, 30× 42×	25 x 35 cm 70 x 70 cm, Op	—	Also enlarger-projector. Extra cost for attachments.
Microdiascope-35 (24)	77,019 fr	35p, r	10×	40 x 40 cm, Tr	30 w, 110 v	RO. Available illumination.

TABLE I. (Continued)

France (Continued)

Type	Price	Film (card) size in mm	Enlarge-ment	Screen size in inches, and type	Light source	Remarks
Kangaroo Microfilm Reader (25)	$37.50	Sheet film to 100 x 150 mm, 35p, r, ST	—	Op	—	Table or wall projection.
Legofiche I (26)	115,000 fr	Sheet film 70 x 90 105 x 150	5×	75 x 75 cm Tr	—	RO. Mounted on wheels.
Lectoclair I (27)		35p, r, and sheet film	12×	—	—	Table or wall projection. Translucent screen available.
Lectoclair II & III	180,000 fr	35p, r, and sheet film	12×, 15×, 25×	60 x 60 cm	—	RO. Also used as enlarger.
Lectra de Sermex (28) Type A	60,000 fr– 80,000 fr	35p, ST, SH	10×	Variable	—	Types A, B, C, same apparatus, different heads. RO table or wall projection. Also enlarger.
Type B	As above	16p, ST, SH	25×	Variable		
Type C	As above	Sheet film 105 x 150. 35p, ST, SH	—	Variable		

TABLE I. (Continued)

France (Continued)

Type	Price	Film (card) size in mm	Enlargement	Screen size in inches, and type	Light source	Remarks
Lecto-Film "Panera-tic" (29)						
Model P 45	225,000 fr	35p, r, and sheet film	20×	45 x 45 cm	200 w, 110–120 v	Weight 100 kg.
(Lecto-Film) Model P 80	250,000 fr	35p, r, and sheet film	30×	80 x 70 cm	300 w, 110–120 v	Weight 150 kg.
Model EV 30	65,000 fr	35p, r, and sheet film	8½×	30 x 30 cm	200 w, 100–120 v	Weight 20.5 kg.
Model EV 45	75,000 fr	35p, r, and sheet film	13×	45 x 45 cm	200 w, 100–120 v	Weight 27 kg.
Model LT	25,000 fr	—	11×	—	50 w, 110–120 v	Weight 5 kg. Table projection.
Model M	45,000 fr	35	12×	12.5 x 18 cm	30 w	Weight 6 kg.
Soretex (30)	75,000 fr	35p, r	10×	Tr	100 w, 110–120 v	Combination, camera reader, projector. Projection and positive printer. RO.
Microlecteur (31)						
201	23,450 fr	35p/up, ST	12×, 50×	Variable	70 w, 110–120 v, AC, DC	Wall or table projection. Weight 6 lb.
202	25,900 fr	35p/up, ST	12×, 50×	Variable	30 w, 110–125 v	As above, but AC only.

TABLE I. (Continued)

Type	Price	Film (card) size in mm	Enlargement	Screen size in inches, and type	Light source	Remarks
				France (Continued)		
Lecteur U30D	39,200 fr	Sheet film 105 x 148. 35p/up, r, ST	7.5X, 12.5X, 19X	30 x 30 cm Op	70 w, 110–220 v, AC	U30 DAX 33,175 fr. AC-DC model.
Lecteur U30RD	45,300 fr	Sheet film 105 x 148. 16-35p/up, r, ST	7.5X, 12X, 19X, 25X	30 x 30 cm Op	70 w, 110–220 v, AC	RO-90°. U30 RDAX-40,725 ft. AC-DC model.
Lecteur U45D	53,700 fr	Sheet film 105 x 148, 16-35p/up, r, ST	12.5X, 18X, 29X	40 x 40 cm Op	70 w, 110–220 v, AC	Also wall table projection. U45 DAX 46,925 fr. AC-DC model.
Lector Huet (32)	48,840 fr	35p	10X, 16X	40 x 40 cm Op	200 w, 125 v	Table or wall projection.
				West Germany		
Fotokopist (33)		35p/up, r	10X	30 x 42 cm		
Prado (34)						
150	$124	35p, ST	6X to 72X	Variable	150 w, 110–220 v, AC, DC	Supplemental reading box approx. $45. 8x. Wall projector.
250	$124.50	35p, ST	15X to 120X	Variable	250 w, 110 or 220 v, AC, DC	Replaces former Prado 500. Wall projector, also 2 x 2 slides.

TABLE I. (*Continued*)
West Germany (Continued)

Type	Price	Film (card) size in mm	Enlargement	Screen size in inches, and type	Light source	Remarks
500	$172.50	35p, ST	15× to 120×	Variable	500 w, 110 or 220 v, AC, DC	Replaces former Prado 500. Wall projector, also 2 x 2 slides.
Microstat (35)						
Lesegerät	$121	35p/up, r	12×, 17×	—	50 w, 110–120 v, AC	1 lens only $107. Prices quoted for agents *only*. RO. Table or wall projection.
Universal	DM557	Sheet film 9 x 12 cm.; 16-35p/up, r	—	—	—	Table projection.
Streifen Lesegerät	DM300	16-35p/up	—	—	—	Table projection.
Graphoskop L3 (36)	DM260	Sheet film 9 x 12 cm.; 16-35p/up, r	—	—	50 w, 110–120 v, AC, DC	Table projection (210 x 297 mm)
Phywe Mikro- Lesegerät (37)	DM450	Sheet film 90 x 120 mm, 35p/up, ST	12×, 17×	—	30 w, 110, 125, 150, or 220 v, AC	RO. Table projection.
Microvist (38)						
1	DM265	Sheet film 9 x 12 cm.; 16-35p/up r, ST	15×	—	25 w, 220 v, AC	RO. Table or wall projection.

TABLE I. (*Continued*)

Type	Price	Film (card) size in mm	Enlarge-ment	Screen size in inches, and type	Light source	Remarks
West Germany (Continued)						
(Microvist) 2	DM342	As above	10×	—	—	As above.
Steinheil (39) Universal		—	8×, 12×, 15×	—	50 w, 110–120 v	Table projection.
East Germany						
MikroKopie-Lesegerät (40)		Sheet film 9 x 12 cm.; 16-35p/up, ST	18×	—	110–120 v, AC	Table projection.
Dokumator (41)	DM711	Sheet film 9 x 12 cm.; 35up, r, ST	10½×, 17×	30 x 40 cm, Op	50 w, 110, 120 v, AC, DC	RO. Also projects 5 x 5 glass slides. FAC.
Ikoscop		35p, ST	—	32 x 32 cm	150 w	RO.
Great Britain						
Ediswan (42) Model 1	£54.146	16-35p/up, r, ST	7½×, 12×, 18×, 25×	12 x 12½, Op	48 w, 110 v, 220–250 v, AC	RO. Also wall projections.
Model 2	£78.150d	16-35p/up, r, ST	12×, 20×, 25×, 40×	18 x 17¾, Op	As above	£96 with automatic film gate. RO. Also wall projection.

TABLE I. (*Continued*)

Great Britain (*Continued*)

Type	Price	Film (card) size in mm	Enlargement	Screen size in inches, and type	Light source	Remarks
Kirdon Micro-film Reader (43)	£39.17.6	35 r	—	—	—	Table projection.
Recordak (44) Library Reader Model AH-Type 2	£152	35p/up, r	12×, 24×	18 x 18	200 w, 200–250 v, AC (100–125 v, DC)	—
Recordak Microfilmer	£390	16p/up, r	12×	—	200 w, 110 v	Reader-recorder.
Shackman-Ruthur-stat Reader (45) Model A	£151.17.6	35up, r	18×	18 x 18 Tr	100 w	RO. Portable (casters).
Universal Model	£194.10.0	35up, r	18×	27⅞ x 23, Tr	250 w	As above.
Pilgrim Automatic Microfilm Reader (46)	£65.0.0	35p/up, r, ST	—	Variable	24 w, 110–240 v, AC	RO. Table or wall projection. Also enlarger.

TABLE I. (*Continued*)

Type	Price	Film (card) size in mm	Enlargement	Screen size in inches, and type	Light source	Remarks
				Great Britain (Continued)		
V. C. Film-strip (47)						
Manual Projector	£12.12.0	35, ST	—	Variable	24 w, 12 v	Table or wall projection.
Automatic Projector	£20.0.0	35, ST	—	Variable	24 w, 12 v	As above.
Model A	£12.12.0	35up	—	Variable	—	RO 90°.
Model B	£10.16.0	35p	—	Variable	—	RO.
B. K. Micro-film Reader (48)						
Model 11	£48.10.0	35p/up, r	10×	17 x 17, Op	60 w	RO 90°.
				Italy		
Fotorex (49)						
Model 100	Lit. 80,000	35p	10× to 40×	—	50 w, 110 v	RO. Table projection.
Model 101	Lit. 60,000	35, ST, SH	—	—	—	—
Model 103	Lit. 49,500	35p	10× to 15×	—	30 w	Table projection.

TABLE I. (Continued)

Type	Price	Film (card) size in mm	Enlarge-ment	Screen size in inches, and type	Light source	Remarks
Italy (Continued)						
(Fotorex) Model 105	Lit. 24,000	35	10× to 30×	—	30 w	—
Model 107	Lit. 32,000	35 ST	—	—	—	—
Model 109	Lit. 68,000	35 r	—	—	—	—
Microcard Reader	Lit. 120,000	Sheet film 7, 5 x 12, 5 cm	—	—	—	—
Phoebus (50)	$125.00	35p, ST	12×	—	100 w, 110–120 v	Table or wall projection. Also 24 x 36 mm. type, $166.00.
Japan						
Leetra 63 (51)	Y 40,000	16-35	10×, 16½×	45 x 50 cm	—	—
Netherlands						
N.D.R. Goebel Reader (52)		Sheet film 90 x 120 mm., 35p/up, ST	17×	—	220, 110 or 130 v, AC	Table or wall projection.
Sweden						
Dokumat (53)	Kr 1,430	35	12×	45 x 45 cm, Tr	100 w, 110–220 v, RO. AC; also 130 v	

TABLE 1 (*Continued*)

Type	Price	Film (card) size in mm	Enlargement	Screen size in inches, and type	Light source	Remarks
				Switzerland		
Type L-1 (54)	Su850	16-35 r, ST	10×	—	50 w	RO. Ceiling or wall projection.
Type L-11	Su698	35p/up	12×	—	50 w, 12 v	Table or wall projection.
Type L-111	Su815	35p/up	12×	36 x 36 cm, Tr	—	Portable.

TABLE I. (*Continued*)

(1) American Measuring Instrument Corp, 240 West 40th St., New York 18, N. Y.

(2) American Optical Co., Instrument Division, Box A, Buffalo 15, N. Y.

(3) Burroughs Corp., Detroit 32, Mich.

(4) Diebold, Inc., Canton 2, Ohio.

(5) Eastman Kodak Co., Rochester 4, N. Y.

(6) Erban Products, Inc., 134-20 Northern Boulevard, Flushing, N. Y.

(7) Federal Manufacturing & Engineering Corp., 199-217 Steuben St., Brooklyn 5, N. Y.

(8) Filmsort Division of Dexter Folder Co., Pearl River, N. Y.

(9) Graphic Microfilm Corp. 112 Liberty St., New York 6, N. Y.

(10) Griscombe Products, Inc., 132 West 21st St., New York 11, N. Y.

(11) Microcard Foundation, Madison, Wis.

(12) Microlex Corp., 1 Graves St., Rochester 14, N. Y.

(13) Microreader Manufacturing & Sales Co., 2217 North Summit Ave., Milwaukee 2, Wis.

(14) Photographic Products, Inc., 6916 Romaine St., Hollywood 38, Calif.

(15) Photostat Corp., Microtronics Division, Rochester, N. Y.

(16) Precision Microfilm Corp., 6615 Tireman Ave., Detroit, Mich.

(17) Readex Microprint Corp., 100 Fifth Ave., New York 11, N. Y.

(18) Recordak Corp. (subsidiary of Eastman Kodak Co.), 444 Madison Ave., New York 22, N. Y.

(19) Remington-Rand, 315 Fourth Ave., New York 10, N. Y.

(20) Atherton Seidell, 2301 Connecticut Ave., Washington 8, D. C.

TABLE I. (Continued)

(21) Documentation Microfilmée, 65 Avenue de Versailles, Paris 16, France.

(22) Imagiscope, 39 Rue Cambon, Paris 1, France.

(23) Microdoc, 5 Rue Rubens, Paris 13, France.

(24) Microfilmex, 75 Rue Saint-Lazare, Paris 9, France.

(25) O. L. deBeauvais, 50 Rue de Truffaut, Paris 17, France.

(26) Photelec, 27 Rue Cousté, Cachan (Seine), France.

(27) Sancar, 197 Boulevard Saint-Germain, Paris 7, France.

(28) Sermex, 69 Rue Caumartin, Paris 9, France.

(29) Société Actar, 197 Boulevard Saint-Germain, Paris 7, France.

(30) Société Alsaphot, 63 Avenue de Villiers, Paris 17, France.

(31) Société de Construction D'Appareils de Précision, 69 Cours de la République, Villeurbanne (Rhône), France.

(32) Société Générale D'Optique, 76 Boulevard de la Villette, Paris 19, France.

(33) Fotokopist G.m.b.H., Westenstrasse 1, Essen, West Germany.

(34) Ernst Leitz G.m.b.H., Wetzler, West Germany.

(35) Lumoprint, Dr. Böger K. G., Hallerstrasse 59, Hamburg 13, West Germany.

(36) Mikrographische Gesselschaft G.m.b.H., Kochstrasse 60, Berlin S. W. 68, West Germany.

(37) Phywe A. G., Postfach 102, Göttingen, West Germany.

(38) **Dr. Rodehuser, Bergkamen: Westfalia, West Germany.**

(39) Optische Werke C. A. Steinheil, Sohne G.m.b.H., Munchen, West Germany.

(40) Falz & Werner, Lutherstrasse 14, Leipsig 0 5, East Germany.

(41) Optik Carl Zeiss, Jena, East Germany.

(42) Edison Swan Electric Company, Ltd., 155 Charing Cross Road, London W. C. 2, England.

(43) Kirdon Electric, Ltd., Factory Yard, Oxbridge Road, Hanwell, London W. 7, England.

(44) Kodak, Ltd., Recordak Division, Adelaide House, London E. C. 4, England.

(45) Ruthurstat, Ltd., 104 High Holborn, London W. C. 1, England.

(46) Visual Communications, Ltd., 17 Denbigh Street, London S. W. 1, England.

(47) Watson, Monasty & Co., 34 Twickenham Road, Teddington, Middlesex, England.

(48) Wray Optical Works, Ltd., Ashgrove Road, Bromley, Kent, England.

(49) Ing. F. Gecchele, Viale Corsica 85, Milano, Italy.

(50) San Giorgio Soc., Via Corsica 21, Genova-Sestri, Italy.

(51) Toho Optical Co., Ltd., 105 I-chome, Shimomeguro, Meguro-Ku, Tokyo, Japan.

(52) Nederlands Document Reproductie N.V., The Hague, Valeriusstraat 28-34, Netherlands.

(53) Dokumat A. B, Nybrokajen 5, Stockholm, Sweden.

(54) Optik A. G., Nordstrasse 22, Chur, Switzerland.

Bibliography

Litchfield and Bennett. ''Microfilm Reading Machines.'' *Special Libraries*, Jan. 1943, pp. 15-20.

Litchfield and Bennett. ''Microfilm Reading Machines: Part II, Construction and Operation.'' *Special Libraries*, Feb. 1943, pp. 45-50.

Litchfield and Bennett. ''Microfilm Reading Machines: Part IV, Technical and Professional Criteria for Choosing a Reading Machine.'' *Special Libraries*, Sept. 1943, pp. 379-384.

H. T. Engstrom. ''Microfilm Selection Equipment in Information Work.'' *Ind. Eng. Chem.*, Vol. 42, pp. 1460-1461 (1950).

G. Miles Conrad. ''User Needs in a Microfacsimile Reader.'' *Amer. Documentation*, Vol. 2, pp. 201-204 (Oct. 1951).

R. S. Elsworth. ''New Horizons with Microfilm.'' *Amer. Documentation*, Vol. 2, pp. 221-228 (Oct. 1951).

Fremont Rider. *The Scholar and the Future of the Research Library*. Hadam Press, New York, 1944.

R. W. Batchelder. ''The Microcard: A Review of Developments in Microfilm and Microcards Including Microcard Readers.'' *Special Libraries*, Vol. 43, pp. 157-161 (1952).

J. Tennant. ''Readex Microprints.'' *J. Doc. Repr.*, Vol. 3, pp. 66-70 (1940).

E. N. Jenks. ''Micro-Editions of Newspapers: A Survey of Developments.'' *Journalism Quarterly*, Fall 1950, pp. 391-398.

Edgar L. Erickson. ''Microprint: A Revolution in Printing.'' *J. Documentation*, Vol. 7, pp. 184-187 (Sept. 1951).

Walter Best. ''Neue Deutsche Aufnahme-und Lesegeräte.'' *Rev. Documentation*, Vol. 17, pp. 97-101 (1950).

Werner Reichelt. ''Technische Hilfsmittel der Mikrodokumentation.'' *Nachr. Dok.*, Vol. 2, pp. 12-13 (1951).

L. J. Van der Wolk and J. C. Tonnon. ''The Microcopy on Flat Film as an Aid in Documentation.'' *Rev. Documentation*, Vol. 17, pp. 134-141, 216-238 (1950).

F.I.D. Manual on Document Reproduction and Selection. Part I, Vol. A. ''Reading Apparatus,'' 222.5, International Federation for Documentation, The Hague, Netherlands.

Report to the Secretary of Commerce by the Advisory Committee on Application of Machines to Patent Office Operations. V. Bush, (Chairman of the Committee) Washington, D. C., Dept. of Commerce, Dec. 1954.

INFORMATION CLASSIFICATION
AND RETRIEVAL

SEMANTIC PERSPECTIVES

The next decade poses the greatest challenge in the development of information retrieval by mechanical means. This cannot be accomplished without exploration and systematization of suitable language and suitable coding for machine use. Alice V. Neil [*] states: "Within the next five years, these machines no doubt will reach a stage where large libraries functioning as nation-wide information centers will have such devices for detailed literature searching. Battelle Memorial Institute hopes to begin reference service using information machines in two years. It is possible that within fifteen years machines geared to small homogeneous library collections will be available on a commercial scale to individual institutions and companies. The special librarian is, therefore, faced with the necessity for learning new nomenclature and new techniques. He will be called upon to converse intelligently about coding, floating information, 'Semantic factoring,' etc. He will need to know, not only what the principles are, but how to operate a literature machine."

This statement does not presuppose that books and card catalogues will be eliminated. Miss Neil goes on to say "no punch file, machine or manual, can anticipate questions. The data must be fed into the device, put in storage and 'punched out.' Current, active files on fields of specific interest can be maintained à la machine, but it seems highly improbable that the contents of all the books in all the libraries will be conveniently coded in the new fashion. Authors will continue to write. The creative urge and the printed word will not diminish. People who have the desire to write will not find satisfaction in talking into a machine. The

---

[*] "Machines or Books?—A Case for Both," by Alice V. Neil, Librarian, Research Service Division, General Electric Co., Schenectady, New York. Stechert-Hafner Book News, Vol. IX, No. 5, Jan. 1955, pp. 57-58.

writers' continued flourishing will generate publishing. Therefore, we shall continue to have books and printed knowledge and readers. The books already in libraries will still be sought. Nothing can replace the satisfaction obtained from holding and reading the object which we know as a book. As long as we have the printed word, we shall need librarians to classify and catalog and make proper use of knowledge."

How important librarians can become to the process can be foreseen when it is remembered that the librarian, in coding the information for insertion into the machine, has automatically limited the manner in which the information he has so coded can be read out by the machine. If the coding has been well done and anticipates the most probable and even all possible kinds of questions relating to it, the information seeker will obtain the information he desires by asking the right questions to obtain read-out by the machine. If the coding has not been well done, the information seeker will not be able to phrase his question in such manner that the machine "understands" the question asked. In a broad sense, coding provides the multiple paths within the machine by which the information inserted into the machine can be retrieved by search from an information seeker. Coding therefore involves a permissible range of questions about the information coded; in a practical structure 100% retrieval of the stored information is not anticipated because the coding used to insert the information into the machine cannot reasonably be expected to anticipate all the questions that anyone interested may ask about the information so coded and stored. With coding so important, it would seem that an American Standard Coding System to be developed under the guidance of the American Standards Association is a "must" if serious economic waste is to be avoided in the commercial exploitation of equipment to be marketed by the lively, energetic, and well-financed competitors who are now in the field and are to enter it in the future.

In practice the range of permissible questions is also limited by the size of the machine. Since the capacity of a particular machine is finite, it is customary to furnish new paths of access to previously recorded data by providing new coding that increases the permissible range of questions which effect read-out of the information. Such additional codings for a specific bit of data may be added from time to time as it is determined that such new codings are applicable and that the machine has the capacity to handle the additional data.

There are some current observations that librarians, as we know them today, will be delegated to the cataloging and classification of books and similar material, and that information specialists, literature researchers, coding experts, and documentalists will take over on the higher levels of retrieving information. Fortunately, there is a growing cognizance in the field of library education that the aspect of librarianship concerned with improving graphic communication within and among groups of specialists needs educational impetus. One of the pioneers in this movement is Dr. Jesse Shera, who was responsible for activating a Center for Documentation and Communication Research at the Western Reserve University School of Library Science. At this center they have instituted a program for documentation specialists. Included in the curriculum are the first courses offered in any library school in (1) Machine Literature Searching and (2) Language Engineering. This is indicative that educators are aware of future problems and demands.

A decade ago mechanical information retrieval seemed remote and bordered on the fantastic. Vannevar Bush projected his "Memex," a machine that would spew out desired information in response to its controls. Projections such as this have accelerated the development of equipment, and activated the problems of coding or classification. As a result, new fields of science yet to be resolved are being developed. Cybernetics* and information theory are typical areas that are being explored through semantics, philosophy, and mathematics as tools.

Dr. Karl F. Heumann, Director, Chemical-Biological Coordination Center, National Research Council, stated in the Appendix to the Library of Congress Information Bulletin, Sept. 27, 1954:

---

* "A new field of science which attempts to relate the operation of automatic devices to the automatic functioning of the human body's nervous system. Once accomplished, it hopes to evolve a theory blanketing the field of control and communication—both in machines and men." Automation Dictionary, Brown Instruments Div., Minneapolis-Honeywell Regulator Co., Philadelphia, Pa.

The existence of a new and growing body of knowledge, such as information theory, developed for a specialized purpose, brings with it the possibility
that it might apply to fields only remotely connected with its origin. Such
has been the case with information theory, young as it is.

It has occurred to me that information theory might well have a real
importance for the field loosely covered by the terms "library science" and
"documentation." These fields already have a voluminous literature of their
own, but in only a few instances have workers brought these two areas
together. These papers merely signify, I am sure, the beginning of a period
of great use of information theory by librarians and documentalists.

The problem of classification is an old one in library economy and today
it remains unsolved for books, in the opinion of Dr. J. N. Shera. Yet the need
for subject classification is greater than ever, and scientists and librarians are
joining to work in this field . . . .

The crux of the problem was stated by Bush in 1945 :*

The real heart of the matter of selection, however, goes deeper than a lag
in the adoption of mechanisms by libraries, or a lack of development of devices
for their use. Our ineptitude in getting at the record is largely caused by the
artificiality of systems of indexing. When data of any sort are placed in
storage, they are filed alphabetically or numerically, and information is found
(when it is) by tracing down from subclass to subclass. It can be in only one
place, unless duplicates are used; one has to have rules as to which path will
locate it, and the rules are cumbersome. Having found one item, moreover,
one has to emerge from the system and re-enter on a new path. The human
mind does not work that way. It operates by association . . . . Man cannot
hope fully to duplicate this mental process artifically, but he certainly ought
to be able to learn from it. In minor ways he may even improve, for his
records have relative permanency. The first idea, however, to be drawn from
the analogy concerns selection. Selection by association, rather than by indexing, may yet be mechanized. One cannot hope thus to equal the speed and
flexibility with which the mind follows an associative trail, but it should be
possible to beat the mind decisively in regard to the permanence and clarity
of the items resurrected from storage.

Attempts are being made to develop new classification systems,
systems applicable to mechanical search. Dr. Mortimer Taube and
associates† developed the Uniterm System, which is based on the
association of ideas. Dr. Taube proposes indexing a representative

---

* "As We May Think," by Vannevar Bush, Atlantic Monthly, July 1945,
pp. 101-108.

† "Storage and Retrieval of Information By Means of the Association of
Ideas," by Mortimer Taube and associates, American Documentation, Vol. VI,
No. 1, Jan. 1955, pp. 1-18.

selection of documents using his system and then preparing a manual dictionary of associations covering the terms used in a Uniterm index followed by setting up a representative number of dedicated-position cards for terms in the system and, finally, building a working model of the display mechanism.

Dr. J. W. Perry, Allen Kent of Western Reserve, and members of the Battelle Memorial Institute, Columbus, Ohio, have explored the use of machines for the retrieval of information and bibliographic control in a series of articles in *American Documentation.* In a recent article they state :*

> Modern electronic searching equipment does not impose limitations on the degree of detail of analysis of the subject content of documents. Appropriate terminology must be selected to designate substances, devices, other spatio-temporal entities, attributes, processes, conditions, and abstract concepts. Encoding of terms selected to characterize the subject content of documents enables important aspects of meaning to be rendered explicit in a form convenient for defining selecting operations. A wide range of symbolism may be needed to denote such aspects of meaning. Similarly, additional symbols may be needed and used in denoting important relationships such as those between things and their attributes, processes and things being processed, produced, or consumed, processes, and conditions.

The volume of material that is spoken, recorded, and printed keeps pace with our industrial and intellectual progress. Technological and scientific developments contribute to the morass of information that has to be searched for guides to further development. The search for the resolution of these related problems has given impetus to new techniques that will remove the present barriers imposed upon information retrieval.

ELECTRONIC PERSPECTIVES

Various types of machines have been and are being devised to solve information search and retrieval problems. Some equipment is in the theory stage, other in blueprint or prototype form and there are still other types that are being refined. No one type of design will be applicable to *all* search problems. Specific problems may require specific design. There will be development and broad-

---

* "Machine Literature Searching, VII, Machine Functions and Organization of Semantic Units," by Luehrs, Kent, Perry, and Berry, American Documentation, Vol. VI, No. 1, Jan. 1955, pp. 33-39.

ening of applications and correlation and integration of various types of equipment. Information may be recorded in one form, transmitted in another form, and reproduced at an immediate or distant terminus in still another form. New types of photographic miniaturization, "video tape recording," high speed flatbed facsimile transmission, closed circuit television, electrostatic storage tubes, and magnetic core memory devices are realities now. But the refinement of these devices and the search for still others continues.

Ralph R. Shaw, former librarian of the United States Department of Agriculture, devised for the Department a "Rapid Selector" developed from principles suggested by Dr. Vannevar Bush. 35mm microfilm is used, one-half of which records text, the other half of which records subjects or index entries in the form of opaque dots. These dots are screened or examined by a photocell through a mask which is punched with holes representing the subject sought. The selector's photoelectric eyes can scan the film at the rate of 60,000 subjects a minute. A master key card is inserted in the selector, the film is scanned, and copies are produced by projections of the desired information into a copying camera, without stopping or slowing down the operation. The potential for such a device is the recording of vast amounts of information that requires compact storage which must be available on demand. In theory it is possible to search the entire catalog of the Library of Congress in about 45 minutes and at the same time produce copies of catalogue cards of any desired subjects while the machine is in operation.

A French development using microfilm is the Filmorex system. Dr. Jacques Samain has published an illustrated booklet in French describing this system.* "This system uses rectangular microfilm units measuring 72 by 45mm, divided into two sections. One contains the reproduction of the document or an abstract (up to two full pages), and the other contains a pattern of transparent and opaque spots representing code numbers for the subjects discussed or for bibliographical data. Twenty 5-digit code numbers can be used. They need not be in any particular order. The microfilm

---

* This booklet may be obtained from Filmorex, 74 Rue des Saints-Perés, Paris 7. The system has been discussed by H. L. Brownson in "Filmorex System for Electronic Selection of Microfilm Cards," American Documentation, Vol. IV, No. 1, Jan. 1953, pp. 29-30.

units are cut from a continuous photographic film 72mm wide. A two-lens camera photographs both sections at once. Before the film is cut, it can be reproduced in as many copies as may be wanted for distribution to centers equipped with selectors. The units may be kept in random order and fed into an electronic selector which scans them at the rate of 600 a minute or selects those with any particular code number or combination of numbers. Those selected can be read directly with a standard microfilm reader, or they can be reproduced or enlarged by ordinary processes."

Emik A. Avakian, an electronics expert, has devised the Automatic Microfilm Information System (AMFIS). In a revised report he states:*

AMFIS employs a mechanism that can store as many as 3 million documents. By keying document serial or accession number on a ten digit key-board the operator can project a legible image onto a viewing screen at center of desk, or at remote points, within a few seconds. Documents are reproduced in less than half a minute by standard techniques such as photostat or Xerography. Reports may be microfilmed on 8, 16, or 35mm film. Twenty-inch strips of microfilm are inserted into a holder, which is scroll-like in arrangement and holds 1000 such strips, which may be replaced in less than 30 seconds. Thus AMFIS presents a solution to the limitations imposed by the unidimentional character of micro-film reels. The desk viewer is standard and the remote viewer employs a flying spot scanner. The basic mechanical components were patented under the title of the Stored Function Calculator, U. S. Patent No. 2,610,791. The unit described used 16 scrolls but more could be added. Browsing is possible and similar in operation to standard microfilm readers. It is particularly applicable to information storage problems where immediate access is essential for reference or reproduction purposes.

A photoelectric scanner was developed at the Massachusetts Institute of Technology, in collaboration with the International Business Machines Co., to help in literature searches. It operates with punched cards, scanning up to 1000 a minute. The card is kicked out when a match is found. This technique may be applicable to punched cards with microfilm inserts. Cards can be organized or alphabetized so that only predetermined subject sections have to be scanned. This is not as quick as the use of magnetic tape, but cards can be conveniently sorted, whereas generally the

---

* ''The Automatic Micro-Film Information System (AMFIS),'' Nov. 20, 1953. Available from Emik A. Avakian, 429 Westchester Ave., Crestwood (Tuckahoe 7), New York.

entire magnetic tape must pass through a machine to get one item.

Numerous approaches are being attempted to resolve the problem of machine translation of language. When solved, this will have tremendous impact in such things as patent search and various scientific fields as well as important military applications.

The development of prototype equipment is fantastically expensive. Such pioneering for a specific need has to be left to large research operations, in industry, libraries, or government. A "Report to the Secretary of Commerce by the Advisory Committee on Application of Machines to Patent Office Operations," of December 22, 1954,* analyzed the problem of mechanization as it applies to Patent Office operation. The Committee, headed by Dr. Vannevar Bush, explored the specific problems of the Patent Office, sought "solution of the interrelated classification and equipment development problems" and attempted "to determine ways and means by which far-reaching improvements may be realized." They analyzed the "use of punched cards combined with electronic, analytical and computing mechanisms; the systems based on magnetic recording techniques; and the systems based on photographic methods with photo-electric analysis of codes." The report outlines a primary problem:

The creation of a classification and indexing system so that machinery can be effectively used for searching is an intellectual problem of formidable proportions because it involves a diversity of complex subject-matter fields. Decisions as to the type and extent of index entries or selection criteria, including their relation to different possible levels of data storage and retrieval, must be made before it is practical to specify the desired characteristics of a machine or combination of machines.

We have given much thought to the nature of the machinery which would be fully applicable. It should be highly flexible, a dynamic rather than a static affair, capable of embodying the experience of examiners as it proceeds, so arranged that it can assist in its own coding, of such nature that it can readily be extended to encompass the great field of scientific literature when that becomes mechanized as it must, and so constructed that interchange with industry is facilitated.

The report stressed cooperative effort between experts and for "further effective teamwork between government and industry." The Committee concluded that "mechanization of a substantial portion of the search process is certainly coming." It should result in marked improvement in the operations of the Patent Office that

---

* For sale by the Department of Commerce, Sales and Distribution Division, Room 6227, Commerce Building, Washington 25, D. C. $1.00.

will be of great and continuing benefit to industry in this country. The Committee is convinced that it would be unwise to enter into an attempt to mechanize the entire search operation of the Patent Office in all of its phases at one time because of the rapid rate at which the application of machines to similar problems is advancing. It appears wise to permit the development to proceed step by step, taking full advantage of the latest advance available as each step is taken."

Time after time, respondents to the inquiries of the Committee emphasized the problems of classification. One of the respondents, the Federal Telephone and Radio Co., of Clifton, New Jersey, presented one statement in its reply that represents an aspect of search that is often overlooked: "In most cases the major problem is not the machine nor the method by which the information is presented. Most users would settle for an automatic method by which they were told where to find what they are looking for—the answer which the machine must give. It has been said that sometimes the searcher does not know what he is looking for until he has found it and there is more than a grain of truth in this thought . . ."

Appendix III of the report covers "The Status of the Data Handling Art" in all the current aspects under development. For example, "photographic glass disks that provide storage densities of the order of 100,000 to 1,000,000 bits per square inch. Using a combination of flying spot scanning techniques and rotation of the disk itself at about 800 rpm, it should be possible to read this digital information at data rates of up to 1,000,000 bits per second, or the information equivalent of about 2000 conventional punched cards in one second." One of the most promising systems mentioned in the report is the Kodak Minicard System being developed by the Eastman Kodak Co.* It might be called micromation, that is, the application of microphotographic techniques to automatic search. Minimation would be another descriptive term encompassing a portion of the trade name. A large portion of a paper on this system,† which explains it in detail, is reproduced here.

---

* Eastman recently signed agreements with Magnavox Co. giving to each other world rights to manufacture, use, lease, or sell the Minicard system or units thereof.

† "The Application of the Kodak Minicard System to Problems of Documentation," by Tyler, Myers and Kuipers, American Documentation, Vol. VI, No. 1, Jan. 1955, pp. 18-30.

THE APPLICATION OF THE KODAK MINICARD
SYSTEM TO PROBLEMS OF DOCUMENTATION*

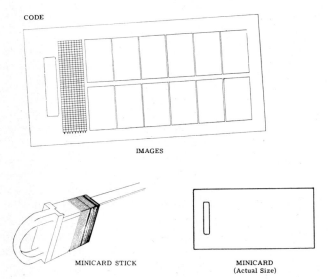

Fig. 1. The Kodak Minicard

I. PHOTOGRAPHY
FOR INFORMATION SYSTEMS

The desirable characteristics of photographic recording mediums for systems of handling information are well known; they include unsurpassed resolution properties and capacity for information storage; the abilities to reach high recording and playback rates for digital information; the properties of permanence, durability, and visibility; and, especially important, the ability to combine digital and graphic information in one record.

Although photographic recording mediums have many advantages for information-handling purposes, they have not been fully exploited up to this time because certain difficulties have had to be overcome first. For instance, the high storage capability can only be used to good advantage if, in reading out information from the record, registration is of a sufficiently high dimensional accuracy; to make use of all the potentialities for image resolution which are present in existing photographic materials, special optical components must be provided; and the chemical processing step which is required in photography often is a source of inconvenience. These and many other problems have been recognized and given direct attention in the development work that has been going on.

In the research and development program of the Eastman Kodak Company, there has been continuing progress in several fields of investigation so that some of the earlier difficulties have now been eliminated. New photographic materials have been made available. There have been improvements in techniques for photographic processing during the past few years. Means have been devised for handling, transporting, and manipulating small pieces of film through all the required operations in an information system. Equipment has been built which has been able to record and read out digital information from a photographic medium at high rates of speed. In the read-out of digital information, the requirements for the registration of a photographic record with extreme dimensional accuracy have been met. All these advances are being incorporated in a general information-handling system which is now under development by the Eastman Kodak Company.

This system, called the "Kodak Minicard System," has features which make it useful for a wide variety of information-system requirements. The system uses as the information medium a small piece of film called the "Minicard." The Minicard is illustrated in Figure 1. It is relatively small and has a slot which facilitates the handling of the card in the system. Both digital information and photographic images may be carried on the Minicard. If required, the Minicard may be used for digital information only. The capability for handling code provides the means for controlling manipulation and for doing computation. The capability for handling graphic images permits large amounts and varied types of information to be carried in the system in directly usable form.

The general characteristics of the Minicard can be shown clearly by making some comparisons with microfilm and punched cards. Microfilm has been widely used for certain types of information handling and has been effective especially where the high information storage capacity could be used to advantage. Microfilm in continuous roll form, however, has certain limitations where information must be manipulated, rearranged, and sorted, or where information must be added to or removed from a file. Punched cards, on the other hand, have desirable characteristics for manipulating, rearranging, and sorting information in a system. They can be removed from or added to a file readily. However, the information storage capacity of punched cards is of a low order, and this is a

disadvantage for many information-system requirements.

The Kodak Minicard combines the desirable characteristics of microfilm and punched cards. The Minicard has the high storage capacity of microfilm, has the abilities for manipulation which are characteristic of the punched card, and handles digital and graphic information in a single record medium.

We can summarize the general capabilities of the Kodak Minicard System in terms of two important characteristics of information mediums. Every information record can be said to have a certain activity in a system. In general, this is a measure of the number of times the record is filed, sorted, referred to, or handled. The record can also be characterized in terms of the number of bits, characters, or symbols contained per record. By plotting "record activity" against "quantity of information per record" we have a useful means of comparing the abilities of information systems. As illustrated in Figure 2, information mediums, such as punched cards and microfilm, fall on different areas on this plot. It will be noted that there is an area indicated which is not being served by punched cards or microfilm. The Minicard System not only can serve in the areas now occupied by punched cards and microfilm, as shown on the plot, but the system offers new capabilities in the region which has no satisfactory medium at present, that is, where there is a

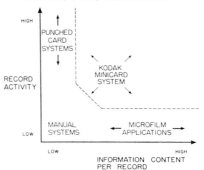

Fig. 2. Information Handling Systems
Areas of Application

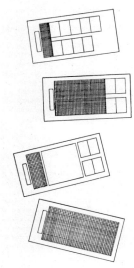

PERSONNEL

    PERSONNEL RECORDS
    MEDICAL RECORDS
    JOB DESCRIPTIONS
    TIME STANDARDS

MATERIALS

    PURCHASE RECORDS
    MATERIALS SPECIFICATIONS
    INVENTORIES
    ACCOUNTS PAYABLE

PRODUCTS

    ENGINEERING DRAWINGS
    PARTS LISTS
    PRODUCTION SCHEDULES
    CATALOGS, PRICE LISTS

CUSTOMERS

    ORDERS, CORRESPONDENCE
    CREDIT INFORMATION
    ACCOUNTS RECEIVABLE
    SALES RECORDS

Fig. 3. Kodak Minicard System
Possible Business Applications

requirement for high record activity and high quantity of information per record.

    The development of the Kodak Minicard System has been undertaken with the view that the system has broad application. Not only will it have advantages for handling all types of documentary information, but it will be attractive for other information requirements, such as computer and business applications, as well. In Figure 3 we have suggested some of the areas where the Minicard System may be used to advantage in business operations.

II. THE KODAK MINICARD SYSTEM

    The first application of the Kodak Minicard System has been made with reference to the problems of handling documentary information. The following description of the Minicard, as well as basic operations and equipment of the system, relates largely to the documentation situation. It should be emphasized, however, that the Kodak Minicard System is capable of handling information of all types and that the development of this system will not be limited to the documentary field, but will range much farther.

    In Figure 4 we have listed the equipment included in the Kodak Minicard System.[1] The items have been arranged under three convenient headings relating to the major functions in the system: making, manipulating, and using Minicards.

    Note: The equipment referred to in this paper is now in various stages of design and construction and will not be generally available for some time. The equipment listed within parentheses in Figure 4 is being planned but will not be completed with the first group of machines which is now being made.

For Making Minicards

    Typewriter-Tape Punch
    Camera
    Duplicator
    Film Processor
    Film Chopper
    (Converter: Microfilm to Minicards)
    (Converter: Punched Cards to
               Minicards)
    (Converter: Magnetic Tape to
               Minicards)

For Manipulating Minicards

    Fine Sorter
    Block Sorter
    Selector
    (Automatic File)
    (Collator)
    (Rapid Access Memory)

For Using Minicards

    Viewers
    Code Printer
    Enlarger
    Print Processor

Fig. 4. Equipment for the Kodak
Minicard System

*A. The Minicard — Its Format, Information
Capacity, and Handling in the System*

The Minicard is a piece of photographic film
16 mm by 32 mm in size. Near one end of the
Minicard is a slot which permits the card to be
handled by means of a metal "stick." In Figure 1
the Minicard format is indicated in outline and a
diagram illustrates a typical stick.

The Minicard carries digital information in
the form of clear or opaque dots, and in addition
it may carry images of documents. This is
illustrated in Figure 5. The available area of
the Minicard can be used for code or images in
any desired proportion. A single Minicard may
contain from zero up to a maximum of twelve
image areas. Each image area may be a record
of copy equivalent to a legal-size page, 8-1/2 by
14 inches. With twelve images on a Minicard,
there is still space for coded information for
manipulation purposes. Should a document

require more record space than is available on
a single Minicard, the additional information,
either code or image, can be put on a second,
third, or more Minicards, as required. Provision has been made to handle a group of Minicards together in the operations of the system.

The maximum amount of digital information
which can be carried on the present Minicard,
when it carries no graphic images, amounts to
seventy columns of 42 bits each, or a total of
2,940 bits. The arrangement of dots, timing
channel, and images is shown in Figure 5. Any
arrangement of code patterns required by a specific situation is permissible. For the purpose
of information retrieval, the dot patterns are
entered in fields which serve certain functions.
As indicated in Figure 5, the first two columns
are used as a sorting field. These columns remain blank in the master Minicard, permitting
code to be added in the duplicating operation.
The added code can then be used for sorting purposes. Following the sorting field, several columns of code are used for a control field. In
this field, code is entered to designate such
items as the file number and the number of
cards per group. Following the control field,
there is an open field that receives the index
data to be used in searching. As the name indicates, this is an open-ended field. There are
no limitations to the order or quantity of data
which can be entered in this field. In the present coding system being used for Minicards, six
bits are required to designate a single alpha-
numeric character. Thus, seven alpha-numeric
characters may be designated by one column of
bits.

Minicards are not handled manually but on
metal sticks. These sticks serve as a means of
handling cards between machines and of entering
or removing cards from the files. A standard
stick has a capacity of 2,000 Minicards. The
speed of handling Minicards in the machines of
the system has been brought to a high level
wherever it has not been limited by a manual operation. For operations such as sorting and selecting, a handling speed of 1,800 cards per
minute is reasonable to attain in the Minicard
System.

The cost of Minicards compares very favor-
ably with conventional forms of punched cards
and microfilm. Minicards are in the same cost
range as punched cards if the comparison is
made card for card. On the basis of digits or
bits per card, Minicards have a cost advantage

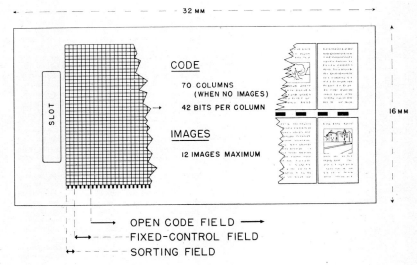

Fig. 5. Minicard Format

over punched cards which amounts to a factor of many times. Similarly, on an image-cost-per-area basis, Minicards have a considerable advantage over conventional microfilm since a greater image reduction has been achieved with Minicards.

B. *Making Minicards – Camera Operations, Encoding, Processing*

For making Minicards, a camera is required to perform two basic functions: the exposure of code patterns and the exposure of document images on photographic film. The film in the camera is in roll form. This is cut into separate Minicards after processing.

The encoding step, which amounts to a kind of input of digital information into the system, is accomplished with the use of typewriter-tape punch equipment. With the use of a typewriter keyboard, a code pattern which corresponds to the alpha-numeric characters is punched into paper tape. Usually, the punching of paper tape

precedes the camera operation so that a roll of paper tape may have the index data for particular documents punched into it and verified without taking up camera time. In addition to code input from paper tapes, code may be entered directly from a keyboard at the camera. It is possible, too, to provide automatic devices for entering code from punched cards or magnetic tape. From punched paper tapes, the camera exposes the code pattern rapidly and automatically, and after all the code has been exposed, the camera is ready for the next step, the exposure of document pages. The document-exposure operation is under the control of an operator. Except for the positioning of documents, the operation of the camera is largely automatic. The photography of document pages is done at a reduction ratio of 60 to 1, which is considerably beyond the reductions now being used in conventional microfilming. Document copy up to a maximum of 8-1/2 by 14 inches can be recorded on one image frame. Both line and continuous-tone copy can be reproduced with very satisfactory quality. This is made possible by the characteristics of the sensitized film and by the nature of the processing. In the Kodak Minicard System, a much lower contrast is maintained than is usually the case for photographic copying purposes.

After the camera operations of exposing the code and images, the photographic film is processed in roll form. The Minicard Film Processor is entirely automatic and very compact in size. Processing is rapid, and the processed film after drying can be passed immediately through a device called a film chopper. This device cuts the film into individual Minicards and stacks them on a Minicard stick. The Minicards can then be used at once in the various machines of the system.

C. Duplicating Minicards

Although duplicating Minicards is essentially the straightforward operation of making a contact printing exposure from a Minicard to roll

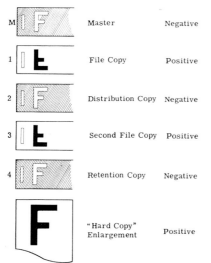

M		Master	Negative
1		File Copy	Positive
2		Distribution Copy	Negative
3		Second File Copy	Positive
4		Retention Copy	Negative
		"Hard Copy" Enlargement	Positive

Fig. 6. Duplicating — Generating Sequence

film, additional capabilities have been added to the duplicator. In the duplicating step, provision has been made for adding code to the Minicard. This capability is of great importance and makes the duplicator a key piece of equipment in the system rather than just a useful accessory.

In the description of the Minicard code field, reference was made to the sorting field. This field consists of the first two columns, which remain blank in the master Minicard. In making duplicates from the master, code may be entered in these columns. This may be done from punched tapes or by direct input from a typewriter keyboard. It will be noted that the entire code field, as well as all images on the Minicard, is duplicated, but in the sorting field additional code is entered as desired. The code entered during the duplicating operation is used for sorting and organizing files by machine. This is a feature which is especially important for large files.

The duplicating capability of the Kodak Minicard System makes it possible to disseminate documentary material widely from a document center. Duplication is possible to more generations than is usually the case in photographic systems. Very acceptable prints can be made from sixth-generation Minicard duplicates. The generations of Minicard duplicates which might be made by a document center are shown in Figure 6. It is required, of course, that the machine equipment be able to handle both positive and negative Minicards of any generation in all the operations of the system.

D. Sorting Minicards

Included in the Minicard System are machines for performing various sorting operations. Sorting is carried out by the same principle as in conventional punched-card machines. Cards are fed one at a time past a reading station which sorts on one digit at a time in a designated code column, the cards being directed to one of ten receiving magazines. Sorting can be done on both numeric and alphabetic characters.

In what is known as the "fine sorter," two sets of ten receiving magazines, each with a reading station preceding it, are arranged in a closed circle. Minicards are transported around this circle by a rotary carrying mechanism. Each magazine is capable of both receiving and feeding cards. These features have made it possible to program this machine to sort successively to any number of digits without attention by an operator. The small size of the Minicard makes this sorter a very compact machine.

In another sorter, which is called a "block sorter," the reading station and magazines function much as in the fine sorter, although cards are moved by a linear transport mechanism. As the name indicates, this sorter can separate cards into blocks or groups. It is an advantage of this design that it is possible to attach file magazines directly to the sorter. Sorting can thus be done directly into the file. File units consist of either 10-magazine or 100-magazine units, each magazine unit having a capacity of 2,000 Minicards. Because of the small size of the Minicard, these file units can be easily handled and attached or removed manually from the sorter. Provision is made to index a 100-magazine file unit to receive Minicards into any of its magazines when placed in position on the sorter.

E. Selecting Minicards

It is an essential function of an information-handling system to be able to select information on the basis of specified question data. In the Minicard Selector, searching capability has been provided to a high degree — probably beyond the requirements of information systems which have been proposed thus far.

basis of anything beyond what has been entered in the Minicard code fields. As has already been described, any data which can be expressed in alphabetic or numeric characters can be entered in any order in the open field of the Minicard. A great deal of flexibility has been achieved by providing a means of labeling, by a suitable identification symbol, each code word entered in the code field. Boundary specifications can also be made in order to specify that certain code words or characters must be associated in a search.

In the operation of the selector, Minicards are fed from a storage magazine at handling speed, past a reading head where all data are read out of the Minicard code field. These data are examined in the electronic circuitry in the selector, and, wherever the Minicard code data are recognized as satisfying the specifications of the question data which have been set up in the selector, the Minicard is selected and directed into a receiving magazine. Minicards that have not been selected pass into a different magazine.

The question data are set up in the selector by means of a typewriter keyboard or a punched-tape input and also by switches on a control panel. The question words, numbers, or characters are entered by the typewriter keyboard or punched tape. The logical specifications and boundary specifications are set up on the control panel. The logical relations of conjunction, disjunction, and negation may be specified in the question. All words or characters may be recognized on the basis of equality. It is also provided that, in some question-word positions, recognition may be on the basis of "less than" or "greater than." Thus, ranges of numbers or characters may be selected. Figure 7 gives a brief summary of the Minicard Selector control specifications.

QUESTION SPECIFICATIONS.	
Characters, Words	— Set up in Selector by Keyboard or Punched Tapes

Logical Specifications
  Conjunction
  Disjunction
  Negation
	— Set up on Selector Control Panel

Recognition of Equality, Inequality	Set up on Selector Control Panel
Boundary Specifications	Set up on Selector Control Panel

Fig. 7. Minicard Selection — Control

The selector capability is directly related to the method by which coded data have been entered into the code field of the Minicard record. Selection, of course, cannot be made on the

F. Minicard Viewers

Although the Kodak Minicard System may be able to store, handle, select, and deliver information very acceptably, a great measure of the system's success will depend upon the satisfactory performance of the

devices for viewing the information on Minicards. Two types of viewers will be made
available, a personal-type viewer and a desk-
type viewer. The personal-type viewer will be
portable and of low cost. The desk-type viewer
will combine a projection-type viewing system
with a semiautomatic mechanism for feeding
Minicards from standard-size sticks. There
will be controls for indexing to particular image positions on a Minicard. After viewing,
Minicards may be separated by directing them
into different receiving magazines in the viewer.
The desk-type viewer is intended to give the
greatest convenience for viewing or scanning a
fairly large number of Minicards.

G. Enlarging Minicard Images

Although information in the Minicard System
can be made available by viewing devices, enlargements of Minicard images to original size
will also have to be supplied to many users of
the system. The enlarger is an automatic device which may be set to supply either enlargements of all the images on a Minicard or an enlargement of the first image frame only. It may
be convenient to make the first image frame on
the Minicard the record of the document abstract. Thus, it would be possible to supply
rapidly, on demand, enlargements of only the
abstracts from a group of Minicards. Enlargements from Minicard images to microprint can
be made if required. This will be of interest to
information centers which make extensive use of
microprint and now have microprint readers
available. Where the bulk and cost of full enlargements become a disadvantage, enlargement
to microprint images may well be considered.
Processing of the sensitized material which has
been exposed in the enlarger may be done rapidly. Both wet and dry processes are available.

H. Minicard Files

Reference has already been made in this discussion to Minicard files in connection with the
operation of sorting directly to the file. The
Minicard files are made up of aggregates of the
standard magazine which is designed to receive
the full capacity of a Minicard stick — 2,000
Minicards. For certain purposes, it will be
convenient to handle Minicards in 10-magazine
file units; in other cases, 100-magazine file
units. Minicards can be removed manually from

the magazines of the file units by means of the
Minicard stick. A 100-magazine file unit occupies a volume of about a cubic foot. The information capacity of this unit is roughly equivalent to the documentary material which can be
kept in 100 conventional four drawer letter files.
For a file of 2,000,000 Minicards, roughly
equivalent to 1,000 file cabinets of documentary
material, the Minicard magazines will occupy a
cabinet about 15 by 30 by 50 inches in size. The
work area and storage file of some 10,000,000
Minicards could be placed conveniently on a
floor area of about ten by ten feet.

III. CAPABILITIES OF THE KODAK MINICARD SYSTEM WITH REFERENCE TO PROBLEMS OF DOCUMENTATION

A. Machines for Documentation

In the last decade or so, there has been an
increasing pressure from the public which uses
information to see that something is done about
the difficulties of disseminating, storing,
searching, and using documentary information.
As the amount of this information has continued
to build up, the difficulties for the people de-
siring to use the information have increased.
For some time there has been the hope that
modern machines would rapidly relieve many of
the difficulties, but progress in this connection
has been somewhat disappointing. There are
indications that, up to the present, record mediums have not had the proper characteristics
for information-handling purposes. Storage requirements and input-output characteristics of
available machine systems have not been entirely suitable for what has been needed. Consequently, there has been little incentive to
attempt to apply these machine systems to documentation purposes, especially to the needs of
the larger document centers.

The Kodak Minicard System has many characteristics which can help to satisfy the present
documentation needs. Especially for larger
files does the system have attractive features.
The outstanding capabilities of the system for
documentation are listed in Figure 8. The discussion which follows points out how these capabilities give the Minicard System certain advantages over systems which have been available
up to this time.

SUMMARY

SOME CAPABILITIES
OF THE KODAK MINICARD SYSTEM
FOR DOCUMENTATION

1. The system handles graphic and digital
   information in one record medium.
   The Minicard, a discrete record unit,
   has a high information capacity and a
   high activity capability.

2. The system has an efficient record
   duplicating capability.

3. Document information in the system
   may be delivered directly

4. The system provides the input-output
   convenience and file space advantages
   required for large files.

5. The system has capabilities for
   organizing files by machine. This
   makes possible relatively short search
   times for large files.

6. The system has searching capability
   to satisfy the requirements of present
   information systems.

Fig. 8.

These insights into the potential of micromation or other techniques of automatic search make some of our present practices of microrecording seem antediluvian by comparison. But for certain applications and for economic reasons, many of our present forms of microrecording will remain in use.

PRESENT CLASSIFICATION TECHNIQUES

We have seen that classification is the basic problem in machine applications of information retrieval. Likewise it is the basic problem with our present forms of microrecording. Some forms of microrecords facilitate search due to decimal arrangements; others are flexible and may be adapted to different systems with different degrees of suitability.

Microfilm, like color television of a few years ago, has a variety of mutually incompatible coding or indexing systems available, no one of which would be adequate for even our presently known needs for machine search. It will require an American Standard Coding System to be developed under the guidance of the American

Standards Association to make it possible for data to be inserted which can be retrieved for the greatest good of the greatest number of individuals.

No matter what the system, files of microrecords must be indexed in order to facilitate search. The entire procedure may be undertaken either by the commercial company that photographs or processes the microrecord or by the owner of the original records. Determining the type of system of indexing, coding, or cataloging for a limited number of items is not difficult because the micro-record normally is classified in the same manner as the original record. The physical characteristics of the microrecord facilitate rather than retard search. Mechanical or electronic selection may become feasible where such selection was not possible with the original record because of its size. Such classification will appear on the finished microrecord whether it is an individual Microcard, Readex Microprint, film strip, sheet film, or reel of microfilm. The problem is that of classifying or arranging the entire microrecord collection in a form that will expedite reference. It is necessary to use housing, containers or cabinets, with proper guides for the microrecords despite the classification on each individual microrecord. Vertical files to house Microcards or microfilm, or suitable shelving for Readex Microprint and Micro-lex may have to be purchased. Sometimes it is possible to utilize existing equipment, but proper housing of microrecords is an intrinsic part of facilitating search. Equipment that is not capable of containing the microrecord collection adequately should not be employed.

Microprint (Offset-Printed Micro-opaques)

Each microprint sheet of the Readex Microprint Corporation is 6 by 9 inches in size. The classification on the individual sheet conforms to the original record. Each sheet may contain as many as 100 pages of a book in a uniform arrangement of 10 rows, each containing 10 pages (Figure 1). If the microprint is that of a newspaper, the arrangement may be a series of 5 rows of 5 pages each, depending on the size of the original newspaper page. Such uniformity makes use in a projector comparatively easy. The numerical sequence of pages conforms to the original record.

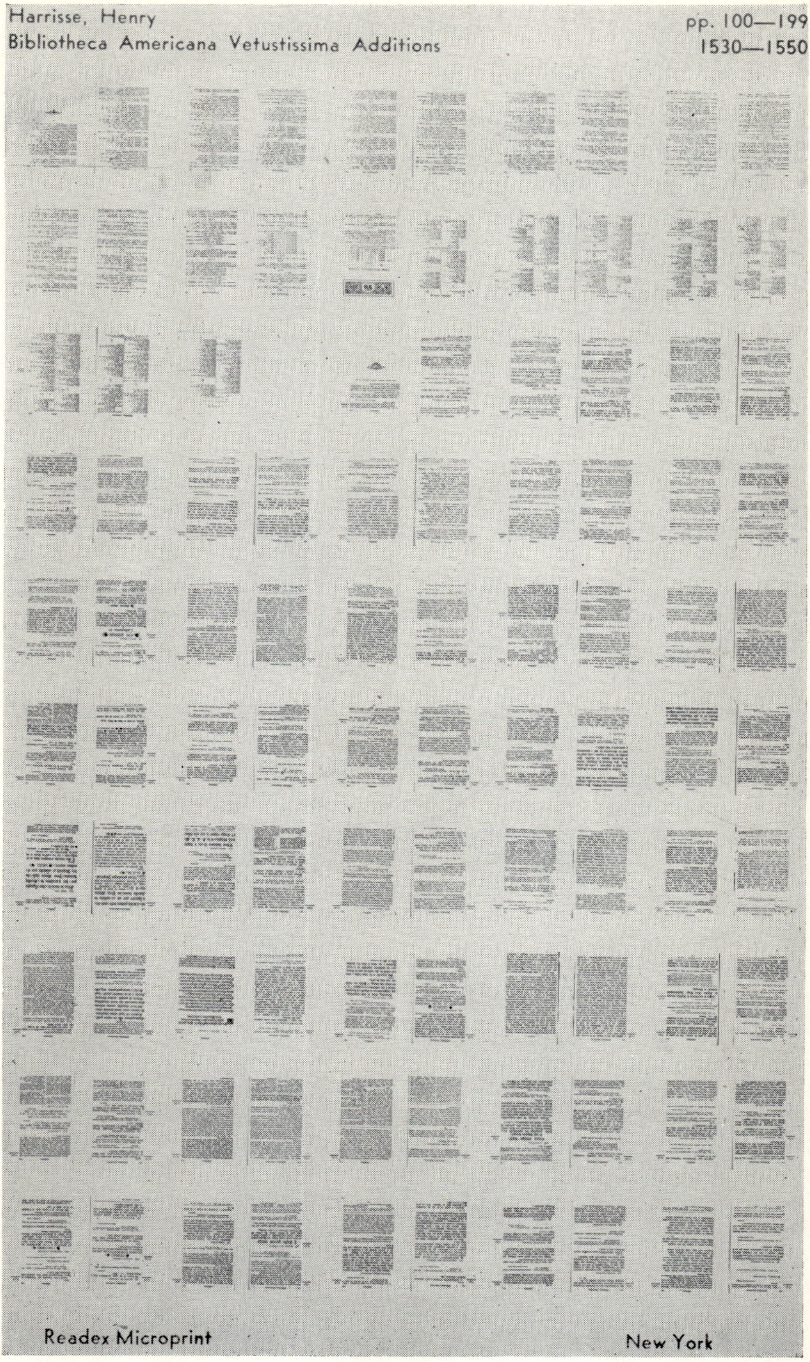

FIG. 1. Readex Microprint. (Courtesy of Readex Microprint Corp.)

Microprint sheets are normally kept in cloth-bound slip cases. A slip case holds approximately 3 inches, or over 200 sheets, of microprint. Each sheet contains the title of the original work, the inclusive pages on the sheet, and, if necessary, the date. This information can be read without enlargement. The slip case can be classified or cataloged in the same manner as a book, and because of its size it can be placed under its proper classification on library shelving with an existing book collection. Chronological arrangement of the slip cases is preferable if the material recorded is a periodical or newspaper. Microprint can also be filed in a filing cabinet without the slip case. Guides may then be utilized to sectionalize the sheets. If microprint is classified according to an existing system along with other books, the catalog card should identify the work as a microprint edition. (Colored catalog cards may be used to indicate microrecords.)

Microcards (Photoprinted Micro-opaques)

Microcards are positive photographic prints (opaque) 3 by 5 inches in size. A card usually contains from 36 to 48 pages of copy, but it can contain as many as 100 pages. If necessary, both sides of the card can be used. The number of pages on a card depends on the size of the original copy and the reduction factor used. Normally the cards are viewed in a projector, but they can be consulted easily with a small hand lens about eight- or ten-power. The hand lens is not desirable for extensive reading.

At the top of each Microcard, or on the reverse side, are classifications or titles which are visible without enlargment. These classifications may conform to those of the original records. They may be a code number, an accession number, or any other type of classification. The title and date of the recorded material and, for periodicals, the date and volume and page numbers may also appear, and there may be a notation that a card is one of a series on a given subject (Figure 2). Such notations, being visible without enlargement, facilitate search and filing.

Because of their size, Microcards are normally housed in drawers 3 by 5 inches in vertical files. The drawer label should indicate the contents, and guides should be employed to group the Microcards properly. When the Microcard edition is that of a book or periodical and its classification conforms to that of other

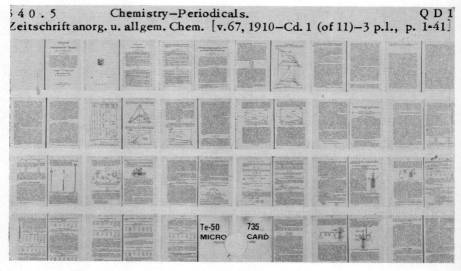

FIG. 2. Microcard. (Courtesy of Microtext Publishing Corp.)

works contained in a library, the catalog card should show that the edition is in Microcard form and should give the precise location (cabinet and drawer) of the Microcard edition.

Standards for Microcards were established by the National Microcard Committee of the American Standards Association, and there have been some slight amendments. The revision of August 15, 1953, to the Microcard Code is now (1955) in the hands of Sectional Committee PH5 of the Association. It has to be submitted to the Association for approval.*

Microlex

A relatively new technique in opaque microrecords is the product of the Microlex Corporation of Rochester, New York. Basically they are reproducing photographically from a sheet film negative 200 pages of a book on each side of a card approximately 6½ by 8½ inches in size (see Figure 3). This is another variation of a decimal arrangement to facilitate search. It is particularly

---

* For guidance in titling, cataloging, and classification of Microcards, it is reproduced in Appendix F, pages 419 to 422.

FIG. 3. Microlex. (Courtesy of Microlex Corp.)

unique in the volume of material recorded on one card. This company also markets a reader to accommodate this card. The original objective was to produce in microrecord form legal material which because of its nature, requires a larger format than the conventional Microcard. Primarily these microcards consist of reported cases, but other types of legal literary work may be adapted. The Microlex Corporation plans to offer some of the subscription publications made up of the units of the *Annotated Reports System* of the Lawyers Co-operative Publishing Company which contains more than 800 volumes. Publication for other publishers will also be undertaken in the legal and other fields of publishing where the subject matter is sufficiently consecutive and voluminous.

Microfilm

Microfilm is normally housed in vertical filing equipment of sizes that vary with the microfilm application; for example, material may be recorded in the form of reels or frames inserted in jacket cards or envelopes, or as individual positives and negatives of 70mm film.

Labeling Reel Boxes. Reels of microfilm should be kept in cardboard reel boxes (4 by 4 by 1 9/16 inches) in outside dimensions. The cardboard should be as free as possible of sulfur. Each reel box should plainly indicate the contents of the reel on the box label and be placed on the narrow end in the cabinet drawer with the label face up. Supplemental data can be recorded on the side of the reel box if there is insufficient room on the label (Figure 4). The rows of microfilm boxes or cartons can be keyed to indicate the correct position of the cartons within the drawer. Varicolored ink, marking crayon, or plastic tape may be used to show the correct sequence. Diagonal lines can be made for a series of 10 boxes or the entire row (Figure 5). The colors may be varied according to row or drawer. Any misfiled reel box is instantly revealed by such a system. The information at the beginning of the reel should correspond with that on the reel box label as a precaution against filing a reel in the wrong box. If identical information of this nature appears at the beginning and end of each reel, there may be a tendency for the user not to rewind reels unless "start" or "end" targets are used. The drawer label should note the contents of each row of reel boxes. Classification of the reels normally follows that

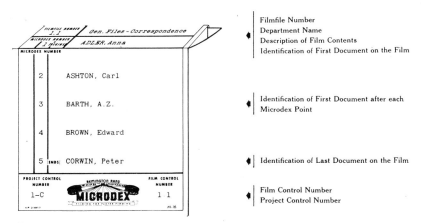

FIG. 4. Reel box with labels. (Courtesy of Remington Rand, Inc.)

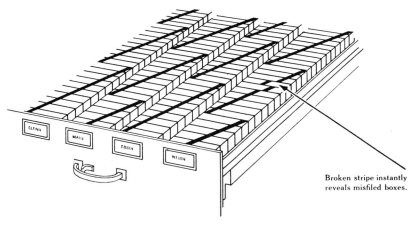

FIG. 5. Film storage cabinet. (Courtesy of Remington Rand, Inc.)

of the original documents. For printed works, the catalog card should show that the edition is available in microfilm form, in addition to its physical location.

Ballou and Rather * point out some of the problems involved in classifying and organizing microfilm collections at large public

---

* "Microfilm and Microfacsimile Publications, by Hubbard W. Ballou and John Rather, *Library Trends*, October 1955, p. 186.

and college libraries. They state that "a 1947 review of microfilm cataloguing at thirteen large research libraries showed that these libraries were nearly evenly divided between using some variety of accession number alone and using such a number in connection with classification letters. An informal survey in 1950 seemed to indicate a trend toward broad classification."

Indexing Microfilm Reel Contents. Certain types of necessary signals and information must be prepared and microfilmed with the original material. Such procedure facilitates search and, when necessary, certifies the authenticity of the microfilm record.

Some of this identification can be the same type size as the original record. It is desirable to have subdivisions prepared in type sizes that are in sufficient contrast to the original material. Such emphasis easily attracts the eye of the user and enables him to locate material more quickly. Each microfilm reel should have a special title of its own that is visible to the naked eye despite any title page that the microfilm work may have. This enables the reel contents to be identified readily.

Guides or targets should appear on the microfilm reel in the following sequence:

(a) Special titling of microfilm reel (exaggerated type size).

(b) Under certain circumstances, information indicating who made the reel, when, and under what auspices should follow the special title. This may be a declaration of intent (Figure 6) to show that the industrial records microfilmed are actually those of the company concerned. It may also certify the destruction of original records. Such certificate should be signed and dated by the person authorized to do so.

(c) Title page or title guide to film contents.

(d) Index to contents.

(e) Subdivision guides should be placed in their proper sequence throughout the film. If there are no subdivisions or subheadings, guides may be used to separate the reel content at regular intervals.

(f) Correction targets should be placed immediately after any error detected by a camera operator and rephotographed immediately following the correction target.

(g) A certification of the authenticity of the contents of the film may be desired (Figure 7). It should contain the name of the

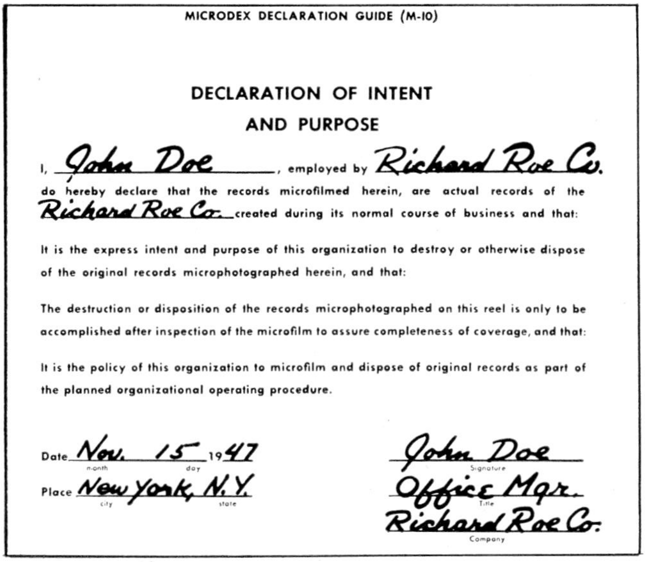

MICRODEX DECLARATION GUIDE (M-10)

DECLARATION OF INTENT
AND PURPOSE

I, John Doe, employed by Richard Roe Co.
do hereby declare that the records microfilmed herein, are actual records of the Richard Roe Co. created during its normal course of business and that:

It is the express intent and purpose of this organization to destroy or otherwise dispose of the original records microphotographed herein, and that:

The destruction or disposition of the records microphotographed on this reel is only to be accomplished after inspection of the microfilm to assure completeness of coverage, and that:

It is the policy of this organization to microfilm and dispose of original records as part of the planned organizational operating procedure.

Date Nov. 15 1947 (month, day)
Place New York, N.Y. (city, state)

John Doe (Signature)
Office Mgr. (Title)
Richard Roe Co. (Company)

FIG. 6. Declaration of intent. (Courtesy of Remington Rand, Inc.)

owner of the records, the precise records contained on the reel, and a statement to the effect that the filming meets the requirements of the National Bureau of Standards; it should be signed by the camera operator.

(h) The declaration of intent can be repeated, if desired, at the end of the film.

(i) Material that was missing during the original filming or photographically unsatisfactory can be spliced on at the end of the reel in the form of an appendix. Such material should be preceded by an appendix target (Figure 8) indicating the start of the appendix. It should be followed by a target indicating the end of the appendix (Figure 9). Both targets should state the reasons for the appendix and be signed by the camera operator.

In some cases additional "start" and "end" targets may be used to indicate the beginning and the end of the microfilm reel. If the title frame is repeated at the end of the reel, it is necessary to use an "end" target. An omission target may be inserted by a camera operator when an omission is noticed, or it can be inserted in correct sequence in the original material by the persons prepar-

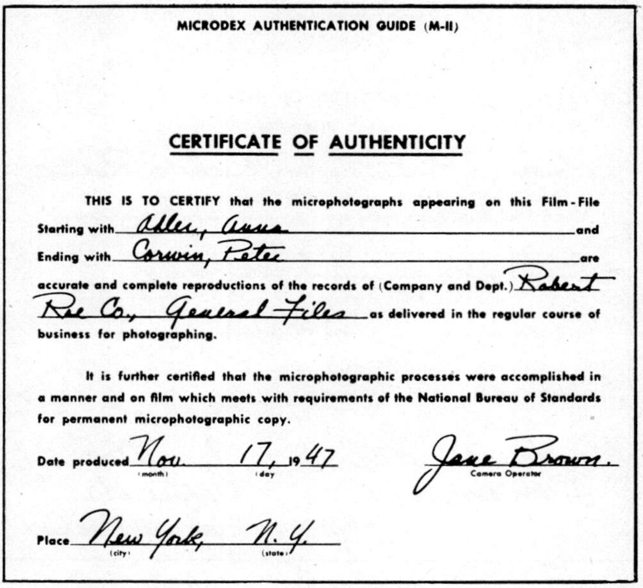

MICRODEX AUTHENTICATION GUIDE (M-II)

CERTIFICATE OF AUTHENTICITY

THIS IS TO CERTIFY that the microphotographs appearing on this Film - File

Starting with *Adler, Anna* and

Ending with *Corwin, Peter* are

accurate and complete reproductions of the records of (Company and Dept.) *Robert*

Rae Co., General Files as delivered in the regular course of

business for photographing.

It is further certified that the microphotographic processes were accomplished in a manner and on film which meets with requirements of the National Bureau of Standards for permanent microphotographic copy.

Date produced *Nov. 17, 19 47*   *Jane Brown.*
       (month)   (day)   Camera Operator

Place *New York, N. Y.*
       (city)   (state)

FIG. 7. Certificate of authenticity. (Courtesy of Remington Rand, Inc.)

FIG. 8. Target indicating start of appendix.
(Courtesy of Remington Rand, Inc.)

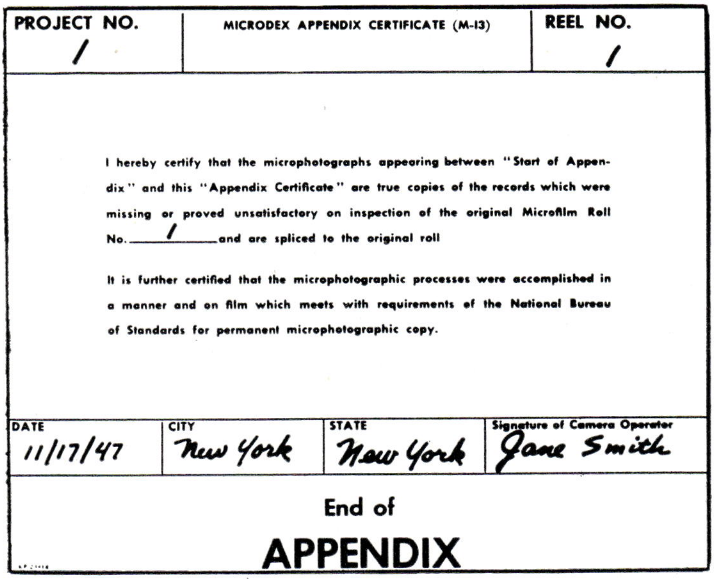

PROJECT NO. *1*	MICRODEX APPENDIX CERTIFICATE (M-13)	REEL NO. *1*

I hereby certify that the microphotographs appearing between "Start of Appendix" and this "Appendix Certificate" are true copies of the records which were missing or proved unsatisfactory on inspection of the original Microfilm Roll No. *1* and are spliced to the original roll

It is further certified that the microphotographic processes were accomplished in a manner and on film which meets with requirements of the National Bureau of Standards for permanent microphotographic copy.

DATE *11/17/47*	CITY *New York*	STATE *New York*	Signature of Camera Operator *Jane Smith*

End of
APPENDIX

Fig. 9. Target indicating end of appendix. (Courtesy of Remington Rand, Inc.)

ing the material for photographing. Resolution charts and density targets may also be included for additional guidance.

Individual problems may create variance in the style and placement of targets. Targets provided by microfilming companies may be adequate, but generally the arrangement of targets follows the procedure outlined in the preceding paragraphs, although it may be varied to meet individual problems.

Indexing Sheet Film. 70mm film and sheet film, transparencies in positive or negative form, are indexed in much the same manner as Microcards (Figure 10). Again, the system of indexing follows that of the original records, and necessary data, including classification, coding, and accession numbers, can appear at the top of each positive or negative. Sheet film (or microfiche) is prepared in the usual photographic film sizes, 45 by 60, 60 by 90, 90 by 120mm, and so on, but many library formats are in the range 75 by 125, 74 by 104, 100 by 150, 104 by 148mm. There are larger sizes but they are not commonly used.

(a) ACCESSION RECORDS. For purposes of recording it may be

Fig. 10. Title on sheet film. (Courtesy of Nederlands Document Reproductie N. V.)

preferable to use simple accession numbers in order of accession (Figure 11) when photographing original record in sheet form in order to reduce the time consumed in printing or hand lettering data pertaining to the original material recorded on each sheet film positive or negative. This is feasible if one or more duplicate negatives are kept in storage and if an accession record is kept of the number and contents of each piece of sheet film, positive or negative. An accession list corresponding to the accession numbers appearing on the sheet film must be kept in book form, or on file cards if interfiling is necessary. The accession record should also indicate the contents of each piece of sheet film.

(b) ALPHABETICAL CATALOG. It is also advisable to maintain an alphabetical catalog of the sheet film in conjunction with the accession list or record. This might be arranged by title, subject, or whatever indexing procedure is followed with the original records. It should also contain the accession number. If both an accession list

FIG. 11. Accession number and classification on jacket of 70mm.
positive. (Courtesy of University Microfilms.)

and an alphabetical catalog are maintained, it is possible to replace readily any sheet film positives or negatives that are misfiled, damaged or lost. When accession numbers are mounted with the original record before photographing, supplemental indexing or classification, which may appear on the protective jacket, cannot cause confusion. If additional prints are made and cross-filed under the appropriate classification or heading, the accession and alphabetic index can be eliminated. This procedure will increase the volume of the file and therefore may not be desirable in some files because of the increased consumption of space and the lack of protection against loss. This procedure may be employed for 70mm microfilm and for larger sizes of sheet film including photographic negatives.

Sheet film should be inserted in protective jackets to prevent abrasion due to handling and general use. Protective jackets may be paper and opaque, or transparent and made from acetate. Acetate jackets have the advantage of giving greater protection to the sheet film if it is used for projection, because the jacket can be kept on the sheet film even in a reader. However, both types of

jackets can be classified in any manner desired to indicate the
contents of sheet film. Acetate jackets can be obtained slightly
larger than the sheet film with an opaque white band on one
edge of the jacket that can be used for classification or indexing
purposes. A special ink must be used to make such identification on
acetate jackets.

Cumulative Microfilm. Originally microfilm was available only
in reel form, and there was some criticism because of the inability
to locate a specific image quickly in a long reel of film. There were
also occasions when several persons made simultaneous requests for
different images on the same reel of film. These difficulties have
been removed by the use of "cumulative" or "open-end" microfilm
which consists of jacket or aperture cards into which individual
frames or strips of microfilm have been inserted. Multiple readers
are used when it is necessary to service more than one person
simultaneously. These cards vary in size, color, construction, and
application. There are standard sizes, but cards can be varied to
contain one or more sizes of microfilm if desired. This technique
has made it possible to index a single microfilm image or a portion
of an image by using aperture cards or jackets to index several
microfilm frames relating to the same subject.

The cards may be constructed of paper or acetate or combinations of both. Classification and indexing can appear directly
on the jacket or aperture card. Punched aperture cards may be
used for mechanical search.

In the United States some of the principal distributors for
these cards are: Remington Rand, 315 Fourth Avenue, New York;
and the Filmsort Division of the Dexter Folder Co., 50 South Pearl
Street, Pearl River, New York. Remington Rand uses card jackets
into which individual frames or strips of microfilm may be inserted.
They also have available cards laminated with acetate that seal in
and protect the microfilm strips.

Filmsort manufactures the greatest variety of jacket and
aperture cards. They offer jacket cards that accommodate several
frames of microfilm of one size and permit the insertion of
several frames of microfilm of a different size. The acetate jackets
contain apertures for the insertion of identification of the microfilm record (Figure 12). They also have acetate cards to which
paper has been attached, across the top or bottom for notations or

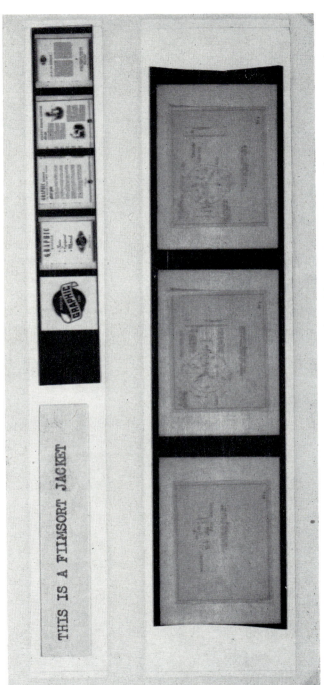

Fig. 12. Filmsort jacket. (Courtesy of Filmsort Division of Dexter Folder Co.)

classification of the contents of the card. A third type of card is made from regulation card stock with apertures to accommodate the desired film size; acetate is laminated to the card stock over the openings to permit the insertion of strips of film. An insertion tool is provided which can be used for insertion or extraction of film. One of their newest developments is the Vidifile jacket. This is a transparent acetate jacket with sealed ends. The strips or frames of film are inserted through a slit that runs the entire length of the pocket for each strip or series of frames. Filmsort also manufacture an aperture or window card which consists of acetate laminated to the card stock and an adhesive protected by a glassine covering. The glassine covering is peeled off and an individual microfilm frame pressed to the adhesive on the acetate. Permanent adhesion takes place under slight pressure. Such aperture cards can be used for mechanical search and coded accordingly (Figure 13).

Paper positives (instead of film positives) may be made directly from the film negative. The trade names are "Microtape" and "Microstrip." They can be made to adhere to an ordinary ragstock file card of any size and interfiled according to any classification. Although a film transparency is "sharper" than an opaque, this method of using paper positives is more economical because it eliminates the expense of jacket or aperture cards through the substitution of less expensive file cards yet permits classification in the same manner.

Film Strips. Strips of microfilm containing 10 images are commonly employed in Europe* (Figure 14). The film strips may be kept in individual jackets upon which classification entries can be made, or they may be kept in a holder which will accommodate 5, 10, 15, or more strips (Figure 15). The holder in turn can be inserted in a pouch in one side of a thin cardboard slip case (¼ by 6 by 9 in.). The other side of the slip case has room for a complete index of each microfilm frame or strip. A title label giving general contents of the slip case can be pasted on the inside of the cover, and the spine of the slip case has room for an accession or classification number. Material housed in this manner can be placed on shelving along with material of similar nature; a card

---

* In France 35mm film strips are commonly 210mm in length and usually contain 10 pages as microframes and a title or classification guide to the strip.

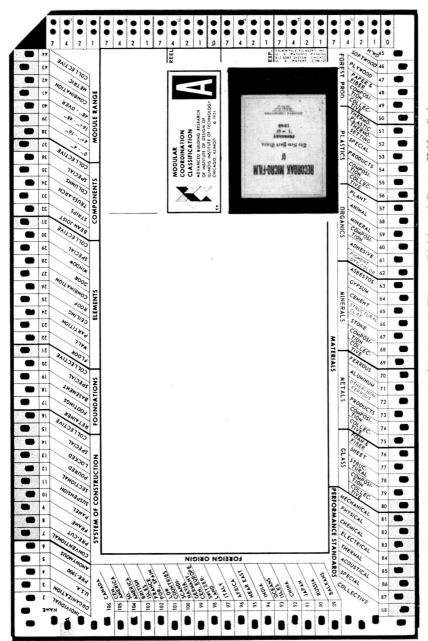

FIG. 13. Filmsort aperture card. (Courtesy of Filmsort Division of Dexter Folder Co.)

FIG. 14. Film strip. (Courtesy of Carl Zeiss, Jena.)

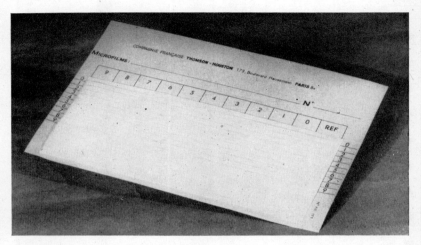

FIG. 15. Filing pouch. (Courtesy of Thomson-Houston Cie.)

catalog would be necessary to locate the material. There are numerous variations of this method of classifying strip film.

SECURITY CONTROLS

The problem of the control of military reports, classified matter, or such data that are restricted for security reasons has been considered in various meetings and conferences by numerous professional associations and societies. Closed meetings on the subject have also been held by government agencies and government contractors.

In general, each agency, department, contractor, or unit concerned has its own detailed regulations, procedures, and practices based upon applicable laws, Executive Orders of the President, and upon its own administrative practices and orders. For the most part, the broad descriptive regulations of each agency are not classified and are available to any interested person. Details as to the specific procedures applicable in a particular case are ordinarily available only to those who "need to know." For this reason detailed information as it applies to a specific situation should always be obtained directly from the facility, agency, or department concerned to assure that the intent of such procedures is fully met and to avoid misinterpretation of the purposes and methods of the specific procedures that apply. Such information is readily available from the cognizant security control officer for those who "need to know." In military organizations, such as the U. S. Army, it is customary for the security control officer to be an intelligence officer. Typical data for the Department of the Army are found in Army Regulations 380-5, 310-5, and SR380-405-5.

Some unclassified manuals covering government regulations regarding classified matter are obtainable from the Government Printing Office, others are restricted and are available under certain circumstances from the issuing agency involved. The pattern for basic security requirements can be found in Executive Order 10501 of November 5, 1953, 18 Fed. Reg. 7049 (1953). This revoked Executive Order 10290 of September 24, 1951, 16 Fed. Reg. 9795 (1951). Some but not all of the laws involving safeguarding information are listed in Part 1—Section E (pages 20-28) of the "Digest of the Public Record of Communism in the United States," published in 1955 by the Fund for the Republic, Inc., New York City.

The function and operation of Federal agencies and others that maintain libraries containing classified or restricted data are adequately covered in an excellent volume* written by Bernard M. Fry, Deputy Chief, Technical Information Service, Atomic Energy Commission. In particular the sections on processing, cataloging, storage, and control procedures are extremely useful.

Microcards are being used to provide necessary availability and space reduction of certain current and out-of-print technical reports. One method used to promote the security of classified material on Microcards by making it readily identifiable is the

---

* "Library Organization and Management of Technical Reports Literature," Bernard M. Fry, Studies in Library Science No. 1, 1953, The Catholic University of America Press, Washington 17, D. C.

result of experiments with various dyes by Mr. Ford W. Bowers of the Photographic Department of Dow Chemical Company. The dyes are those used in coloring textiles, especially cotton, and they have no effect on the photographic image, gelatin, or paper stock other than the coloring. Tintex and crocein scarlet (photographic negative retouching color) were used. The procedure employed was that of making a highly concentrated solution by dissolving the dye in hot water, then cooling it to room temperature, and finally filtering it before using. Other cloth dyes may work equally well. This technique of "color-coding" micro-opaques may have other applications aside from identifying classified material.

Usually any library, organization, or business has some type of record or records that do not involve national security but are restricted in use. No one technique can be prescribed that can be utilized in all cases of this type. Each situation has to be analyzed individually. Equipment and system manufacturers can suggest certain approaches, but, if more rigid restrictions are desired, some of the controls employed by government agencies in maintaining classified data may be employed or modified as necessary.

A Security Suggestion

When an original document such as an application blank or other statement is executed under oath, it is strongly recommended that *all* copies shall be *exclusively* photographic copies derived solely from the original document. Such copies may be made as enlargements, if desired, from the primary microfilm original negative.

In the event that more than a single ribbon copy of a document exists and all such copies are executed under oath, small discrepancies among such documents that may occur unintentionally or otherwise cast serious doubt upon the validity of the documents and strongly suggest that such documents are worthless as evidence in a court of law.

Bibliography

Frank W. Bobb. "Applying Microfilm in a War Agency." *Special Libraries,* Feb. 1948, pp. 50-52.

"Microfilms and Microcards; Their Use in Research; A Selected List of References." Card Division, Library of Congress, June 1950, Washington, D. C. 55c.

L. J. v.d. Wolk and J. C. Tonnon. "The Microcopy on Flat Film as an Aid in Documentation." *Rev. Doc.* XVII (1950), fasc. 5, 8.

R. S. Schultze. "The Role of Microfilm and Microcard." Week-end Conference Papers of the London and Home Counties Branch of the Library Association, Oct. 1951.

R. W. Batchelder. "The Scope and Value of the Microcard." *Special Libraries,* May-June 1952, pp. 157-161.

Manual on Document Reproduction and Selection. International Federation for Documentation, The Hague, Netherlands, 1953-1954, 2 vols. $7.10.

Vernon D. Tate. "Microreproduction and the Acquisitions Program." *Library Trends,* April 1955.

"Microfilming of Engineering Drawings and Records." By A. H. Rau, Engineering General Division, General Electric Co., Schenectady, N. Y. Data Folder No. 3707, Oct. 1946.

"Microdex," Remington Rands' New System for Indexed Microfilming. F-179, Remington Rand Inc., 1948.

Leonard F. Paine. "Cataloging Audio-Visual Materials." Wilson *Library Bulletin,* May 1949, pp. 699-701, 711.

Ralph H. Carruthers. "Titling of Microfilm Editions." *Amer. Documentation,* Vol. 1, No. 4, pp. 190-193 (Oct. 1950).

Wm. P. Southard. "Indexing Microfilmed Records." *Systems,* August 1951, pp. 17, 30.

Ben Milnitsky. "Classifying Negatives and Prints." *Industrial Photography,* Jan.-Feb., 1954, pp. 36-40.

"The Cataloguing of Films and Filmstrips." *UNESCO Bulletin for Libraries,* Vol. 9, Nos. 5, 6, pp. 98-101 (May-June 1955).

"A Guide to Indexing on Diebold Flofilm." Diebold, Inc., Canton 2, Ohio.

Taube, Gull, and Wachtel. "Unit Terms in Coordinate Indexing." *Amer. Documentation,* Vol. 3, No. 4, pp. 213-218 (Oct. 1952).

Taube, and Wachtel. "The Logical Structure of Coordinate Indexing." *Amer. Documentation,* Vol. 4, No. 2, pp. 67-68 (April 1953).

Francis Bello. "The Information Theory." *Fortune,* Dec. 1953, pp. 48, 136-141, 149-158.

C. S. Wise and J. W. Perry. "Multiple Coding and the Rapid Selector." *Amer. Documentation,* Vol. 1, No. 2, pp. 76-83 (April 1950).

J. W. Perry. "Information Analysis for Machine Searching." *Amer. Documentation,* Vol. 1, No. 3, pp. 133-139 (Aug.. 1950).

Calvin N. Mooers. "Coding, Information Retrieval, and the Rapid Selector." *Amer. Documentation,* Vol. 1, No. 4, pp. 225-229 (Oct. 1950).

Calvin N. Mooers. "Zatocoding Applied to Mechanical Organization of Knowledge." *Amer. Documentation,* Vol. 2, No. 1, pp. 20-32 (Jan. 1951).

Brian C. Vickery. "Some Comments on Mechanical Selection." *Amer. Documentation,* Vol. 2, No. 2, pp. 102-107 (April 1951).

J. H. Shera. "Effect of Machine Methods on the Organization of Knowledge." *Amer. Documentation*, Vol. 3, No. 1, pp. 15-20, (Jan. 1952).

Carl S. Wise. "Multiple Word Coding vs. Random Coding for the Rapid Selector." *Amer. Documentation*, Vol. 3, No. 4, pp. 223-225 (Oct. 1952).

J. W. Perry. "Specialized Machines of the Future for Handling Broad Ranges of Subject Matter." *Amer. Documentation*, Vol. 4, No. 1, pp. 22-26 (Jan. 1953).

Yehoshua Bar-Hillel. "The Present State of Research on Mechanical Translation." *Amer. Documentation*, Vol. 2, No. 4, pp. 229-237 (Oct. 1951).

* J. W. Perry, Allen Kent, and Madeline M. Berry. "Machine Literature Searching: I, A General Approach. II, Problems in Indexing for Machine Searching." *Amer. Documentation*, Vol. 5, No. 1, pp. 18-25 (Jan. 1954).

* Allen Kent, Madeline M. Berry, and J. W. Berry. "Machine Literature Searching: III, Making Indexes Amenable to Machine Searching. IV, Collection of Terminology." *Amer. Documentation*, Vol. 5, No. 2, pp. 92-100 (April 1954).

* Allen Kent, J. W. Perry, and Madeline M. Berry. "Machine Literature Searching: V, Definition and Systematization of Terminology for Code Development." *Amer. Documentation*, Vol. 5, No. 3, pp. 166-173 (Aug. 1954).

* J. W. Perry, Madeline M. Berry. "Machine Literature Searching: VI, Class Definition and Code Construction." *Amer. Documentation*, Vol. 5, No. 4, pp. 238-244 (Oct. 1954).

* Fred U. Luehrs, Allen Kent, J. W. Perry, and Madeline M. Berry. "Machine Literature Searching: VII, Machine Functions and Organization of Semantic Units." *Amer. Documentation*, Vol. 6, No. 1, pp. 33-39 (Jan. 1955).

* Allen Kent, Madeline M. Berry, Fred U. Luehrs, and J. W. Perry. "Machine Literature Searching: VIII, Operational Criteria for Designing Information Retrieval Systems." *Amer. Documentation*, Vol. 6, No. 2, pp. 93-101 (April 1955).

* J. W. Perry, Allen Kent, and M. M. Berry. "Machine Literature Searching: IX, Operational Functions of Automatic Equipment." *Amer. Documentation*, Vol. 6, No. 3, pp. 166-174 (1955).

* J. W. Perry, Allen Kent, and M. M. Berry. "Machine Literature Searching: X, Machine Language; Factors Underlying its Design and Development." *Amer. Documentation*, Vol. 6, pp. 242-254 (1955).

J. Heston Heald. "The Reports Librarian and National Security." *Amer. Documentation*, Vol. 3, No.3, pp. 138-143 (Aug. 1952).

Earle V. Lee. "New Developments in Distribution and Dissemination." *Amer. Documentation*, Vol. 3, No. 3, pp. 176-181 (Aug. 1952).

---

* Also published with additional material in one volume by Interscience Publishers Inc., New York, 1956.

"Restricted Dissemination of Information and Its Social Implications."
  Amer. Documentation, Vol. 4, No. 3, pp. 115-122 (Aug. 1953).
Ford W. Bowers. "Identification of Microcards Containing Classified Material." *Amer. Documentation*, Vol. 5, No. 1, p. 29 (Jan. 1954).
W. N. Locke and A. D. Booth. *Machine Translation of Language*. John Wiley and Sons, New York, 1955.
Working papers from the Conference on the Practical Utilization of Recorded Knowledge—Present and Future, held at Western Reserve University School of Library Science, Jan. 16-18, 1956.
  Pre-conference Paper No. 1. "A System of Documentation Terminology."
  Pre-conference Paper No. 2. "Report of the Committee on Cooperative Information Processing."
  Pre-conference Paper No. 3. "Report of the Committee on the Research and Decision Making Process."
  Pre-conference Paper No. 4. "Report of the Committee on the Present Status of Education Programs for the Training of Librarians, Documentalists, and Information Specialists."
  Pre-conference Paper No. 5. "Report of the Committee on the Characteristics of Recorded Information."
  Pre-conference Paper No. 6. "Report of the Committee on the Inventory of Methods and Devices for Analysis, Storage, and Retrieval."
  Pre-conference Paper No. 7. "Report of the Committee on Ways and Means in which Research Workers, Executives, and Others Use Information."

STORAGE

The problem of storage is inherent in any record retention program. It exerts an important influence on all aspects of the program: which items shall be documented; which shall be stored for future reference, and which destroyed; which shall be kept in active storage, and which in inactive storage; the length of period of retention; the manner of preservation; and the actual cost of storage. (See "Record Storage" in Chapter II.)

Once a document has been acted upon, it must be either destroyed after review or preserved and stored for future reference.

STORING ORIGINAL DOCUMENTS

According to the National Records Management Council, Inc., of New York, to maintain an ordinary letter-size file cabinet in an average business office, for example, costs about $29 per year. A typical cost for floor space in such an office is $8 per square foot per year; since the average cabinet occupies about 2 square feet while closed, $15 of the $29 cost can be assigned to rent alone. For purposes of rough calculation, we may assume that the operating cost of a stored file cabinet in active storage is about equal to twice the rental cost of the space it occupies.

The National Records Management Council, Inc., of New York, has prepared these figures on the cost of maintaining a single letter-size file cabinet for a year:

	Active storage	Inactive storage
Total cost per cabinet	$29.00	$3.00
Rental space per cabinet	15.00	2.15
Rental space per square foot	8.00	1.00

All physical materials deteriorate with age. An original document, for example, can best be preserved if it is stored:

(1) free from harmful light (to retard fading);

(2) in an inert atmosphere (to retard chemical change);

(3) in a controlled atmosphere with constant humidity and constant temperature (to avoid dimensional changes with their attendant stresses and strains in the record material);

(4) sealed against foreign matter and material (to avoid contamination);

(5) protected against handling (to avoid physical damage).

In round figures, it may be said that it costs roughly 10 times as much to have an original document accessible (in active storage) as it does to store it in inaccessible fashion (in inactive storage). Because live storage costs are so high compared with inactive storage costs, many businesses make it a practice to clear out their files once a year to limit the active files to a single current year.

The importance of the costs of storage space and the implications of such costs in terms of facilities should not be underestimated, especially in areas where land values and construction costs are high, as they are in centrally located sections of large cities. If, for example, such storage space costs $8 per square foot per year, and microfilming is employed with a space reduction factor of 10, the equivalent unit storage cost drops to 80¢ per square foot per year. If we can, through a very high level of engineering and management skill, reduce the space cost by utilizing the high space reduction factor of 100, the equivalent unit cost drops to only 8¢. In all cases, a very important criterion of the effectiveness of the installation is the accessibility of the desired documents to the users. An effective library or record center with a large space reduction factor, for example, will probably have a wide variety of high-quality reading and reproducing instruments for use with its microrecords as well as excellent machine searching equipment for locating the documents of interest at a moment's notice.

The need for standard storage recommendations has just been recognized within Committee PH5 of American Standards Association in Proposed American Standard Practice for Storage of Film (First Draft Dated December 2, 1954). It is reproduced here in full because of its importance.

American Standards Association, subcommittee PH 5-1

First Draft Dated December 2, 1954

Proposed American Standard

PRACTICE FOR STORAGE OF MICROFILM

1. Scope

1.1 The recommendations contained in this standard refer to the storage of exposed and processed microfilms containing microphotographs, in roll, strip, sheet or card form, regardless of size.

2. Definitions

2.1 Microfilm. Microfilm, for purposes of this standard, shall be of the type as defined in Section 2.1 of the American Standard Practice for 16 and 35mm Microfilms, Z38.7.8-1947, or the latest revision thereof approved by the American Standards Association, Inc.

2.2 Microphotographs. A microphotograph, for purposes of this standard, shall be as defined in Section 2.2 of American Standard Practice for 16 and 35mm microfilms, Z38.7.8-1947, or the latest revision thereof approved by the American Standards Association.

2.3 Materials. Film base or stock for microfilm shall be of the type defined in American Standard Definition of Safety Photographic Film, Z38.3.1-1943, or the latest revision thereof approved by the American Standards Association, Inc. Microfilm having a combustible base, such as cellulose nitrate, is not considered in the recommendations of this standard. Exposed and processed microfilm shall be of the type defined in American Standard Specifications for Films for Permanent Records, Z38.3.2-1945, or the latest revision thereof approved by the American Standards Association, Inc.

2.4 Type of Storage

2.4.1 Commercial Permanence. The term Commercial Permanence shall be applied to storage of microfilm the preservation of which does not have to extend beyond a period sufficient for general business purposes. As an example, and not by way of limitation, such a period might cover a span of up to 25 years.

2.4.2 Archival Permanence. The term Archival Permanence shall be applied to storage of microfilm the preservation of which is to be carried to the maximum period obtainable.

2.4.3 Fire Protective Storage. Reference is made to Section 3.4 of this standard.

3. General

3.1 Humidity during Storage. Optimum relative humidity of the air in contact with stored microfilm is between 40% and 50% RH. Humidity essentially above the optimum has a deleterious effect to a greater extent than humidity ranging below the optimum. Exposure to conditions above 60% RH will tend to destroy the gelatine of the microfilm, due to formation of mold, and will eventually cause buckling of the film base. Consistent exposure to humidity below 25% RH will tend to produce brittleness of the film base.

3.2 Temperature during Storage. Optimum temperature for storage of microfilm is in the range between 60F and 80F. Consistent temperatures above 95F will eventually reduce the pliability of the film base, and temperatures substantially below 32F will result in brittleness of the film base as well as of the emulsion layer. The most important aspect of temperature is its effect on relative humidity causing conditions beyond the range stipulated in Section 3.1 of this standard. Storage temperatures below the dewpoint of the air in rooms serving the handling of microfilm, involve problems of condensation of moisture upon removal of the film from its storage container.

3.3 Air-borne Impurities. Dust and other air-borne, solid particles, when deposited on microfilm, interfere with legibility, and reactive types of dust will cause fading or staining of the emulsion layer. Gaseous impurities consisting of sulphurous and other active compounds, tend to react with the silver contained in microfilm emulsions. This standard contains recommendations for protection against solid and gaseous impurities.

3.4 Fire Protection. Effective protection of microfilm against the hazards of fire does not only involve measures to prevent exposure to high temperatures as well as to fire-fighting liquids and vapors but also calls for protection against contact with steam at temperatures exceeding about 200F. Tests indicate that microfilm, when stored at 50% RH, will not be distorted when subjected to dry heat of 250F, for a period of six hours; at 300F dry heat, there will be some warpage but individual frames or images can still be printed, while at 350F dry heat the distortion will generally make reproduction by printing impossible. However, in the presence of steam, temperatures of 200 to 225F will produce severe distortion, cause adhesion between convolutions of layers of film and, under prolonged exposure or upon condensation of steam effect melting of the emulsion. Where fire protection is a specific storage requirement, all storage elements shall be chosen for protection against excessive temperature as well as against the presence of steam.

4. Reels

4.1 Microfilm in roll form shall be wound on reels of the type specified in American Standard Dimensions for Reels for Processed 16 and 35mm Microfilm, Z38.7.17-1946, or the latest revision thereof approved by the American Standards Association, Inc. The material used for the reels shall be non-corrosive such as plastic compounds or non-ferrous metals. Steel, if used, must be well protected by lacquer, tinning or other corrosion-resistant finish, but steel reels are not recommended for archival storage. Materials used for reels, or for the protection of steel reels, shall not develop reactive gases when subjected to temperatures of up to 350F. Rubber bands, for confining microfilm on reels, are not recommended, but, if used, shall consist of sulphur-free compounds.

5. Storage Containers

5.1 Classification. Containers used to hold individual rolls, strips, sheets or cards, are classified as open type, closed type, sealed type and fire-protective containers.

5.2 Open Containers. Envelopes of paper, glassine or plastic foil, folding and other cartons, and file folders if used for film strips in jackets and for frames in card apertures, shall be considered open containers giving free access to ambient air. When in direct contact with the surface of microfilm, the material used for envelopes, jackets, folders and cartons, and also the adhesive used for seams and joints, shall be subject to the Specifications of American Standard for Photographic Filing Envelopes for Storing Processed Photographic Films, Plates and Papers, Z38.8.21-1950, or the latest revision thereof approved by the American Standards Association, Inc.

5.3 Closed Containers. Cans of round or other shape with telescoping or slip-type lids, shall be classified as closed containers, and the material used shall consist of steel well protected by tinning, and preferably lacquer coating, non-corrosive metals or plastic compounds. Closed containers are not considered air-tight and give limited access to ambient air.

5.4 Sealed Containers. Requirements for sealed containers are met by closed containers of round shape, fabricated from impermeable materials, with friction-type lids. Telescoping lids can be used but the joint shall be sealed by two wraps of pressure-sensitive adhesive tape having low permeability. If tape is used, bi-annual retaping of joints is recommended. Other types of seals such as screwed and gasketed covers, or low temperature-type soldering can be used but these methods involve factors of high cost and interefere with ready removal of film. Sealed containers are considered air-tight.

5.5 Fire Protective Containers. Sealed containers are suitable for fire protective storage if they are fabricated from a material which will not be affected, ignited or distorted by temperatures up to 350F, and if they are provided with friction lids, or with telescoping lids sealed by two wraps of pressure-sensitive adhesive tape of a type which has low permeability and will maintain the seal under temperatures up to 350F (such as silicon-type tape). If tape is used, bi-annual retaping of joints is recommended.

6. Storage Housing

6.1 General Type. All microfilm, regardless of the type of container used, should always be stored in separate cabinets, preferably drawer-type cabinets, constructed of steel or other non-combustible material.

6.2 Fire Protective Housing. Fire-resistive safe cabinets rated by the Safe Manufacturers National Association for one hour, two hour or four hour exposure will, for the period of their ratings, maintain an internal temperature of 350F or below. As indicated in Section 2.4.3 of this standard, a temperature of 350F dry heat will seriously distort microfilm records but will not destroy them. For complete preservation of stored microfilm, fire-resistive safe cabinets or housings equipped with equivalent insulation, preferably applied to the exterior of the casing, shall be placed as recommended in Section 7.3 of this standard.

7. Storage Rooms

7.1 Microfilm of Commercial Permanence. A separate storage rom for microfilm of commercial permanence will generally not be required, provided conditions as recommended in Section 8 of this standard are maintained.

7.2 Microfilm of Archival Permanence. The value of microfilm kept for archival purposes makes it advisable to provide a separate storage room, preferably in the form of a vault.

7.3 Fire Protection. For full protection against exposure to fire and associated hazards, safe cabinets of the fire-resistive or insulated type as recommended in Section 6.2 of this standard, shall be placed within fire-resistive vaults constructed in accordance with applicable recommendations of the National Board of Fire Underwriters.

7.4 General Requirements. Rooms and areas used for storage of microfilm should contain provisions for inspection and viewing of the film, such as space and handling facilities. Good housekeeping is essential.

8. Conditions of Air

8.1 Limits of Humidity and Temperature.

   8.1.1 *Microfilm of Commercial Permanence.* Humidity shall not, for extended periods of time, exceed a maximum of 60% RH and a minimum of 25% RH. Temperature shall not, for extended periods of time, exceed a maximum of 95F and a minimum. of 35F.

   8.1.2 *Microfilm of Archival Permanence.* Humidity shall at all times be maintained between 40% and 50% RH, and temperature shall be maintained in the range between 60F and 80F.

8.2 Methods of Air Conditioning.

8.2.1 *Microfilm of Commercial Permanence.* The limiting conditions recommended in Section 8.1.1 of this standard may be maintained either within individual storage housings or within the storage room.

Conditions within individual housings may be maintained by means of commercial air conditioning units or by connections to a supply of properly conditioned air. Provided temperature is held between 50F and 90F, suitable conditions of humidity within a cabinet may be obtained by the use of open containers holding a saturated aqueous solution of a compound, as well as an excess of such compounds so constituted that equilibrium is kept with the humidity of ambient air. Containers shall be located such as to prevent contamination of stored film, as by spillage. Individually conditioned housings shall be arranged to permit interior circulation of air, and joints of doors and drawers should be reasonably air-tight.

For conditions within storage rooms, commercial (comfort) air conditioning if maintained within recommended limits, shall be considered satisfactory but provisions shall be made for humidification of the air during heating periods.

8.2.2 *Microfilm of Archival Permanence.* Conditions of humidity and temperature as specified in Section 8.1.2 of this standard, shall be maintained within the storage room or vault, by means of an independent air conditioning system.

8.2.3 *Fire Protection.* Air conditioning installations for fire-resistive vaults, and particularly self-closing fire control dampers in ducts carrying air to or from the storage vault, shall be constructed in accordance with recommendations contained in National Board of Fire Underwriters' pamphlet No. 90 ''Standards of the National Board of Fire Underwriters for the Installation of Air Conditioning, Warm Air Heating, Air Cooling and Ventilating Systems.''

8.2.4 *Sealed Container Storage.* Microfilm to be stored in sealed containers as defined in Sections 5.4 and 5.5 of this standard, shall be preconditioned for a period of not less than 24 hours, by holding the film under conditions of humidity and temperature specified in Section 8.1.1 of this standard for commercial permanence or Section 8.1.2 for archival permanence. During the preconditioning period, film shall be kept open or in open containers as defined in Section 5.2 of this standard. Preconditioning is also required whenever the film is removed and replaced in sealed containers.

For microfilmed records of commercial permanence, the limits of humidity specified in 8.1.1. of this standard need not be held in the space surrounding the sealed containers. However, temperatures in the storage space or housing should be maintained within a range which does not permit the air within the sealed containers to exceed the humidity limits specified in Section 8.1.1 of this standard.

8.3 Control of Air Conditioning. Mechanical air conditioning systems, when used, should be equipped with adequate automatic controls capable of main-

taining conditions of humidity and temperature as recommended in Section 8.1 of this standard. Chemical means for purposes of humidity control shall be maintained in proper condition by periodic disposal of surplus water absorbed from the air, as well as replacement of evaporated water and of the compound employed.

8.4   Protection Against Air-borne Impurities.

8.4.1   *Air-borne Solids.* Air supplied to storage housings or storage rooms containing microfilm, shall be cleaned by means of filters adequate to retain at least 90% of the dust and other air-borne solids contained in the outside air.

8.4.2   *Baseous Impurities.* While chemical means of removal for gaseous impurities are possible they are not recommended due to complex apparatus and maintenance involved and due to the hazards of operating failure. Where gaseous impurities are present to a substantial degree, protection shall be provided by storage of microfilm in sealed containers as per Section 5.4 or 5.5 of this standard.

9. Condensed Storage Recommendations

See page 333.

Bibliography

Storage of Microfilms, Sheet Films, and Prints, Eastman Kodak Company, 1946.

"The Effect of Heat and Steam on Processed Microfilm," Eastman Kodak Report MF-207, February, 1954.

International Critical Tables, Section "Laboratory Methods for Maintaining Constant Humidity."

"Protection of Microfilm Records against Loss by Fire," *Burning Facts*, Safe Manufacturers National Association, Vol. 1, No. 9, 1951.

National Board of Fire Underwriters' pamphlet No. 90, "Standards of the National Board of Fire Underwriters for the Installation of Air Conditioning, Warm Air Heating, Air Cooling and Ventilating Systems."

"Summary Report of Research at the National Bureau of Standards on the Stability and Preservation of Records on Photographic Film," *NBS Miscellaneous Publication* M162, May 1939.

9. Condensed Storage Recommendations

All reference numerals pertain to sections of this standard

	Type of storage	Special provisions	Storage containers	Storage housings	Storage rooms	Conditions of air	Remarks
9.1	Commercial permanence	Without specific fire protection	5.2 or 5.3	6.1	7.1, 7.4	8.1.1, 8.2.1, 8.3, 8.4.1	
9.2	Commercial permanence	With specific fire protection	5.5	6.2	7.3, 7.4	8.1.1, 8.2.1, 8.2.3, 8.2.4, 8.3, 8.4.1	
9.3	Commercial permanence	Storage in sealed containers	5.4 or 5.5	6.1 or 6.2	7.1 or 7.3, 7.4	8.2.4	
9.4	Archival permanence	Without specific fire protection	5.2 or 5.3	6.1	7.2, 7.4	8.1.2, 8.2.2, 8.3, 8.4.1	
9.5	Archival permanence	With specific fire protection	5.5	6.2	7.3, 7.4	8.1.2, 8.2.2, 8.2.3, 8.2.4, 8.3, 8.4.1	
9.6	Commercial or archival permanence	Protection against air-borne, gaseous impurities	5.4 or 5.5	To be selected in accordance with requirements of applicable Sections 9.1, 9.2, 9.3, 9.4 or 9.5.		9.1, 9.2, 9.3, 9.4 or 9.5.	All microfilm in sealed containers shall be preconditioned as per Sec. 8.2.4.

PRESERVATION

Webster defines preservation as "the act or process of preserving or keeping from injury and decay." Since preservation of the original document for long periods of time is quite costly and frequently not desired and since if so preserved, the original would not be accessible for use, the solution to the problem is to preserve the subject matter of the document by the use of a photographic facsimile. To reduce storage and maintenance costs this is done in microrecorded form. Since the making of copies from all or part of a microfilm facsimile original negative always results in physical damage, due to handling, to the negative so used, a separate microfilm original facsimile negative must be made if archival storage is an important requirement of the specific preservation problem. The use of but a single microfilm facsimile original negative for both purposes constitutes a risk, often an uncalculated risk of large magnitude, that may or may not be justified by the additional cost of making the extra microfilm negative for archival storage and the cost of that storage.

The permanence of silver images of a microfilm negative and the like can be predicted; ASA PH4.12-1954 describes the American Standard Method for Indicating the Stability of the Images of Processed Black-and-White Films, Plates, and Papers.* The basic method involves accelerated testing, a procedure very common in the evaluation of the probable performance of materials.

STAGES OF STORAGE

Storage is related very closely to the accessibility of the document and its subject matter. For convenience in analysis, storage may be divided into three stages:

Stage 1. The first-generation original facsimile microrecord is kept in *inactive* (dead) storage. Such storage shall be under the most suitable physical conditions that the installation can afford. Material stored in stage 1 storage should be inspected periodically to ascertain that its objectives are being realized, and to correct any inadequacies discovered.

---

* Since its criteria and methods are often the subject of almost wild conjecture in nontechnical circles, it is reproduced in its entirety in Appendix G, pages 423 to 426.

Stage 2. The preprint microrecord, preferably a first-generation original facsimile, the microfilm from which end-use copies are directly made, is in *active* (live) storage under the most practicable physical conditions—preferably in an air-conditioned space with normal space with normal room temperatures and humidities such as was described on page 326. Such storage should assure ready availability of preprint films for the making of end-use copies.

In the event of loss or damage to the preprint microrecord, an intermediate copy may be made as a replacement master copy; this would be photographically printed from the preserved facsimile original that would be temporarily withdrawn from stage 1 storage for the purpose. Immediately after the replacement master copy is made, the preserved facsimile original would be promptly returned to stage 1 storage; in the process of making such master copy, every precaution practicable would be taken to reduce to an absolute minimum the physical damage done to the preserved facsimile original in such use.

It should be anticipated that end-use copies made from the replacement master copy are rarely capable of providing as good quality in end-use copies as those made from the first-generation facsimile original previously used. At least one and more often two generations of copies are added between the original facsimile and the end-use copy. Owing to the large magnitude of the quality losses in the copying process, best quality in end-use copies is obtained when the number of print generations between original facsimile and end-use copy is kept to a minimum; in practice, this means two generations only, the original and the end-use copy made directly from that original.

Stage 3. When made in anticipation of a user's requirements, end-use copies shall be available for immediate use, yet stored under the best practicable day-to-day conditions of constancy of temperature and humidity that the installation can afford. This requirement is ordinarily satisfied when such copies are stored in an air-conditioned office.

STORAGE OF RAW FILM

It is definitely unreasonable to expect two rolls of the same emulsion lot of film to show similar characteristics if one has been

stored for a long period near a heated radiator or steam pipe and
the other under more normal conditions. The temperature of a
microfilm storage place for raw film should not exceed 70°F.
Under such conditions most microfilm may be stored as long as a
year and even longer from the date of manufacture to the date of
exposure and development if this simple precaution is observed.
To assure that roll-to-roll variations in a particular emulsion are
quite small, special pains are taken by film manufacturers in storing
raw film to *assure* that the variations due to differences in storage
temperature and storage time will be kept to a minimum. It is
reasonable to expect that, after raw film has left the manufacturer's
custody and is in the hands of the user, full advantage will be taken
of whatever storage facilities are available to assure the minimum of
deterioration due to storage. Performance degradation due to improper storage results in fog, loss of image detail and clarity, and
also of loss of sensitivity. These factors may be measured by sensitometry, the analysis by suitable numerical measurements of the
properties of photographic materials.

MICRORECORD STORAGE

Microrecords are stored in protective cans or envelopes. American Standard ASA Z38.8.21-1950 describes the American Standard
Requirements for Photographic Filing Envelopes for Storing Processed Photographic Films, Plates, and Papers.* If microrecords are
carefully stored, it is obvious that the facsimile original is not so
accessible as the original documents would be in live storage. A
study of the formats with which microfilms are recorded will give
a clue to the loss of accessibility to be expected in practice.

Accessibility also implies the ability to locate the desired document at the desired time with a minimum of elapsed time for document searching and presentation, and at a minimum cost for locating
and presenting it to the user. In practice, the desired document or
portion of a document is represented by a single small photographic
image which cannot be read with the naked eye, located at a small
specific point crosswise and at a small specific point lengthwise
among many documents similarly recorded on the same film roll,
strip, or frame. The microrecord containing the desired image may

---

* Reproduced in Appendix G, pages 427 and 428.

be housed in file cabinets or shelving, classified according to the needs of the user. A well-organized system of cataloging the recorded documents is at least as important as when the original documents themselves are stored for reference. To make microrecording practical, the cataloging system will take into account the physical limitations of the forms of microrecords actually used as well as their subject matter.

PROTECTION OF RECORDS AGAINST
DISASTER AND WAR DAMAGE

Fire, flood, explosion, theft, sabotage, and war—all can result in the destruction of records. Any or all of them can cause complete or partial cessation of operations. Reconstruction of operation can be expedited if initial planning includes protection, duplication, and dispersal of records. Protection of records against fire, flood, and theft requires limited duplication and dispersal of records in fire- and flood-resistive vaults. Protection against bombing, of course, requires a more extensive dispersal and protection plan. (See Chapter II for a detailed discussion of the problem.)

Bibliography

"Storage of Microfilms, Sheet Films, and Prints," Eastman Kodak Co., Rochester, N. Y., 1946.
William O. Offenhauser, Jr., 16mm Sound Motion Pictures, Interscience, New York-London, 1949, Chapter XI, "Preservation and Recording," pp. 355-363.

APPENDIX

APPENDIX A

*Recommendations for Retention of Records by Departments**

ACCOUNTING, AUDITING, EXECUTIVE, AND ADMINISTRATIVE DEPARTMENTS

Permanent retention

Annual reports	Contracts and agreements	Inventory records
Appraisals		Investment records
Assets and property records	Consolidated balance sheets	Leases
Audit reports	Constitution and by-laws	Letters of credit
Authorizations and appropriations for expenditure	Control ledgers	Licenses
	Corporate records	Minutes of meetings
Bank statements and reconciliation	Correspondence, executive	Mortgages
		Real estate acquisitions
Bond and bondholders' records	Cost sheets	Property records
	Deeds	Research data
Building plans and specifications	Destruction records	Royalty records
	Dividend checks	Safe deposit vault records
Capital stock ledgers	Drafts paid	
Capital stock certificates	Easements	Signatures
Certificates of incorporation	Financial statements	Statistical reports
	Franchises	Stock and stockholders' records
Charter	General code and cipher books	
Check books		Stock transfer records
Checks, cancelled, and stop payment notices	General books of account (journals and ledgers)	Stop payment orders
		Tax records
Claim files	House organs	Trial balances
		Water rights

7 years

Accounts receivable	Manifests	
Accounts payable	Miscellaneous reports	
Charge sales slips	Notes, cancelled	
Consular invoices	Notes, receivable	
Correspondence, general	Priority records	
Credit tickets	Tabulating cards	
Departmental reports	Vouchers	
Deposit books and slips		

3 years

Requisitions on stores or for purchases

2 years

Petty cash records
Proxies

7 years after expiration

Insurance policies
Insurance schedules

3 years after expiration

Bonds, surety
Fidelity bonds

* From ''Business Records Classification and Retention Recommendations,'' Diebold, Inc., Canton 2, Ohio.

341

Until expiration	4 years after duration	Optional
Options	Contracts, war	Cancelled stock certificates
		Retired securities

ADVERTISING DEPARTMENT

Permanent retention	7 years	Optional
Correspondence, executive	Contracts with agencies, engravers, lithographers, and printers	Department form proofs
Market investigations		Dummies and layouts
Publication file	Correspondence, general	Inquiries record
	Mailings record	Inventory of advertising material
	Orders for advertising	Manuscripts
	Production, progress, and job records	Newspaper clippings
	Requisitions for advertising	Photographs and photostats
		Sketches
		Testimonial letters

COST DEPARTMENT / CREDIT AND COLLECTION DEPARTMENT

Permanent retention	7 years	
Cost production and job summary records	Application for credit	Collection file
	Credit authorization records	Time payment contracts and promissory notes
7 years		
Labor distribution records	Credit files—commercial reports, financial statements, letters of reference, etc.	
Time and earning records		

ENGINEERING AND RESEARCH DEPARTMENT

	Permanent retention	
Analysis and compound records	Formulas	Plant inventory and machine location records
Blue prints, drawings, sketches, tracings, index cards, charts, and graphs	Laboratory production records	Plant layout charts
	Machine and product production records	Production, progress, and job records
Die and tool records	Maps	Research data file
Experiment and test records	Operating reports	Specification sheets
Flow or work and material charts	Order procedures	Templates
	Patterns	Time cards and reports
	Planning summaries	Work or shop orders

7 years
Uncollectible accounts

ESTIMATING AND PRICING	LEGAL DEPARTMENT	
7 years	Permanent retention	
Correspondence	Case files, affidavits, tes-	Patents and applications
Estimates	timony, depositions,	for tax files, returns,
Price records	etc.	briefs, appeals
Quotations	Claims, evidences, and	Trade marks and appli-
Specifications	proofs	cations for
	Copyrights and applica-	Titles and mortgages,
	tions for dockets	deeds
	Information file, briefs,	
	etc.	

MAILING DEPARTMENT

3 years	
Parcel post insurance receipts	Registered letter receipts

ORDER DEPARTMENT

	3 years	
Acknowledgments of orders	Orders, filled	Returned goods record
Inspection records	Orders, unfilled	Shipping notices and reports
Notices of orders billed	Order register	
	Order replacement record	

ORGANIZATION STUDIES

Permanent retention		7 years
Payroll records	War bond delivery receipts	Personnel records
Pension plan records		Reference letters
Payroll receipts	Workmen's compensation reports	Time and motion studies
Social security records		Time records
Retirement records	Receipted pay checks	Unclaimed wage record
State wage reports	Receipted time tickets	
Unemployment insurance reports	Discharge tickets	Optional
	Any evidence of payment for service	War bond pledges

PERSONNEL DEPARTMENT

Permanent retention	7 years	3 years
Accident records	Employee case histories	Assignment and garnishee records
Employee savings fund records	Employee contracts	
Federal wage records	Employment releases	**Optional**
Group insurance records	Fingerprint records	Minors' salary releases
Invention assignment forms	Hospital plan records	

PURCHASING DEPARTMENT

Permanent retention	3 years	
Contracts with suppliers	Acknowledgment of orders	Quotations
Invoices	Correspondence	Requisitions, purchase
Price list files	Printed forms inventory	Source of supply and catalog files
	Priority requisitions	Specifications
	Purchase and cost records	Summary of purchases
	Purchase orders, filled and unfilled	Vendors' record

SALES DEPARTMENT

Permanent retention	7 years	2 years
Confidential contracts	Charts and graphs	Closed accounts
Contracts with representatives, agents, distributors, etc.	Contracts with customers	**Optional**
	Correspondence	Applications for sales
	Expense accounts	Employment bulletins
	Filled contracts	
	Mailing lists	
	Market investigations and reports	
	Postwar plans	
	Prospect records	
	Sales records and summaries	
	Sales territory layouts, maps, etc.	
	Salesmen's reports	
	Special orders	
	Turnover comparisons	
	Users' records	

	SERVICE DEPARTMENT		STORES DEPARTMENT

3 years	Permanent retention	3 years
Complaints and service record	Stock record	Receiving reports
Correspondence		Requisitions
Returned goods and replacements record		Tool record

TRAFFIC DEPARTMENT

7 years	3 years	Optional
- Claims	Delivery receipts	Bills of lading—straight
Correspondence	Export declarations	and order
	Express receipts	
	Freight bills	
	Inspection reports	
	Packing lists	
	Rate records	
	Receiving reports	
	Routing reports	
	Shipping instructions	
	Shipping reports	
	Weigh bills	

Title 32—National Defense *

CHAPTER XX—OFFICE OF CONTRACT SETTLEMENT, GENERAL SERVICES ADMINISTRATION

[Regulation 11, Rev. Mar. 4, 1953]

Part 2011—Preservation of Records

Authorization to war contractors under certain conditions to destroy contract records

Pursuant to section 443 of the act of June 25, 1948 (62 Stat. 705; 18 U. S. C. 443) the following policies, principles, methods, procedures, and standards are prescribed to govern the destruction of records of war contractors which are governed by such act.

---

* From *Federal Register*, March 7, 1953.

Authority: §§ 2011.1 to 2011.12 issued under sec. 1, 62 Stat. 705, as amended; 18 U. S. C. 443.

§ 2011.1 *Scope of regulation.* (a) This regulation applies to:

(1) Any records of a war contractor relating to the negotiation, award, performance, payment, interim financing, cancellation or other termination, or settlement of a war contract of $25,000 or more,

(2) Any records of a war contractor and any purchaser relating to any disposition of termination inventory in which the consideration received by any war contractor or any Government agency is $5,000 or more, and

(3) Any records of a war contractor which by the war contract are required on termination to be preserved or made available.

(b) The term "war contract" which is defined in the Contract Settlement Act of 1944 as meaning either a prime contract or subcontract, has the same meaning herein. It is not limited to terminated contracts, but, except where otherwise limited by the context, also includes continuing or completed contracts.

(c) As used herein, the term "records" includes, but is not limited to, books, ledgers, checks and check stubs, payroll data, vouchers, memoranda, correspondence, inspection reports, and certificates, and cost data where involved in final payment or settlement of the contract.

§ 2011.2 *Responsibility of the war contractor.* (a) Pursuant to section 443 of the act of June 25, 1948, the war contractor shall preserve for the period of time stated below records essential to determining the performance under the war contract and to justifying the settlement thereof; any determination that certain records are not essential and need not be retained is made at the contractor's risk in accordance with the requirements of such act.

(b) Since the Contract Settlement Act defines "war contractor" as a holder of either a prime contract or a subcontract, the subcontractor has the same responsibility to preserve his individual contract records as does the prime contractor, and many dispose of such records in accordance with the provisions of this regulation without approval of the prime contractor unless required by the subcontract.

§ 2011.3 *Records not to be destroyed for stated period.* (a) Except as provided in § 2011.4, at the conclusion of the time period stated below, final disposition of the contract records which he is required to preserve is in the discretion of the war contractor and requires no authorization from the Office of Contract Settlement, or (unless required by the war contract) by the contracting agency:

(1) Five years after such disposition of termination inventory by such war contractor or Government agency, or

(2) Five years after the final payment or settlement of such war contract, or

(3) December 31, 1951,

whichever applicable period is longer, *Provided, however,* That where the termination inventory has been disposed of, or final payment or settlement of the war contract has been made on or after December 31, 1950, the above five-year period is reduced to three years.

(b) Nothing herein shall be construed:

(1) As affecting the requirements relating to records under any law other than the Contract Settlement Act of 1944, or

(2) As prohibiting the destruction of records, the destruction of which is not otherwise prohibited, or

(3) As authorizing the destruction of records where the contract is in litigation or under investigation, or

(4) As requiring the photographing of records of war contractors, or

(5) As affecting the requirements of the Comptroller General of the United States for preservation and submission of records, or

(6) As reducing the period of time for retention of records as provided for in any war contract as that term is defined in this regulation.

§ 2011.4 *Partial settlements, exclusions or exceptions.* (a) The period prescribed by § 2011.3 for retaining records commences:

(1) On the date the war contractor accepts the final payment or settlement offered by the agency which contracted with him, or

(2) Where the war contractor does not accept such payment or settlement, on the date when the period prescribed by law for appeal or other action contesting such payment or settlement expires, or

(3) Where an appeal or other action contesting such payment or settlement is filed, on the date of final determination of such appeal or other action.

(b) Where the settlement is not complete, or there are exclusions or exceptions to the settlement, the records of the parts or items which are settled are eligible for destruction at the end of the period prescribed in §2011.3 dating from such settlement, except that all records pertaining to such exclusion or exception must be retained for the prescribed period from its date of settlement.

§ 2011.5 *Duplicate copies.* Duplicate or extra copies of the contract records need not be retained.

§ 2011.6. *Authorization to destroy if photographs are retained.* Subject to the provisions of § 2011.1, any records to which this regulation applies and which can be reproduced through photography without loss of their primary usefulness may be destroyed, *Provided, however,* That clearly legible photographs thereof are made and preserved in accordance with the conditions and standards set forth herein. Any number of copies of the record may be

destroyed, provided one such photograph of the record is preserved. The terms
''photograph,'' ''photographing'' and ''photography'' include, but are not
limited to, ''microphotograph,'' ''microfilm,'' ''microphotographing'' and
''microphotography.''

§ 2011.7. *Features which photography would not clearly reflect.* If there
is any significant characteristic, feature, or other attribute of a record which
photography would not clearly reflect, as for example that the record is a copy,
or is an original, or that certain figures thereon are red, the record shall not
be destroyed unless prior to being photographed it is marked so that the
existence of such characteristic, feature, or other attribute is clearly reflected.
When a number of the records to be microfilmed have in common any such
characteristic, feature, or attribute, an appropriate notation identifying the
characteristic, feature, or attribute with the records to which it applies may be
placed at the beginning of the roll of film instead of on the individual records.

§ 2011.8. *Arrangement, classification and self-identification of records.* At
the time of photographing, the records shall be so arranged, classified and self-
identified as readily to permit the subsequent examination, location, identification and reproduction of the photographs thereof.

§ 2011.9 *Minimum standards for film and processing.* The minimum
standards for film and processing used in the production of photographs shall
be those set forth in the ''Standards for Temporary Record Photographic
Microcopying Film'' issued by the National Bureau of Standards under date
of October 25, 1943, and set forth below as Exhibit A.

§ 2011.10 *Certificate of authenticity.* The photographs shall have attached
thereto a certificate or certificates that the photographs are accurate and complete reproductions of the records submitted by the war contractor or purchaser and that they have been made in accordance with the standards and requirements set forth in this regulation. Such certificate or certificates shall be
executed by a person or persons having personal knowledge of the facts covered
thereby.

§ 2011.11 *Additional special requirements for microfilm.* In the case of
microphotographs, a microfilm of such certificate or certificates shall be photographed on each roll of film. The photographic matter on each roll shall com-
mence and end with a frame stating the nature and arrangement of the records
reproduced, the name of the photographer and the date. Rolls of film shall not
be cut. Supplemental or retaken film, whether of misplaced or omitted documents or of portions of a film found to be spoiled or illegible or of other matter,
shall be attached to the beginning of the roll, and in such event the certificate or certificates referred to in § 2011.10 shall cover also such supplemental
or retaken film and shall state the reasons for taking such film.

§ 2011.12. *Indexing and retention of photographs.* The photographs shall
be indexed and retained in such manner as will render them readily accessible
and identifiable and will reasonably insure their preservation against loss by
fire or other means of foreseeable destruction. They shall be retained for the
period of time during which, except for this regulation, the destruction of the
original records would have been prohibited.

Note: The record-keeping requirements contained herein have been approved by the Budget Bureau in accordance with the Federal Reports Act of 1942.

Initially issued January 24, 1945. Revised March 4, 1953.

RUSSELL FORBES,
Acting Administrator.

Exhibit A

Standard for Temporary Record Photographic Microcopying Film
(Gelatin-Silver Halide Emulsion Type)

The exposed and processed film shall be of such a type that no serious loss in the quality of the image shall result within five years after processing when the film is kept under ordinary storage conditions. All film shall be of 16mm or 35mm size either perforated or unperforated as specified.

Detailed Requirements

Film base. The film base shall be the slow burning cellulose-acetate type known as ''safety'' film. The thickness of the film base and emulsion shall be 0.0055 ± 0.0010 inch.

Emulsion. The emulsion or light sensitive coating shall be composed of silver-halide crystals of a size distribution entirely suitable for microcopying use, uniformly dispersed in a thin layer of high grade gelatin on one side of the film base. The white-light and spectral sensitivities shall be such that accurate and complete copies of the documents are obtained with the usual exposure and development technique.

Processing. The film shall be developed with the usual organic developing agents such as ''Metol,'' hydroquinone, glycin, etc., compounded to produce a silver image essentially black. Developers producing stained or colored images are not to be used. The films shall be fixed in the usual sodium thiosulphate fixing bath. Fixing baths containing ammonium thiosulphate shall not be used. No intensification or reduction of the developed image is permitted.

Hypo content of emulsion. The hypo (sodium thiosulphate) content of the processed film shall not exceed 0.02 mg per square inch of film. The hypo content shall be determined by the method of Crabtree and Ross in the Journal of the Society of Motion Picture Engineers, Vol. 14, p. 419 (1930).[1] One square inch of film ($1\frac{5}{8}''$ of 16mm film or $\frac{3}{4}''$ of 35mm film) is immersed in a shell vial $\frac{3}{4} \times 4''$ containing 10 ml of the following solutions:

Potassium bromide	25 grams.
Mercuric chloride	25 grams.
Water to make	1 liter.

After the sample has remained in the above solution for 15 minutes the turbidity is compared with that of three similar shell vials containing the above solution, one with no hypo, one with 0.02 mg, and one with 0.03 mg hypo (Na_2S_2O). The comparison is made in a darkened room using a mercury lamp for illumination. The shell vials should rest on a black surface, the light entering from one side of the vials. The criterion is that the turbidity of the tested solution should not exceed that of the one having 0.02 mg. of hypo.

----

[1] In this article (p. 426) the sensitivity of the mercuric chloride test is given as 0.05 mg of hypo without stating the volume of solution or area or length of film. This value is obviously for 1 foot of film since with ordinary care 0.005 mg per frame of 35mm film (1 square inch) is detectable.

Flexibility. Flexibility is determined by means of a Pfund folding endurance tester used as described by Weber and Hill, National Bureau of Standards Miscellaneous Publication M158, obtainable from the Superintendent of Documents, Government Printing Office, Washington, D. C., price 5 cents.

Processed film, conditioned at 65% relative humidity, shall stand at least 16 single folds in the Pfund tester (19mm between jaws) without breaking. Film aged 72 hours at 100° C. and conditioned at 65% relative humidity shall not lose more than 25% in folding endurance of the original sample.

Burning time test. A sample 16 inches long shall be cut from the 16mm or 35mm film to be tested All gelatin layers shall be removed by washing in warm water or treatment with an enzyme such as pancreatin. After drying for at least 24 hours, the sample shall be marked 2 inches from each end and perforated with holes approximately 0.12 inch in diameter along one edge at intervals of about 1¼ inches, if sample is not already perforated. A wire having a diameter of not more than 0.020 inch shall be threaded through the perforations on one side at points approximately 1¼ inches apart.

The wire holding the dried sample is stretched horizontally between two supports permitting the sample to hang vertically from it. The bottom corner of one end of the sample is ignited. The time which elapses from the moment the flame reaches the first mark until the flame reaches the second mark shall be recorded as the burning time. If the sample does not ignite or if it does not completely burn, the burning time is recorded as infinite. The test shall be made in a room free from draughts. At least three tests shall be made. The burning time shall not be less than 45 seconds.

NATIONAL BUREAU OF STANDARDS,
   October 25, 1943.
         [F. R. Doc. 53-2124; Filed, Mar. 6, 1953; 8:55 a. m.]

Protection of Business Records — *Supplemental Data*

LEGALITY OF MICROFILMED RECORDS

The principal reasons for duplicating records by microfilm or other means are to enable organizations to continue operations without unnecessary delay and to prevent large financial loss in case the originals are destroyed. In the vast majority of cases the duplicate records would be used, after any disaster, without the necessity to consider their possible use in court. A small percentage, however, may be needed in law suits and the legality of their reproductions must be considered.

Laws often seem technical and illogical. Nevertheless they are usually made in the interest of justice. The rules for presenting evidence in court, designed to prevent fraud, have undergone gradual changes since medieval times to keep abreast of changing conditions in human affairs.

Centuries ago, only primary evidence was allowed in lawsuits and the loss of an original document affecting property or contract rights could prove disastrous. Today secondary evidence may be introduced to prove the contents of an instrument that is not available.

---

* Reprinted by courtesy of the Commerce and Industry Association of New York, Inc., 99 Church St., New York 7, N. Y.

Primary Evidence

Original documents are considered the best or primary evidence. Books or entries therein, made in the regular course of business, have been admitted as primary evidence in 47 states. This has been expressly provided for in 30 states by statutes. There seems to be no statute or case in point in Nevada.

Before books or entries therein are admitted in evidence, a proper foundation must be laid. Each jurisdiction has its own requirements. Some statutes require proof when the original entrant is unavailable or absent from the jurisdiction. Others require only that entries were made in the regular course of business.

Most state courts have admitted or indicated that entries made in the regular course of business are admissible where the entries are verified by one who has been responsible, and do not require personal knowledge of the entries by the verifying witness.

By act of Congress (Federal Statute 28 U. S. C. A. Sec. 695) special authority was granted concerning records made in the regular course of business. This act encouraged the court in one leading case (U. S. v. Manton, 309 U. S. 664, page 844), to admit photographic facsimiles of checks as primary evidence.

Rules governing the procedure in the District Courts of the United States, in all suits of a civil nature, are covered by the Federal Rules of Civil Procedure (28 U. S. C. A. Sec. 723c). Rule 43a permits the admission of evidence under whichever one of the tests of admissibility is most favorable.

Secondary Evidence

When originally documents are lost, destroyed or otherwise unavailable, secondary evidence may be introduced to prove the contents, provided the original documents would have been competent as primary evidence. Secondary evidence, however, cannot be received without accounting for the original and is not admissible without proof that the original is lost, destroyed or otherwise beyond the power of the party to produce it.

Before secondary evidence is admitted the motive or cause of destruction or loss of the original documents is carefully examined. The secondary evidence will be admitted where there is no indication of fraud, but if the motive or cause of loss or destruction of the originals is not free from suspicion the secondary evidence will not be admitted.

Secondary evidence is now generally admissible to prove the contents of original records that have been destroyed in the ordinary course of business if the proponent removes, to the satisfaction of the court, any suspicion of fraud.

Photographic Evidence

For more than 70 years photographs have been presented to courts as evidence. In early cases the courts expressed grave doubts as to the accuracy of photographs due to distortions, but since then great progress has been made in photographic equipment and in the science of photography. Now, the courts no longer entertain doubts as to the accuracy of the photographs. In fact, the photographic reproductions of documents have an advantage in that they may be enlarged to help detect forgeries or alterations.

Generally, photographic or photostatic copies are regarded as secondary evidence. They are subject to the best evidence rule and the original records must be accounted for. When failure to produce the original documents has been explained and it has been shown that photographic copies are true and accurate reproductions the courts have admitted them as secondary evidence.

However, recent statutes and decisions indicate a legislative intent to make photographic reproductions primary evidence. Some state courts admit photographic copies of documents without compliance with the best evidence rule.

Title 28 of the United States Code was amended by Public Law 129 on August 28, 1951. This amendment to the law permits photographic reproductions of business records and assures them the same acceptance in evidence in Federal courts as would the originals they replace.

Many states have permitted the recording of public documents by the photographic or photostatic method and have expressly provided that such reproductions shall have the same legal value as the original records. Photostats, for example, are commonly used for recording deeds, mortgages, wills and other documents in county clerks' offices.

Whether microfilm is held as primary or secondary evidence, the laying of a foundation for its admission must be made. Usually a proper foundation for photographic evidence is laid by authentication and verification. This may generally be done by:

1. Establishing the existence, at one time, of the original document and its competency as evidence in the particular case.
2. Showing the reason for the loss, destruction or unavailability of the original. An accurate copy by microfilm, preserving the contents exactly as in the original, should overcome any presumption of fraud.
3. Establishing the accuracy of the microfilm process. The accuracy of microfilm shows authenticity.
4. Following the jurisdictional statutes or case laws in verifying the microfilm records.

Photographic Prohibitions

The photographing of certain documents has been prohibited by law. This covers the following:

Obligations or securities of the United States Government, including:

Bonds	Coupons
Certificates of Indebtedness	United States Notes
National Bank Currency	Treasury Notes
Gold Certificates	Certificates of Deposit
Silver Certificates	Fractional Notes

Bills, checks or drafts for money, drawn by or upon authorized officers of the United States.

Stamps and other representatives of value, of whatever denomination, which have been or may be issued under any Act of Congress.

Coins or money in any form.

Adjusted compensation certificates for veterans of the World War.

Amateur radio operators' licenses.

Automobile licenses, drivers' licenses and automobile titles in certain states.

Certificates of citizenship or naturalization.
Copyrighted material (without permission of the owner of the copyright).
Immigration papers. Passports.
Obligations of any foreign government, bank or corporation.

In certain cases this prohibition against photocopying the above documents does not apply. When it is necessary to copy a legal document on which there is a cancelled revenue stamp, this may be done by authority of Sec. 402.2 of Internal Revenue Bulletin No. 7 entitled ''Reproductions Authorized'' which reads as follows:

''Authority is hereby given to make, hold and dispose of black and white reproductions of cancelled United States Internal Revenue Stamps provided that such reproductions are made, held and disposed of, as part of, and in connection with the making, holding and disposition for lawful purposes of the reproductions of the documents to which such stamps are attached.''

Also, it does not apply to film recordations of United States and foreign securities by various classes of corporations, associations, partnerships and individuals who handle such securities in the ordinary course of business.

Under former regulations, only banks and banking institutions were authorized to make confidential film records of United States securities, checks, warrants and paper money. Film records of foreign securities were not authorized.

New regulations, issued January 24, 1951, on Treasury Department releases S2579, extend the authority to make confidential film records of United States securities to members of established stock exchanges and to investment bankers and dealers in Government securities who are members of either the Investment Bankers Association or the National Security Dealers Association.

Under the amended regulations confidential film records may also be made of notes, bonds, obligations, or other securities of any foreign government, bank, or corporation, by the same classes of individuals and institutions authorized to make film records of United States securities, if these individuals or institutions handle foreign securities in the ordinary course of business.

Only film records of a type whch can be projected upon a screen are authorized. Prints, enlargements, or other reproductions may not be made unless special permission has been obtained from certain designated Treasury officials. Such permission may be granted by the Secretary of the Treasury, the Treasurer of the United States, the Commissioner of the Public Debt, and the Chief of the Secret Service. While the amended regulations give authority to make film records of United States securities to various classes of corporations, associations, partnerships, and individuals who may hold such securities in their possession, Treasury Department officials stated that such film records will not in and of themselves be sufficient to establish ownership as a basis for the issue of duplicate United States securities under the Act of July 8, 1937, as amended (U. S. C., title 31, section 738a). That statute requires proof of ownership, as well as proof of loss, theft, or destruction in the case of registered securities and proof of destruction in the case of bearer securities before maturity or call for redemption. In many instances it is required that the owner file a bond of indemnity. A film record establishes only the fact that at the time the record was made, if that date can be ascertained, the security was in the possession of the party making the film. It does not prove continued ownership, which ownership as well as proof of destruction would necessarily have to be established to the satisfaction of the Secretary of the Treasury before a duplicate United States security could be issued under the statute.

Reference Material

Statutes and leading cases, bearing upon the admissibility of business records and photographic reproductions as evidence in various jurisdictions are listed as follows:

List A. Statutes and cases showing what proof is needed to admit secondary evidence when original documents have been lost or destroyed.

List B. Statutes and cases recognizing the admissibility of books or entries therein, made in the regular course of business, and what proof, if any, is required to lay a proper foundation.

List C. Statutes providing for the recording of photographic or photostatic copies of documents in county clerks' offices, etc.

List D. Statutes providing for the admission of microfilm as primary evidence.

List A

Statutes and cases showing what proof is needed to admit secondary evidence when original documents have been lost or destroyed.

Alabama	Rodgers v Crook (1892)	97 Ala. 722, 725
	Bracken v The State (1895)	111 Ala. 68, 71
	May Hosiery Mills v Mumford Cotton Mills (1920)	205 Ala. 27, 29
California	Bagley v Eaton (1858)	10 Cal. 126, 148
Colorado	Breen v Richardson (1883)	6 Col. 605, 607
Connecticut	The Bank of the U. S. v Sill (1823)	5 Conn. 106, 111
	Woicicky v Anderson (1920)	95 Conn. 534
Georgia	Wenar v Stocks (1933)	177 Ga. 127
Illinois	Blake v Flash (1867)	44 Ill. 302, 304
	Bank of Sandoval v First Nat. Bank (1920)	216 Ill. App. 571
Indiana	The Anderson Bridge Co. v Applegate (1859)	13 Ind. 339, 340
	Rudolph v Lane (1877)	57 Ind. 115, 118
	Beem v Beem (1923)	193 Ind. 481, 490
Iowa	Murray v Olberding (1899)	107 Iowa 547
Kentucky	Shields v Louis (1899)	49 S.W. 803
	Reynolds v Cooper (1922)	193 Ky. 763

Maine	Tobin v Shaw (1858)	45 Me. 331, 347
Maryland	Wright v The State of Maryland (1898)	88 Md. 436, 438
Massachusetts	"The Count Joannes" v Bennett (1862)	87 Mass. (5 Allan) 169, 173
	Stone v Sanborn (1870)	104 Mass. 319, 325
	Smith v Holyoke (1873)	112 Mass. 517, 521
Michigan	Shrimpton & Sons v Netzorg (1895)	104 Mich. 225, 227
	Davis v Teachout's Estate (1901)	126 Mich. 135, 137
	Munroe, Boyce & Co. v Ward (1919)	207 Mich. 369, 380
	People v Sharp (1884)	53 Mich. 523, 525
Minnesota	City of Winona v Huff (1866)	11 Minn. 119, 128, 130
Missouri	Skinner v Henderson (1846)	10 Mo. 205, 207
	Stephen v Metzger (1902)	95 Mo. 609, 621, 622
	Leighty v Murr (1916)	194 Mo. Ap. 156
Montana	State v Welch (1899)	22 Mont. 92, 96
New Mexico	DePalma v Weinman (1911)	16 N. M. 302, 314 232 U. S. 571
New York	Steele v Lord (1877)	70 N. Y. 280
	Mason v Libbey (1882)	90 N. Y. 683
N. Carolina	Pollock v Wilcox and Andrews (1873)	68 N. C. 46, 51
Ohio	Bevis v Am. Railway Exp. Co. (1922)	17 Ohio App. 73, 75
	Janchar v Cerkvenik (1930)	35 Ohio App. 519, 520
S. Carolina	State v Head (1892)	38 S. C. 258, 260
Tennessee	Anderson v Maberry (1871)	58 Tenn. 653, 655
	Eagle Furniture Stores v. Jones (1937 Texas)	110 S. W. (2d) 610
United States	Riggs v Tayloe (1824)	9 Wheaton (U. S.) 483

List B

Statutes and cases recognizing the admissibility of books or entries therein, made in the regular course of business, and indicating what proof, if any, is required to lay a proper foundation.

Alabama	1928 Code of Ala., sec. 7701	
	Title 7 Code of Ala. (1940) sec. 415	
	Ziliak and Schafer Milling Co. v Moore	222 Ala. 254
	Brewer v State	223 Ala. 568
	Dean v Thames	234 Ala. 388
Arizona	1939 Arizona Code Anno., sec. 23-314	
	Cooper v Francis	36 Ariz. 273, 279
	School Dist. No. 1 v Whiting (1940)	56 Ariz. 334

Arkansas	Walter L. Pope's 1937 Digest of Statutes of Arkansas, sec. 5144 St. Paul Fire & Marine Ins. Co. v. Am. Food Prod. Co. (1927 C.C.A. 8th E.D. of Ark.)	21 F (2d) 733,736
California	1941 Code of Civil Procedure, sec. 1953-e to 1953-h Patrick v Fitzlaff People v Kuder	46 Cal. App. 243 98 Cal. App. 206, 216
Colorado	Vol. 3, 1935 Colo. Statutes Anno. C 63, Sec. 14 Hobbs v Breen (1923) Walker v Drogmund (1937)	74 Colo. 277 101 Colo. 521, 74P (2d) 1235
Connecticut	C 305 Cumulative Supp. to General Statutes 1930, sec. 1675 c 1931 General Statutes of Conn., secs. 5601, 5607, 5610, 5878 Brown v Canty State v Hayes (1941)	115 Conn. 226, 228 127 Conn. 543, 18 Atl. 2d 895
Delaware	1935 Revised Code of Delaware, sec. 4701, 4704A sec. 19A (1945) Edsall v Rockland Paper Co. (1937)	194 Atl. 115
Florida	Florida Statutes Anno. (1941) Sec. 90.21 Court Rules, 1946, Common Law, Rule 63	
Georgia	1933 Georgia Code, Title 38, sec. 310 Crump v Bank of Toccoa (1930)	41 Ga. Ap. 505
Hawaii	Rev. Laws 1945, sec. 9902 Shuman Carriage Co. v Paxson	27 Hawaii 161
Idaho	Vol. 1 Idaho Laws Anno. (1943) Sec. 16-415 to 16-419 Kent v Richardson Henderson v Allis-Chalmers Mfg. Co. (1944)	8 Idaho 750 65 Idaho 570
Illinois	Smith-Hurd Ill. Anno. Statutes, ch. 51, sec. 3 People v Small (1926) National Malleable Casting Co. v Iroquois Steel & Iron Co. (1929) White v Parish (1939)—(23 N.E. 2d 939)	319 Ill. 437 333 Ill. 588, 598 301 Ill. App. 172
Indiana	Polus v Conner (1931) Shneider v State (1942)	92 Ind. Ap. 465 220 Ind. 28
Iowa	C. 268 Laws of 52nd Gen. Assembly sec. 3 Laws of 1946, sec. 303.12, 622.27 to 622.30 Farmers Trust & Savings Bank v DeWolf Olson v New York Life Ins. Co. (1941) (295 N.W. 833) Roberts Estate (1942) (3 N.W. 2d 161)	212 Iowa 312 229 Iowa 1073 231 Iowa 1088

Kansas	Corrick's 1935 Gen. Statutes of Kansas, C 60, sec. 2869	
	Bank v Gragg (1916)	98 Kan. 318
	Mulich v Graham Ship By Truck Co. (1946)	162 Kan. 61, 65 (174P 2d 98)
Kentucky	Louisville & Nashville R.R. Co. v Daniel (1906)	122 Ky. 256, 265
	Denunzio Fruit Co. v Louisville & Nashville R.R. Co. (1938)	276 Ky. 168
Louisiana	Vol. 1 Civil Code of La., sec. 2279	
	Willard Storage Battery Co. v Caddo Transfer & Warehouse Co. (1926)	160 La. 910
Maine	Revised statutes 1944, C 100, sec. 133,146	
Maryland	Flack's 1935 Code of Maryland, Article 35, sec. 54A	
	Article 35 of the Anno. Code of Md., sec. 68	
Massachusetts	Laws of Mass., Vol. 8, Chap. 233, sec. 77, 78, 79A	
	Taylor v Harrington (1922)	243 Mass. 210
	Standard Oil Co. of N. Y. v Malaguti (1929)	269 Mass. 126, 128
Michigan	Vol. 21 Mich. Statutes Anno., sec. 27.902	
	Hartford Fire Ins. Co. v Baker	257 Mich. 651, 654
	People v Lewis (1940)	294 Mich. 684
Minnesota	Vol. 11 Minn. Statutes Anno., sec. 145.30 to 145.33	
	Vol. 38 Minn. Statutes Anno., sec. 600.01 to 600.04	
	Tiedt v Larson	174 Minn. 558, 563
	Johnson v Burmeister	182 Minn. 385
	H. F. Shepardson Co. v Central Fire Ins. Co. (1945)	220 Minn. 401
Mississippi	Hayes v Nat. Surety Co. (1934)	169 Miss. 676, 693
Missouri	Mo. Laws 1945, p. 1427 H.S.H.B. 626, sec. 1-4	
	Welch-Sandler Cement Co. v Mullin	31 S.W. (2d) 86, 89
Montana	Revised Code 1935, Sec. 10598.1-10598.4	
	Smith v Sullivan	58 Mont. 77, 83
	State v Smart	81 Mont. 145, 150
Nebraska	Vol. II Revised Statutes of Neb. 1943, sec. 25-1212	
	Redding v Posten	109 Neb. 197
	Brownell v Adams	121 Neb. 304, 314
New Hampshire	State v Mark Shinborn (1866)	46 N. H. 497
	Roberts v Claremont Power Co. (1917)	78 N. H. 491, 493
	Geralds v Champlin (1944)	93 N. H. 157

New Jersey	N. J. Statutes Anno., Sec. 2:98-27.1	
	Cockran and Meloney v Rutter (1908)	76 N. J. L. 375
	Autocan Sales & Service Co. v Scheurer (1922)	97 N. J. L. 560
	Grobart v Passaic Valley Water Comm. (1943)	134 N. J. L. 413
New Mexico	Vol. II N. M. Statutes 1941, sec. 20-219 (1945)	
	McKenzie v King	14 N. M. 375, 380
New York	Civil Practice Act, sec. 374a	
	Mason v Libbey	90 N. Y. 683
N. Carolina	General Statutes of N. Carolina 1943, sec. 8-42 to 8-45	
	Fireman's Ins. Co. v Seaboard Airline R.R. (1905)	138 N. C. 42, 45
	Edgarton v Perkins (1931)	200 N. C. 650
N. Dakota	Vol. 3 N. D. Revised Code of 1943, sec. 31-0801	
	Fargo Mercantile Co. v Johnson	47 N. D. 304
	Spies v Stang	56 N. D. 674
	Baldwin Piano Co. v Wylie	63 N. D. 216
Ohio	Page's Ohio Gen. Code Anno., sec 12102-22 to 12102-25	
	Burr v Shute	2 C.C. (N.S.) 343
	Bennett v Shaw	12 C.C. 574
	Lumpkin v Met. Life Ins. Co. (1945)	75 Ohio app. 310
Oklahoma	Oklahoma Statutes 1941, Title 12, Sec. 501	
	Clover v Neely	116 Okla. 155, 157
	Harsha v Mock	139 Okla. 181
	Maney v Cherry	170 Okla. 469
	Oil Field Operating Co. v Eureka Tool Co. (1937)	74 P (2d) 377
Oregon	Oregon Compiled Laws Anno. 1941, secs. 2-819 to 2-819c	
	Warren Construction Co. v Grant	137 Oregon 410, 418
	Pacific Trading Co. v Sim Ins. Office Ltd.	145 Oregon 211, 219
Pennsylvania	Purdon's Penn. Statutes, Title 28, secs. 63, 91a-91d	
	Harkin's v John Hancock Mut. Life Ins. Co. (1944)	154 Pa. Supr. 387
	Specktor v Victory Ins. Co.	282 Pa. 429, 432
	Ingram v City of Pittsburgh (1942)	346 Pa. 45
Porto Rico	1911 Revised Code of Porto Rico, Art. 48, Sec. 7607	
Rhode Island	Gen. Laws of 1938 Anno. C538, Sec. 1	
	1946 Jan. Sessions Laws C1770	
	Cargill v Atwood	18 R. I. 303, 304
	Cicca & Co. v Antonelli	51 R. I. 280
S. Carolina	Currie v Davis (1924)	130 S. C. 408, 415
	State v Johnston (1928)	149 S. C. 195, 207

S. Dakota   Vol. II, S. D. Code of 1939, Sec. 36.1001

Tennessee   Williams, Shannor & Harsh 1932 Code of
                   Tenn., Sec. 9733

Texas   Vernon's 1936 Texas Statutes, Art. 3737,
                   3737a
                   1939 Supplement, Art. 3737c
                   Watson Co. v Lone Star Service Station   16 S.W. (2d) 151,
                   (1929)   153
                   J. M. Radford Grocery Co. v Porter   17 S.W. (2d) 145,
                   (1929)   148

United States   U. S. v Manton   2 Cir. 107F(2d)
                                                                  834, 844

Utah   Revised Statutes of Utah, Title 104, ch.
                   48, Sec. 11 (2)
                   Shepard v Denver & Rio Grande R.R. Co.
                   (1915)   45 Utah 295, 318

Vermont   Laws 1939, No. 48
                   Crowley v Goodrich (1945)   44 Atl. 2d 128
                   Griffin v B. & M. R. R.   87 Vt. 278, 292
                   Squires v O'Connell   91 Vt. 35, 38

Virginia   French v Virginia R. R. Co. (1917)   121 Va. 383
                   White Sewing Mach. Co. v Gilmore Fur
                   Co. (1920)   128 Va. 630, 645
                   Ratliff v Jewell (1929)   153 Va. 315, 327

Washington   Remington's Rev. Statutes of Wash. Anno.
                   1947 Suppl., Sec. 1263-1 to 1263-5
                   Goodwin Co. v Schwaegler   147 Wash. 547
                   Still v Swanson   175 Wash. 553, 556

W. Virginia   State v Larue (1925)   98 W.Va. 677, 690
                   State v Martin (1926)   102 W.Va. 107, 113

Wisconsin   Wisc. Statutes 1937, Ch. 327, Sec. 24, 25
                   Wisc. Statutes 1945, Sec. 327.25, 327.29
                   F. Dohem Co. Ltd. v. Niagara Fire Ins.
                   Co.   96 Wis. 38, 46
                   Stella Cheese Co. v Chic., St. P., M & O
                   Ry. Co. (1946)   248 Wis. 196

Wyoming   Compiled Statutes 1945, Sec. 3-3122 to
                   3-3125
                   Lewis v England   14 Wyo. 128

List C

Statutes providing for the recording of photographic or photostatic copies
of documents in county clerks' offices, etc.

Alabama   Title 7 Code of Ala. (1940) Sec. 5

Arizona   Arizona Code Anno. (1939) Sec. 17-801

California   Code of Civil Procedure, section 1920 b
                   Probate Code Section 330

Colorado	C.154 Colorado Statutes Anno. (1935) Sec. 18(7) C. 40 Colorado Statutes Anno. (1935) Sec. 35
Connecticut	Cumulative Supplement to the General Statutes, (Jan. Sessions 1931, 1933, 1935) Ch. 5 Sec. 23-C.
Delaware	Laws of Delaware, Volume 42 (1939), Ch. 88
Florida	Compiled Laws of Florida, Sec. 92.29 and Sec. 18.20 (1945)
Georgia	Laws of 1943, Part 1, Title VI.
Idaho	Session Laws 1943, Chap. 81
Illinois	Smith-Hurd Ill. Anno. Statutes, Ch. 116, Sec. 31-38
Indiana	Anno. Indiana Statutes, C. 39, Sec. 49-3901 (1947)
Iowa	Vol. I Code of Iowa 1946, Ch. 422, Sec. 422.61 Fiftieth General Assembly 1943, Chap. 202.
Kansas	General Statutes 1945 Supp. Secs. 75-3506 to 75-3508; Sec. 75-2713
Louisiana	General Statutes—Dart.—Sec. 7872 and 7894
Maine	Rev. Statutes, C. 100, Sec. 145, 146
Maryland	Article 3 Code of Public Local Laws (1930) amended 1947, Sec. 123C
Massachusetts	Laws of Mass., Vol. 8, Ch. 233, Secs. 77, 78, 79A
Michigan	Sec. 3.991 Ch. 16A, Mich. Statutes Anno., amended Oct. 1947
Minnesota	Vol. 29, Minn. Statutes Anno., Sec. 507.11
Mississippi	Miss. Code 1942 Anno., Sec. 878 (1946)
Missouri	Mo. Laws 1945, p. 1427, H.S.H.B. No. 626, Sec. 1-4
Nebraska	Vol. II Rev. Statutes of Neb. 1943, Sec. 25-1281
New Hampshire	C.229 Laws of N. H. 1947
New Jersey	N.J.S.A. 46:19-3 (1944) N.J.S.A. 47:3-2 (1941)
New Mexico	New Mexico Statutes 1941, Secs. 13-403, 13-406 to 13-409
New York	General Municipal Law, Sec. 51-a Public Officers Law 65-a Administrative Code, City of N. Y., Sec. B40-13.1 Surrogate's Court Act, Sec. 16 (C. 19 Laws of N. Y. 1948)
N. Carolina	General Statutes of N. C. of 1943, Sec. 153-9.1 (1945) Public Laws (Session of 1941) Chapter 286
N. Dakota	Vol. 1 N. D. Rev. Code of 1943, Sec. 11-1019 Laws of N. Dakota (1941) Chap. 234
Ohio	Page's Ohio Gen. Code, Sec. 32-1
Oklahoma	Session Laws of Oklahoma 1947 Ch. 18, Secs. 1 to 9, p. 616 Oklahoma Statutes 1941, Title 67, Sec. 91

Oregon	Vol. VI, Oregon Compiled Laws Anno. Secs. 85-401 to 85-404 (1947)
Pennsylvania	Purdon's Penn. Statutes Anno., Title 71, Sec. 205 Purdon's Penn. Statutes, Title 65, Secs. 61-62
Rhode Island	Laws of 1946 (Jan. Session) Ch. 1770
S. Carolina	Code of Laws of S. Carolina, 1942, Vol. 1, Sec. 713 S. Carolina Acts (1942)—Act 678
S. Dakota	Session Laws of S. Dakota (1947) Ch. 168
Texas	Vernon's Texas Statutes (1945 Supplement) Article 6663a
Vermont	Public Acts 1945, No. 26 amending Sec. 1707 of Public Laws Public Acts 1945, No. 200 amending Acts of 1937, No. 229, Sec. 3
W. Virginia	W. Va. Code of 1943, 1947 Supplement, Sec. 5714 (1)
Wisconsin	Wisc. Statutes 1945, Sec. 327.25
Wyoming	Wyoming Compiled Statutes 1945, Sec. 27-705 Revised Statutes of Wyoming 1940 Supplement 30-510

List D

Statutes providing for the admissibility of microfilm as primary evidence.

Alabama	Laws of 1951
Arizona	Laws of 1951, Chapter 62
California	Laws of 1951, Chapter 346
Delaware	Laws of 1951
Georgia	Laws of 1950
Idaho	Laws of 1951, Chapter 173
Indiana	Laws of 1949, Chapter 168
Iowa	Laws of 1951
Maryland	Laws of 1951, Chapter 77
Michigan	Laws of 1949
Minnesota	Laws of 1951, Chapter 125
Nebraska	Laws of 1951
Nevada	Laws of 1951, Chapter 16
New Hampshire	Laws of 1951, Chapter 110
New Jersey	Laws of 1951, Chapter 266
New York	Laws of 1952, Chapter 791
N. Carolina	Laws of 1951
N. Dakota	Laws of 1951

Oklahoma	Laws of 1951
Oregon	Laws of 1949
Pennsylvania	Laws of 1951, Act No. 357, S. B. No. 1512
Tennessee	Public Acts 1949, Chapter 98
Texas	Laws of 1951
Virginia	Laws of 1950, Chapter 332
Washington	Laws of 1949, Chapter 223
Wisconsin	Laws of 1951, Chapter 284

LIMITATIONS FOR CIVIL ACTIONS

(Letters indicate footnote. Figures indicate years.)
O-Oral—W-Written

State	Promissory Notes	Open Accounts	Instruments and Contracts Under Seal	Ordinary Contracts	Domestic Judgments in Courts of Record	Domestic Judgments in Courts not of Record	Foreign Judgments in Courts of Record	Foreign Judgments in Courts not of Record
Ala.	6	3	10	6	20	6	20	6
Alaska	6	6	10	6	10	10	10	10
Ariz.	6(a)	3	6(a)	6-W—3-O(a)	5	5	4	4
Ark.	5	3	5	5-W—3-O	10	10	10	10
Calif.	4 Corp. Notes 6	4	4 if book account of stated account or written contract, if not—2		5	5	5	5
Colo.	6	6	6(b)	6(b)	20	6	6	6
Conn.	6 17 non-neg.	6	17 (18 Real Estate—7)	6-W—3-O	21	21	No prov.	No prov.
Del.	6	3	3	3	No prov.	No prov.	No prov.	No prov.
D. C.	3	3	12	3	12	12	(c)	(c)
Fla.	5	3	20	5-W—3-O	20	4	7	7
Ga.	6	4	20	6-W—4-O	7	7(d)	5	5
Hawaii	6	6	6	6	10	6	6	4
Idaho	5	4	5	5-W—4-O	6	6	6	6
Ill.	10	5	10(r)	10-W—5-O	20	10	5	5
Ind.	10	6	20	20-W(s)—6-O	20	15	20	15
Iowa	10	5	10	10-W—5-O	20	10	20	20

363

LIMITATIONS FOR CIVIL ACTIONS (Continued)

(Letters indicate footnotes. Figures indicate years.)

O-Oral—W-Written

State	Promissory Notes	Open Accounts	Instruments and Contracts Under Seal	Ordinary Contracts	Domestic Judgments in Courts of Record	Domestic Judgments in Courts not of Record	Foreign Judgments in Courts of Record	Foreign Judgments in Courts not of Record
Kan.	5	3	5	5-W—3-O	Kept alive by execution every five years		15	15
Ky.	15(e)	5(f)	15	15-W—5-O	15	15	15	15
La.	5	3	10	10	10(g)	10(g)	10	10
Me.	6	6	20	6	20	6(h)	20	6
Md.	3	3	12	3	12	12	12	12
Mass.	6(i)	6	20	6	20	6	20	6
Mich.	6	6	10	6	10	6	10	6
Minn.	6	6	6	6	10	10	10	10
Miss.	6	3	6	6-W—3-O	7	6	7(j)	6
Mo.	10	5	10	5	10	5	10	5
Mont.	8	5	8	8-W—5-O	10	5	10	5
Neb.	5	4	5	5-W—4-O	Kept alive by execution every five years		5	5
Nev.	6	4	6	6-W—4-O	6	6	6	6
N.H.	6	6	20	6	20	20	20	20
N.J.	6	6	16	6	20	6	20	6
N.M.	6	4	6	6-W—4-O	7	6	7	6
N.Y.	6	6	6	6	20	6(k)	20	6
N.C.	3	3	10	3	10	7	10	7

N.D.	6	6	6(b)	6(b)	10	10	10	10
Ohio	15	6	15	15-W-6.0	21	15	15	15
Okla.	5	3	5	5-W-3.0	Kept alive by execution every five years		1	1
Ore.	6	6	10	6	10(l)	10(l)	10	10
Pa.	6	6	20	6-4(m)	20(n)	20	20	20
R.I.	6	6	20	6	20	20	20	20
S.C.	6	6	20	6	10	10		
S.D.	6	6	20	6	20	20	10	10
Tenn.	6	6	6	6	10	10	10	10
Texas	4	2	4	4-W-2.0	8	10	10	10
Utah	6	4	6	6-W-4.0	8	8	8	8
Vt.	6(o)	6	8	6	8	6	8	6
Va.	5	3	10	5-W-3.0	20	6	10	10
Wash.	6	3	6	6-W-3.0	6	6	6	6
W. Va.	10	5	10	10-W-5.0	10	10	10	10
Wis.	6	6	10-20(p)	6	20	6	10	6
Wyo.	10	8	10	10-W-8.0	5(q)	5(q)	5	5

(a) Instruments executed without the State, 4 years.
(b) Contracts affecting real property, 10 years.
(c) Suit may be brought on a foreign judgment unless statute of limitations has run against it in the jurisdiction where it was entered.
(d) Even though judgments rendered in Courts of Georgia become dormant after seven years, if no execution is issued, or if execution is issued but no return made within seven years, judgment may be revived by scire facias proceedings within three years thereafter.
(e) 5 year period applies, if note is placed on the footing of a bill of exchange.
(f) Actions on a merchant's account shall be instituted within 5 years from the 1st day of January next succeeding the respective dates or times of delivery of the articles charged in the account.
(g) May be revived for additional 10 year periods by action before statute runs against the claim.
(h) Judgments of Justices of the Peace and Trial Justices, 20 years.
(i) Bills, notes, or other evidence of indebtedness, issued by a bank, promissory notes, with attesting witness, as against original payee or his executor or administrator, 20 years.
(j) Domestic Mississippi judgments are valid for seven years. Foreign judgments are same, unless debtor resided in Mississippi when it was rendered, then barred in three years.
(k) Judgment of Court not of Record docketed in County Clerk office, 20 years.
(l) May be renewed for additional ten years.
(m) Uniform Commercial Code provides 4 year statute of limitations as to sales contracts.
(n) Lien on realty, 5 yrs.; judgment good 20 yrs. Judgments may be renewed.
(o) If note be witnessed, 14 years.
(p) If action accrues within the State, 20 years; if outside, 10 years.
(q) May be revived by action brought within 21 years after it becomes dormant.
(r) Vendors lien, mortgage—20 years.
(s) Contract to convey land—15 yrs., contract for payment of money—10 yrs.

Public Law 129 — 82d Congress
Chapter 351 — 1st Session
H. R. 4106

AN ACT

To amend section 1732 of title 28, United States Code, entitled "Judiciary and judicial procedure" by adding a new subsection thereto "To permit the photographic reproduction of business records and the introduction of the same in evidence."

Be it enacted by the Senate and House of Representatives of the United States of America in Congress assembled, That section 1732 of title 28 of the United States Code entitled "Judiciary and judicial procedure" is amended by inserting "(a)" immediately preceding the first paragraph thereof, and by adding a new subsection to read as follows:

"(b) If any business, institution, member of a profession or calling, or any department or agency of government, in the regular course of business or activity has kept or recorded any memorandum, writing, entry, print, representation or combination thereof, of any act, transaction, occurrence, or event, and in the regular course of business has caused any or all of the same to be recorded, copied, or reproduced by any photographic, photostatic, microfilm, micro-card, miniature, photographic, or other process which accurately reproduces or forms a durable medium for so reproducing the original, the original may be destroyed in the regular course of business unless held in a custodial or fiduciary capacity or unless its preservation is required by law. Such reproduction, when satisfactorily identified, is as admissible in evidence as the original itself in any judicial or administrative proceeding whether the original is in existence or not and an enlargement or facsimile of such reproduction is likewise admissible in evidence if the original reproduction is in existence and available for inspection under direction of court. The introduction of a reproduced record, enlargement, or facsimile does not preclude admission of the original. This subsection shall not be construed to exclude from evidence any document or copy thereof which is otherwise admissible under the rules of evidence."

Sec. 2.   The analysis of section 1732 of chapter 115 of title 28, United States Code, immediately preceding section 1731 of such title, is amended so as to read:

"1732.   Record made in regular course of business; photographic copies."

Sec. 3.   The catchline of section 1732, chapter 115 of title 28, United States Code, is amended so as to read:

"1732.   Record made in regular course of business; photographic copies."

Approved August 28, 1951.

European Laws Pertaining to Microrecords

Belgium (January 6, 1953)

"... according to information received from the Belgian Department of Justice, the question of the evidentiary value of microfilm has never come up, in Belgian Courts, as only the original of an act may be introduced as evidence—except in such cases as foreseen in articles 1335 and 1336 of the Belgian Civil Code. As a rule a microfilm is considered as any other copy and has to be certified by a special authority to have any value at all."

Denmark (October 22, 1952)

"... concerning Danish laws on the evidentiary value of microfilm. The Danish Ministry of Justice, to which your inquiry has been submitted, has now informed the Embassy that no such laws exist. It is possible to use microfilm as evidence in Denmark, but in each case it is left to the Court to judge the value thereof just as it is left to the Court to judge the value of all other evidence."

Finland (October 3, 1952)

"... regarding your inquiry of eventual Finnish laws on the evidentiary value of microfilm, I wish to inform you that Finnish legislation does not contain any regulations and there is no legislation in planning. The evidentiary value of microfilm is the same as of photographs or films in general. In this connection I wish to inform you that the Finnish legislation does not either contain any special regulations of the evidentiary value of a photostatic copy. In the practice some courts have given the same evidentiary value to a photostatic copy as to an original document, but this conduct depends on the deliberation of the court or other authority in question."

France (January 27, 1953)

"No laws in existence at the present time."

Great Britain (September 16, 1952)

"In the laws of evidence, there is no provision for microfilm as such. When the law mentions 'copies' the term is not defined to include microfilm but that does not necessarily mean that it is not permitted in the courts as evidence. This would depend upon interpretation of the word 'copies.'"

Italy (October 27, 1952)

"... no particular legislation exists in Italy on microphotography."

Netherlands (May 12, 1953)

"As the use of microfilms in the Netherlands is a comparative novelty, there are no rules in existence as to its admissibility as evidence. The Department of Justice takes the viewpoint that the Court is at liberty to admit such microfilms to the extent it deems fit: there is as yet no jurisprudence concerning this matter."

Norway (December 15, 1952)

"... there are no special provisions in existence in Norway concerning the evidentiary value of microfilm. It may be added that the evaluation of evidence in Norwegian Courts is free. The Court thus after a thorough consideration of the proceedings and the presentation of evidence on the whole decides which facts are to constitute the foundation of the judgment."

Sweden (September 26, 1952)

"... there is no law about the evidentiary value of microfilm. Neither has there been a court decision concerning the evidentiary value of microfilm. The Swedish courts of justice are entitled to a free examination and judgment of the value and the importance of any evidence brought forward by a party. Therefore, the courts do not put the question whether microfilm has an evidentiary value. They would rather ask why the party has presented the document in the form of a microfilm copy and not the original document."

Switzerland (October 23, 1952)

"... there are no provisions on this matter in Swiss law. The evaluation of such evidence is entirely up to the Courts. According to article 962 of the Swiss Federal Code of Obligations, commercial firms are obliged to preserve their books during a period of ten years. Up to date no court decisions are known as to the question whether a firm which preserves microphotostatic copies instead of the originals has fulfilled its duties according to article 962 of the Code."

APPENDIX B

American Standard
Practice For Microfilms

Reg. U. S. Pat. Off.
Z38.7.8-1947

*UDC 778.14

1. Definitions

1.1 Microfilm. Microfilm shall mean a transparent flexible material carrying microphotographs for optical, but not cinematographic, projection or viewing.

1.2 Microphotographs. A microphotograph is a reduced-size photographic documentary reproduction, generally too small to be read by the unaided eye. Microphotographs usually are made for record purposes from documentary material, such as texts or drawings, or from physical objects.

1.3 Reduction. Reduction is the ratio of a linear dimension of the object to the corresponding dimension of the image on the film.

2. Material

2.1 Stock. Microfilms shall be made only on safety (slow-burning) stock as defined by American Standard Definition of Safety Photographic Film, Z38.3.1-1943, or the latest revision thereof approved by the American Standards Association. Microfilms intended for permanent preservation should be made on film stock meeting the American Standard Specifications for Films for Permanent Records, Z38.3.2-1945, or the latest revision thereof approved by the American Standards Association.

2.2 Width and Perforations. 35- and 16-mm stock used for microfilms shall conform in width and perforations, if the latter are present, with the American Standards for Cutting and Perforating Dimensions for 16-Millimeter Silent Motion Picture Negative and Positive Raw Stock, Z22.5-1947; for 16-Millimeter Sound Motion Picture Negative and Positive Raw Stock, Z22.12-1947; and for 35-Millimeter Motion Picture Positive Raw Stock, Z22.36-1947, or the latest revisions thereof approved by the American Standards Association. An additional tolerance of $^{+0.2}_{-1.0}$ percent may be added to the dimensions specified in the above standards at the time the film is first removed from

its original container. Film perforated along both edges, along one edge, or unperforated, may be used.

2.3 Winding. Processed microfilm prints normally are wound with the emulsion out for negatives and with emulsion in for positives. If the supply reel of processed film has a round spindle hole, the film should unwind downward from the right-hand side when the round hole is toward the observer. (See Fig. 1 A.)

LEADING END OF FILM

LEADING END OF FILM

A   B

Fɪɢ. 1
Position of Film on Reel

Nᴏᴛᴇ: Arrow through film indicates direction of light for visual inspection (not as in a reader).

2.4 Film Thickness. The film base used for microfilm should be within the range of 0.11 to 0.17 mm (0.0045 to 0.0065 in.) in thickness.

3. Format and Placement

3.1 Width of Image

3.1.1 On 35-Millimeter Film. The width of the image on 35-mm film shall not exceed 24.0 mm (0.945 in.) on film perforated along both edges; 28.6 mm (1.126 in.) on film perforated along one edge; and 31.75 mm (1.250 in.) on unperforated film.

3.1.2 On 16-Millimeter Film. The width of the image on 16-mm film shall not exceed 10.4 mm (0.410 in.) on film perforated along both edges; 12.7 mm (0.500 in.) on film perforated along one

*Universal Decimal Classification

Approved: December 5, 1947, by the American Standards Association.
Sponsor: Optical Society of America.

369

American Standard

Practice For Microfilms

Z38.7.8-1947

I   II A   II B   III

Fig. 2

Arrangements of Images on Microfilm for General Library Use

(See Fig. 1 B.)

NOTE:

I. Single page of copy arranged lengthwise on the film with the lines of print at a right angle to the edges of the film.

II. Copy arranged with the lines of print parallel to the edges of the film.
   A. Double page (two pages side by side).
   B. Single page.

III. Two pages arranged side by side with the lines of print at a right angle to the edges of the film.

A. WESTERN LANGUAGES WRITTEN FROM LEFT TO RIGHT

Fig. 3

Arrangement of Images on Microfilm for Western Languages Written from Left to Right

(See Fig. 1 B.)

edge; and 15.0 mm (0.590 in.) on unperforated film.

3.2 Separation of Images. When framing in the reader is important, successive images should be separated by at least 0.5 mm (0.02 in.), and on strips of 3 m (10 ft) or longer, the separation should approach this value to conserve film and storage space.

3.3 Film for General Library Use. The images on the film for general library use should be arranged, when possible, as shown in Fig. 2.

3.4 Sequence of Pages. The sequence of pages on microfilms should be such that the first line of the following page is nearest to the last line of the preceding page and the sequence of pages should be orderly for the type of material copied. Fig. 3 shows the preferred arrangement for microfilms of books in Western languages.

4. Leader and Trailer

4.1 When the film is long enough to be stored on reels, a leader and a trailer of 45 cm (18 in.) each should be provided.

5. Title Frame

5.1 When the film is stored on reels, the first image should be the title, or a condensed version of the title, in letters at least 2 mm (0.08 in.) high. The last frame should indicate the end of the film by "End" or other suitable designation.

6. Reels

6.1 Microfilms 7.6 m (25 ft) long or longer should be wound on standard reels as defined in American Standard for Reels for Processed Microfilm, Z38.7.17-1946, or the latest revision thereof approved by the American Standards Association. The position of microfilm on the reel shall be as shown in Fig. 1.

American Standard Definition of

Safety Photographic Film

Foreword

THE American Standard Definition of Safety Photographic Film defines a photographic film which is no more hazardous than common newsprint paper. In order to be classified as Safety Photographic Film, a photographic film must (a) be difficult to ignite, (b) be slow burning, and (c) evolve a limited amount of toxic oxides of nitrogen during decomposition.

The ease of ignition is determined by measuring the time of ignition after subjecting the sample to a uniformly maintained high temperature. The requirement for ease of ignition and the test method are the same as those specified by the British Standard Definition of Cinematograph "Safety" Film (1939) and other European standards for safety motion picture film.*

The rapidity of burning and the method of measuring that characteristic are also the same as specified in the British Standard Definition of "Safety" Film (1939).*

The toxic gases evolved when photographic films of cellulose nitrate are decomposed by heat are oxides of nitrogen, carbon monoxide, and hydrocyanic acid. Laboratory tests made available to the committee indicate that only oxides of nitrogen and carbon monoxide are evolved in sufficient quantities to constitute an appreciable hazard. These tests also indicate that photographic film does not evolve more carbon monoxide than does common newsprint paper when equal quantities of film and paper are decomposed in the same manner.

The maximum quantity of oxides of nitrogen which can evolve when safety photographic film decomposes is limited by stipulating in the definition the maximum nitrogen (present as nitrate) content of the material. Fumes from photographic film that comply with this standard will not be significantly different from fumes evolved from ordinary newsprint paper decomposed under the same conditions.

Photographic films made from materials for which this definition applies but which do not comply in one or more respects are not necessarily hazardous. For example, acetate film may fail to comply with the maximum nitrogen content specified in this definition and still not be significantly more hazardous than common newsprint paper under ordinary conditions.

The committee considered a maximum nitrogen content of 0.72 percent and had some evidence that a safety film containing that proportion of nitrogen was no more toxic than films with a lower content. However, the specification was set at a lower figure to correspond with the current requirements of the Underwriters' Laboratories. The method for measuring the nitrogen content was adopted from the Summary of *Requirements for Slow Burning Cellulose Acetate Film*, Underwriters' Laboratories, Inc, Chicago, Illinois.

The definition of Safety Photographic Film applies only to films, the supports for which comprise cellulose esters of simple fatty acids, combinations of cellulose esters and nitrate, and regenerated cellulose. Should photographic films in the future be made of other materials, this definition may have to be modified and additional requirements incorporated in the definition.

Suggestions for improvement based upon experience gained in the use of this definition will always be welcome. They should be sent to the American Standards Association, 29 West 39 Street, New York 18, N. Y.

The American Standards Association in the past has acted as the secretariat for the project on Photography, ISA 42 of the International Standards Association.

The ASA Committee on Standardization in the Field of Photography was initiated in September, 1938, on the recommendation of a general conference of the American photographic industry following a request from the International Standards Association that the ASA accept the secretariat for ISA Committee 42 on Photography. The Optical Society of America was designated as sponsor for the ASA project.

* These requirements were proposed at the Eighth Congress of International Photography at Dresden in 1931 (*Bericht uber den VIII. Internationalen Kongress fur Wissenschaftliche und Angewandte Photographie*, pp 279–286) and adopted by the Ninth Congress, Paris, 1935 (see *IX⁰ Congress International de Photographie*)

ASA
Reg. U. S. Pat. Off.

Z38.3.1—1943

American Standard
Definition of Safety Photographic Film

O. Scope

Photographic films are classified as safety photographic film if they are difficult to ignite, slow burning, and low in nitrogen content.

1. Ignition Time

1.1 Definition. Film supports for light-sensitive materials are classified as difficult to ignite when the ignition time is greater than ten minutes.

1.2 Method of Measurement. The ignition time of photographic films is measured as follows:

1.2.1 *Sample.* A sample 35 mm long and 8 mm wide shall be cut from the film to be tested. The sample shall be free of perforations as far as is practicable. All gelatin layers shall be removed by washing in warm water, and the sample shall then be dried for at least 12 hours by being suspended freely in air having a temperature of 18 C to 22 C and a relative humidity of 40 to 50 percent.

1.2.2 *Procedure.* The test shall be made in an electric resistance oven, the interior of which shall be in the form of a vertical cylinder (preferably with a rounded bottom), having a diameter of 70 mm and a mean height of 70 mm. The top of the oven shall be closed by means of a closely overlapping lid, having two holes of 7 mm and 15 mm, respectively, the centers being at a distance of about 15 mm from each other. A thermocouple shall be introduced through the smaller opening, the connecting wires having a porcelain coating fitting tightly into the hole. Alternatively, the temperature in the cylinder may be measured by means of a mercury thermometer, protected from rising heat by means of a cork disk lying a little above the lid.

1.2.3 *Temperature.* The oven shall be brought to, and maintained at, a temperature of 300 C ±3 C. When this temperature is reached, the sample, attached to a thin U-shaped wire hook, shall be introduced through the larger opening. The thermocouple (or the thermometer) and the sample shall be fixed in such a way that the thermojunction (or the mercury bulb) and the center of the sample shall be at an equal depth of about 35 mm.

1.2.4 *Time Interval.* The time interval from the insertion of the sample to the ignition of the sample is recorded as the ignition time.

1.2.5 *Preparation for Tests.* Between tests, the oven shall be thoroughly aired.

2. Burning Time

2.1 Definition. Photographic films having a thickness equal to or greater than 0.08 mm are classified as slow burning when the burning time is not less than 45 seconds. Photographic films having a thickness less than 0.08 mm are classified as slow burning when the burning time is not less than 30 seconds.

2.2 Method of Measurement. The burning time of photographic films is measured as follows:

2.2.1 *Sample.* A sample 35 cm long and 35 mm wide shall be cut from the film to be tested. All gelatin layers are to be removed by washing in warm water. The sample shall then be dried for at least 12 hours by being suspended freely in air having a temperature of 18 C to 22 C and a relative humidity of 40 to 50 percent.

The sample shall be marked at a point 5 cm from one end. The sample shall be perforated with holes 3 mm in diameter along both edges. Perforations are to be at intervals of not more than 32 mm.

2.2.2 *Procedure.* A wire having a diameter of not more than 0.5 mm shall be threaded through the perforations on one side so that the sample is supported at points not more than 32 mm apart. With the wire stretched horizontally and the sample hanging vertically from it, the bottom corner of the marked end is to be ignited.

2.2.3 *Time Interval.* The time which elapses from the moment the flame reaches the mark until the sample is completely burned shall be recorded as the burning time. If the sample does not ignite or if it does not completely burn, the burning time is recorded as infinity.

2.2.4 *Test Conditions.* The test shall be made in a room free from draughts and immediately after the period of drying. At least three tests shall be made.

3. Nitrogen Content

3.1 Definition. Photographic films having a nitrogen content less than 0.36 percent by weight are classified as having a low nitrogen content.

3.2 Method of Measurement. The nitrogen content of photographic films is measured as follows:

3.2.1 *Sample.* After the emulsion is removed, 2.5 grams of support are cut into small pieces and placed in an 800-cc Kjeldahl flask. To this are added 90 cc of 30-percent sodium hydroxide and 10 cc of ethyl alcohol. (Note 1) The sample may be conveniently held overnight at this point.

3.2.2 *Procedure.* The sample is heated on the steam bath, and 25 cc of 30 percent hydrogen peroxide are added slowly, followed by agitation with a stirring rod. When the first portion of hydrogen peroxide is boiled out, another 20-cc portion is added; this is usually sufficient to dissolve the support completely. When the reaction has ceased, the stirring rod is removed and washed down with distilled water. The contents of the flask will now be approximately 200 cc.

3.2.3 *Temperature.* The solution is evaporated over a flame to 75–100 cc volume to remove the last traces of ammonia, diluted to a total of 350 cc with distilled water, cooled, and immediately before connecting the flask to the Kjeldahl apparatus, 2.5 grams of DeVarda's alloy are added quickly. After the flask is connected, about 200 cc of distillate are collected in a 500-cc Erlenmeyer flask containing 50 cc of standard tenth-normal sulfuric acid. The excess acid is back titrated with tenth-normal alkali. (Note 2)

3.2.4 *Method of Calculation.* A blank determination is made on the reagents, using the same quantities that are used in the actual determination. The percent nitrate nitrogen in the sample is calculated as follows:

$$\frac{[(\text{cc acid in blank}) - (\text{cc acid in sample})] \times 0.1 \times 0.014 \times 100}{2.5}$$
$$= \text{percent nitrogen.}$$

NOTE 1. Ethyl alcohol denatured with CP methyl alcohol may be used.

NOTE 2. Three sources of error must be avoided in this test:

(*a*) When evaporating the solution following the peroxide digestion, mechanical loss by entrainment may occur if the solution is boiled down too far. This will give low results.

(*b*) When distilling the sample after addition of the DeVarda's alloy, some alkali may be carried over into the standard acid by entrainment if the distillation is carried too far, or is too vigorous. This will give high results.

(*c*) The total volume of the sample at the time of addition of the DeVarda's alloy must be closely controlled. Too much or too little water added changes the alkali concentration so that the rate of reaction with the alloy and the corresponding reduction of the sodium nitrate present will be erratic.

SPONSOR

Optical Society of America

Approved June 11, 1943
American Standards Association

American Standard
Specifications for
Films for Permanent Records

Z38.3.2-1945

Approved March 28, 1945
American Standards Association

SPONSOR
Optical Society of America

Foreword

The past decade has seen great advances in the use of photographic films in the place of paper documents for the preservation of records. Considerable interest is also being shown in the safe-keeping of pictorial records having legal, scientific, industrial, or historical value. The preservation of film records by national, state, and municipal governments throughout the country, and by banks, insurance companies, and other enterprises, was stimulated by a recognition of the economies in storage space and the ease of reproducing that result from the use of film records.

During the early development period of the art of microcopying documents it was customary to use 35-mm nitrate motion picture films, a material that is inflammable and likely to deteriorate in storage. Today, however, films that have been specifically designed for record purposes are in wide use. They have special photographic qualities that would be of little use in the motion picture field and are, without exception, produced on safety-film base, usually of the cellulose acetate type.

The useful life of cellulose acetate films is conjectural since actual experience with the material extends back only about 35 years. Experience with the material during that time and the result of accelerated aging tests and other studies predict, however, that the material is capable of enduring as long as rag-paper stock under normal storage conditions. This fact was recognized by the 76th Congress of the United States, which passed, in 1940, Public-No. 788, a bill permitting the destruction of certain kinds of original records of the Government after they had been copied on record film meeting the requirements of the National Bureau of Standards. The present American Standard is based on those requirements.

The Pfund folding endurance tester described in this document was designed by Dr. A. H. Pfund of the Johns Hopkins University for the E. I. du Pont de Nemours & Company, Inc, and is made available through the courtesy of the designer and his sponsor.

The American Standards Association in February, 1939, organized a sectional committee designated as Z38 to develop standards in the field of photography exclusive of cinematography. This action followed an invitation issued by the International Standards Association at a meeting in Budapest in September, 1936, for the American Standards Association to take the secretariat for international standardization in photography other than cinematography; and the International Standards Association restricted its project 36 to cinematography with the German standardizing body holding the secretariat.

American Standard
Specifications for
Films for Permanent Records

1. Scope

1.1 Photographic films for permanent records may be considered as processed films ready for storage in repositories. They may also be considered as unexposed, undeveloped photographic films so constituted in manufacture that they will have maximum storage life when properly processed. The present standard is concerned both with raw stock for permanent record films and with the processed films ready for storage. The standard is not restricted to roll films perforated like motion picture films but applies equally well to unperforated roll films and to sheet films.

1.2 This standard deals only with cellulose acetate-type films having gelatine-silver halide emulsions, developed in ordinary processing solutions to produce what is normally called a black-and-white photographic image. Silver halide layers that produce colored images by means of their chemical composition, or treatment in processing, are excluded. Likewise excluded are black-and-white silver halide images that have been chemically altered by treatments after processing, such as reduction or intensification.

1.3 The terminology employed in this standard follows the established practice of the American Standards Association, using the word "shall" in cases where the requirement is mandatory and using the word "should" to denote the advisory status of a recommendation.

2. Definitions

2.1 Permanent Record Film. Permanent record film is photographic material so composed and treated that the image and support shall have maximum keeping quality under ordinary room-storage conditions.

2.2 Raw Stock. Raw stock is sensitized photographic material that has not undergone the process of development.

2.3 Film Base. The film base is the support for the photographic layer or photographic film with the light-sensitive layer removed.

2.4 Photographic Layer. The photographic layer is the light-sensitive medium capable of producing an image by means of the photographic process; specifically a gelatine-silver halide emulsion layer.

2.5 Cellulose Acetate Type Films. Cellulose acetate type films are photographic films composed mainly of cellulose esters of acetic, propionic, or butyric acids.

3. Raw Stock Requirements

3.1 Base. Film for permanent record use shall comply with the following requirements for ignition point, slowness of burning, and low nitrogen content.

3.1.1 Ignition Time. A sample 350 mm (13.78 inches) long and 8 mm (0.31 inch) wide shall take longer than 10 minutes to ignite when placed in an oven at $+300$ C ($+572$ F) as described in 5.1.1.

3.1.2 Rapidity of Burning. A sample 350 mm (13.78 inches) long, 35 mm (1.38 inches) wide and 0.08 mm (0.0031 inch) or more in thickness shall require longer than 45 seconds to burn under the test conditions described in 5.1.2.

3.1.3 Nitrogen Content. Safety film for permanent-record use must contain not over 0.15-percent nitrate nitrogen as determined by the method described in 5.1.3.

3.2 Photographic Layer. Gelatine-silver halide emulsions shall be used for permanent records that are suitable for development either as original negatives, as positive prints from negatives, or as direct positives by the reversal-development process. Photographic materials producing final images composed of dyes shall not be used for permanent record films.

4. Processed Film Requirements

4.1 Base. Film for permanent records, after being processed, shall comply with the following requirements.

4.1.1 Relative Viscosity. The relative viscosity of acetone solutions of processed film which has been heated 72 hours at +100C (+212F) and of unheated film, shall not differ by more than 5 percent when measured according to 5.2.

4.1.2 Stability of pH. The pH of acetone-water solutions of processed film which has been heated 72 hours at +100 C (+212 F) and of unheated film, shall not differ by more than 0.5 pH unit when measured according to 5.3.

4.2 Base Plus Emulsion Layer. After being processed, film for permanent records shall comply with the following requirements.

4.2.1 Flexibility. Processed film, conditioned at room temperature and 65-percent relative humidity shall stand at least 16 single folds in the Pfund tester* (19 mm [0.75 inch], between jaws) without breaking. After 72 hours exposure to a temperature of +100 C (+212 F), the material shall not lose more than 25 percent in folding endurance under the test conditions prescribed in 5.4.

4.3 Emulsion Layer. Processed film for permanent records shall comply with the following requirements.

4.3.1 Color of Image. The developer used and the process of development employed shall have produced a photographic image essentially black and colorless when viewed by transmitted light. Stained or toned images shall not be accepted for permanent-record use.

4.3.2 Residual Thiosulphate Content. After processing, the film shall contain not more than 0.005 mg per square inch of sodium thiosulphate ($Na_2S_2O_3$) as determined by the test method prescribed in 5.5.

5. Test Methods

5.1 Tests for Film Base for Permanent-Record Use.† A sample of film base freed from emulsion shall pass the following tests.

5.1.1 Ignition Time. The ignition time of photographic films is measured as follows:

(*a*) A sample 35 mm (1.38 inches) long and 8 mm (0.31 inch) wide shall be cut from the film to be tested. The sample shall be free of perforations as far as practicable. All gelatin layers shall

be removed by washing in warm water, and the sample shall then be dried for at least 12 hours by being suspended freely in air having a temperature of +18 to +22 C (+64.4 to +71.6 F) and a relative humidity of 40 to 50 percent.

(*b*) The test shall be made in an electric resistance oven, the interior of which shall be in the form of a vertical cylinder (preferably with a rounded bottom), having a diameter of 70 mm (2.76 inches) and a mean height of 70 mm (2.76 inches). The top of the oven shall be closed by means of a closely overlapping lid, having 2 holes of 7 mm (0.27 inch) and 15 mm (0.59 inch), respectively, the centers being at a distance of about 15 mm (0.59 inch) from each other. A thermocouple shall be introduced through the smaller opening, the connecting wires having a porcelain coating fitting tightly into the hole. Alternatively, the temperature in the cylinder may be measured by means of a mercury thermometer, protected from rising heat by means of a cork disk lying a little above the lid.

(*c*) The oven shall be brought to, and maintained at, a temperature of +300±3C (+572 ±5.4F). When this temperature is reached, the sample, attached to a thin U-shaped wire hook, shall be introduced through the larger opening. The thermocouple (or the thermometer) and the sample shall be fixed in such a way that the thermojunction (or the mercury bulb) and the center of the sample shall be at an equal depth of about 35 mm (1.38 inches).

(*d*) The time interval from the insertion of the sample to the ignition of the sample is recorded as the ignition time.

(*e*) Between tests, the oven shall be thoroughly aired.

5.1.2 Rapidity of Burning. The burning time of photographic films is measured as follows:

(*a*) A sample 350 mm (13.78 inches) long and 35 mm (1.38 inches) wide shall be cut from the film to be tested. All gelatin layers are to be removed by washing in warm water. The sample shall then be dried for at least 12 hours by being suspended freely in air having a temperature of +18 to +22 C (+64.4 to +71.61 F) and a relative humidity of 40 to 50 percent.

(*b*) The sample shall be marked at a point 50 mm (1.97 inches) from one end. The sample shall be perforated with holes 3 mm (0.118 inch) in diameter along both edges. Perforations are to be at intervals of not more than 32 mm (1.26 inches).

---

*See Appendix for details of Pfund Folding Endurance Tester.
†Test methods for ignition time, rapidity of burning, and nitrogen content are identical with those specified in American Standard Definition for Safety Photographic Film, Z38.3.1-1943, or latest revision thereof.

(c) A wire having a diameter of not more than 0.5 mm (0.020 inch) shall be threaded through the perforations on one side so that the sample is supported at points not more than 32 mm (1.26 inches) apart. With the wire stretched horizontally and the sample hanging vertically from it, the bottom corner of the marked end is to be ignited.

(d) The time which elapses from the moment the flame reaches the mark until the sample is completely burned shall be recorded as the burning time. If the sample does not ignite, or if it does not completely burn, the burning time is recorded as infinity.

(e) The test shall be made in a room free from draughts and immediately after the period of drying. At least 3 tests shall be made.

(f) Should the sample to be tested be shorter than 350 mm (13.8 inches), the required minimum burning time shall be prorated in accordance with the actual length of the sample.

5.1.3 Nitrogen Content. The film base shall not contain more than 0.15-percent nitrogen combined as cellulose nitrate. The determination for nitrogen shall be made as follows:

(a) Place 2.00 grams of film base, emulsion removed, in an 800-ml Kjeldahl flask. Ninety (90) ml of 30-percent sodium hydroxide and 10 ml of ethyl alcohol are added. The sample is heated on the steam bath or over a low flame, and 25 ml of 30-percent hydrogen peroxide are added slowly with agitation, using a stirring rod or shaking the flask. When the first portion of hydrogen peroxide is boiled out, another 25-ml portion of hydrogen peroxide is added, which is usually sufficient to dissolve completely the film base. The contents of the flask will now be made 200 ml.

(b) The solution is evaporated over a flame to about 75 ml to remove the last traces of ammonia. (During evaporation, mechanical loss by entrainment may occur if the solution is boiled down too far, thus giving a low result.) The solution is then diluted to a total of 350 ml with distilled water and cooled; immediately before connecting the flask to Kjeldahl apparatus, quickly add 2.5 grams of DeVarda's alloy. The total volume of the sample at the time of the addition of the DeVarda's alloy must be closely controlled. Adding too much or too little water changes the alkali concentration so that the rate of the reaction with the alloy and the corresponding reduction of the sodium nitrate present will be erratic. About 200 ml of distillate are col-

lected in a 500-ml Erlenmeyer flask containing 50 ml of standard tenth-normal sulphuric acid. When distilling the sample after the addition of the DeVarda's alloy, some alkali may be carried over into the standard acid by entrainment if the distillation is carried too far or is too vigorous, thus giving a high result. The excess acid is back titrated with tenth-normal sodium hydroxide, using methyl red as indicator.

(c) A blank determination is made on the reagents, using the same quantities that are used in the actual determination. (The difference in the number of milliliters of hydroxide required for the blank and the sample, multiplied by 0.07, gives the percentage of nitrogen.)

5.2 Test for Relative Viscosity. Four (4) samples of processed film weighing 1.000 gram each are cut from the specimen. Two (2) of the samples are heated in air at +100C (+212F) for 72 hours. Each of the samples is dissolved in approximately 95 ml of reagent grade acetone in 100-ml volumetric flasks. Solution may be effected by repeated shakings for one to two hours or allowing it to stand overnight. After solution of the film base is completed and the emulsion has settled to the bottom, the flasks are immersed in a water bath maintained at $+30\pm0.05C$ ($+86\pm0.09F$). When temperature equilibrium has been reached and the volume of the solution adjusted to 100 ml, a 5-ml portion is transferred to an Ostwald pipette immersed in the same constant-temperature bath. The time of flow of the solution through the capillary of the pipette is measured to at least ⅕ of a second. The time of flow is also measured for 5 ml of the pure solvent. Not less than 3 readings should be made for each 5-ml portion. The relative viscosity is then calculated as the ratio of the time of flow of the solution to the time of flow of the solvent. Duplicate determinations shall be made on both the original and heat-treated film sample and the duplicates should agree within ³⁄₁₀ of a second. The change in relative viscosity caused by heat treating shall not exceed 5 percent.

5.3 Test for pH Stability. Four (4) samples of processed film weighing 1.000 gram each are cut from the specimen. Two (2) of the samples are heat treated in air at +100C (+212F) for 72 hours. Each sample is placed in a 200-ml Erlenmeyer flask and dissolved in 100 ml of acetone-water solution containing 10 percent by volume of water. Solution may be effected by repeated shakings for one to two hours or allowing it to stand overnight. After solution of the film base is complete, the pH of the solutions is measured with a glass electrode. The change in pH between the original and aged samples shall not exceed 0.5-pH unit. Duplicate determinations shall be made on both the original and heat-treated film sample and the duplicate shall agree within 0.1-pH unit. Both the water and acetone used shall have been purified by distillation.

5.4 Test for Flexibility.

Flexibility is determined by means of a Pfund folding endurance tester,* used as described below, which is the technique described by Weber and Hill, National Bureau of Standards Miscellaneous Publication M158. While the movable jaw is at its maximum distance from the stationary jaw, the folding endurance tester is fitted with a sample of the material to be tested that has been cut approximately 15 × 50 mm (0.59 × 1.97 inches). The film is folded by moving the free jaw until it touches the stationary jaw and then returning it until it touches the stop plate. The folds are caused to form alternately on opposite sides of the jaws by directing the film with a blunt instrument such as the eraser of a lead pencil. The number of folds sustained by the film before breaking is recorded as the folding endurance. The test shall be carried out with the samples conditioned at room temperature and 65-percent relative humidity.

5.5 Test for Residual Thiosulphate

5.5.1 Mercuric Chloride Method.† The mercuric chloride method of test is used to test the

*See Appendix for construction details.

residual sodium thiosulphate (hypo) content of the processed film.

(*a*) One (1) square inch of film (1.632-inch strip of 16-mm film or 0.75-inch strip of 35-mm film) is immersed in a shell vial 19 × 127 mm (0.75 × 4 inches) containing 10 ml of the following solution:

(1)	Potassium bromide	25 grams
(2)	Mercuric chloride	25 grams
(3)	Water to make	1 liter

(*b*) After the sample has remained in the above solution for 15 minutes, the turbidity is compared with that of 3 similar shell vials containing the above solution, 1 with no hypo, 1 with 0.005 mg, and 1 with 0.010-mg hypo or sodium thiosulphate ($Na_2S_2O_3$). The vials shall be agitated to uniformly distribute the opalescent precipitate. The vials containing the unknown and standard comparison solutions shall be equally illuminated from a light source located on the side opposite to that of the observer and shall be viewed in a darkened room against a black background along a line which makes an appreciable angle (approximately 30 to 45 degrees) with the line of illumination.

(*c*) The light source shall consist of either a mercury vapor lamp in a housing, or a fluorescent lamp (6500 degrees K, daylight type) with shade, or in an illuminator housing, to give only directed illumination, and fitted with an opaque shield to prevent direct light from reaching the eyes of the observer. The criterion is that the turbidity of the tested solution shall not exceed that of the one having 0.005 mg of hypo.

†The mercuric chloride method of test is described in detail by Crabtree and Ross in the Journal of the Society of Motion Picture Engineers, Vol 14, p 419 (1930).

Appendix

Pfund Folding Endurance Tester.

Fig. 1

Assembled View

[NOTE: A lever-actuated counter may be mounted on the instrument to record the number of strokes.

Should the samples tend to break near the jaws rather than at the center of the loop, a stop may be inserted near the stationary jaw to prevent the stationary and movable jaws from touching. This stop should not extend more than 0.020 inch (0.51 mm) from the stationary jaw.]

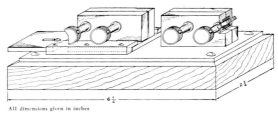

All dimensions given in inches

Fig. 2

Base Construction Details

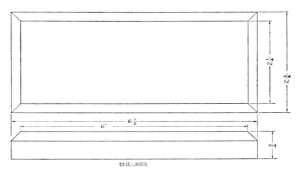

BASE - WOOD

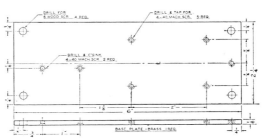

BASE PLATE - BRASS I REQ.

All dimensions given in inches

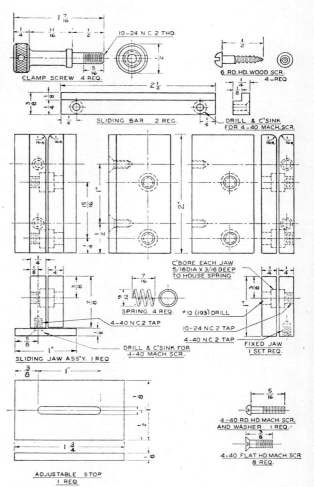

Fig. 3
Construction Details

All dimensions given in inches

American Standard

Dimensions for 16mm Film, Perforated Two Edges

ASA
Reg. U.S. Pat. Off.

PH22.5–1953

Revision of Z22.5–1947
*UDC 778.5

Page 1 of 2 pages

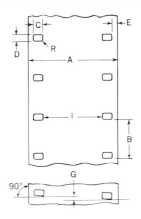

Dimensions	Inches	Millimeters
*A	0.629 ± 0.001	15.98 ± 0.03
†B	0.3000 ± 0.0005	7.620 ± 0.013
C	0.0720 ± 0.0004	1.83 ± 0.01
D	0.0500.± 0.0004	1.27 ± 0.01
*E	0.036 ± 0.002	0.91 ± 0.05
G	Not > 0.001	Not > 0.025
I	0.413 ± 0.001	10.490 ± 0.025
‡L	30.00 ± 0.03	762.00 ± 0.76
R	0.010	0.25

These dimensions and tolerances apply to negative and positive raw stock immediately after cutting and perforating.

* For low-shrink film as defined in Appendix 2, A shall be 0.628 ± 0.001 and E shall be 0.0355 ± 0.0020 in.

† In any group of four consecutive perforations, the maximum difference of pitch shall not exceed 0.001 in. and should be as much smaller as possible.

‡ This dimension represents the length of any 100 consecutive perforation intervals.

Approved December 17, 1953, by the American Standards Association, Incorporated
Sponsor: Society of Motion Picture and Television Engineers

*Universal Decimal Classification

Authors' notes: For 16mm perforated 1 edge (for sound) omit the row of sprocket holes on the left side of the diagram.

For 16mm unperforated film, omit both rows of sprocket holes.

(These Appendixes are not a part of American Standard Dimensions
for 16mm Film, Perforated Two Edges, PH22.5–1953.)

Appendix 1

The dimensions given in this standard represent the practice of film manufacturers in that the dimensions and tolerances are for film immediately after perforation. The punches and dies themselves are made to tolerances considerably smaller than those given, but owing to the fact that film is a plastic material, the dimensions of the slit and perforated film never agree exactly with the dimensions of the punches and dies. Shrinkage of the film, due to change in moisture content or loss of residual solvents, invariably results in a change in these dimensions during the life of the film. This change is generally uniform throughout the roll.

The uniformity of perforation is one of the most important of the variables affecting steadiness of projection.

Variations in pitch from roll to roll are of little significance compared to variations from one sprocket hole to the next. Actually, it is the maximum variation from one sprocket hole to the next within any small group that is important. This is one of the reasons for the method of specifying uniformity in dimension B.

Appendix 2

In the early days of 16mm film the safety base used for this film had the characteristic of shrinking very rapidly to a certain fairly definite amount and then not shrinking much more. Although this film tended to swell at high humidities, nevertheless the shrinkage that occurred in the package before the user received the film was always at least as great as any swell that might occur due to high humidities at the time of use. This meant that the user never encountered film, even at high humidities, that had greater width than that specified in the standards. This meant that camera and projector manufacturers seldom ran into trouble so long as their film gates would readily pass film at the upper limit of the slitting tolerances, namely 0.630 in.

Within the past few years, however, a safety base with lower shrinkage characteristics began to be used. Although this film was less susceptible than the previous film to swelling at high humidities, nevertheless the shrinkage characteristics were low enough so that this shrinkage did not always compensate for the swell at high humidities.

For this reason film slit at the mid point of the tolerance for width, namely 0.629 in., would occasionally swell at high humidities to such an extent that it would bind in film gates designed to pass film with the width of 0.630 in. The manufacturers, therefore, were compelled to slit at the lower edge of the tolerance permitted by the previous edition of this standard. Variations in their slitting width, however, sometimes produced film slit below the limits of the standard.

This revision has therefore been adopted in order that the manufacturers may slit low-shrink film within the standard and still produce film which does not exceed 0.630 in. even at high humidities.

For the purpose of this specification, low-shrink film base is film base which, when coated with emulsion and any other normal coating treatment, perforated, kept in the manufacturer's sealed container for 6 months, exposed, processed, and stored exposed to air for a period not to exceed 30 days at 65 to 75 F and 50 to 60% relative humidity and measured under like conditions of temperature and humidity, shall have shrunk not more than 0.2% from its original dimension at the time of perforating. The final measurement should be made after conditioning the film for 24 hours to a humidity of 55 ± 5%.

This definition of low-shrink film is to be used as a guide to film manufacturers, and departure therefrom shall not be cause for rejection of the film.

American Standard

Dimensions for
35mm Motion-Picture Positive Raw Stock

ASA
Reg. U.S. Pat. Office

PH22.36-1954
Revision of Z22.36-1947

*UDC 778.5:771.5

Page 1 of 2 pages

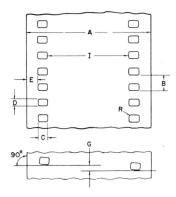

Dimensions	Inches	Millimeters
A	1.377 ± 0.001	34.98 ± 0.03
B	0.1870 ± 0.0005	4.750 ± 0.013
C	0.1100 ± 0.0004	2.794 ± 0.01
D	0.0780 ± 0.0004	1.98 ± 0.01
E	0.079 ± 0.002	2.01 ± 0.05
*G	Not > 0.001	Not > 0.025
I	0.999 ± 0.002	25.37 ± 0.05
†L	18.70 ± 0.015	474.98 ± 0.38
R	0.020	0.51

These dimensions apply to the film immediately after cutting and perforating
This film is used for motion-picture prints and sound recording.

* Method of indicating G is the main change from Z22.36–1947.

† This dimension represents the length of any 100 consecutive perforation intervals.

Approved April 5, 1954, by the American Standards Association, Incorporated
Sponsor: Society of Motion Picture and Television Engineers   *Universal Decimal Classification

Authors' note : For 35mm unperforated film omit both rows of sprocket holes.

Appendix
(This Appendix is not a part of the foregoing Standard.)

The dimensions given in this standard represent the practice of film manufacturers in that the dimensions are for film immediately after perforation. The punches and dies themselves are made to tolerances considerably smaller than those given, but owing to the fact that film is a plastic material, the dimensions of the slit and perforated film never agree exactly with the dimensions of the punches and dies. Shrinkage of the film, due to change in moisture content or loss of residual solvents, invariably results in a change in these dimensions during the life of the film. This change is generally uniform throughout the film.

The uniformity of perforation is one of the most important of the variables affecting steadiness of projection.

Variations in pitch from roll to roll are of little significance compared to variations from one sprocket hole to the next. Actually, it is the maximum variation from one sprocket hole to the next within any small group that is important.

PH22.36-1954

American Standard Dimensions for
70-Millimeter Perforated (and Unperforated) Film
(Cutting and Perforating Standard)

Reg. U. S. Pat. Off.
Z38.1.3-1948
Revision of
Z38.1.3-1941
*UDC 771.53

1. Scope

1.1 This standard is not intended for use in the motion picture field. Its purpose is to provide a film for still pictures and various scientific recording instruments such as oscillographs, electrocardiographs, seismographs, and similar instruments, and in its development no consideration was given to its use for motion picture purposes.

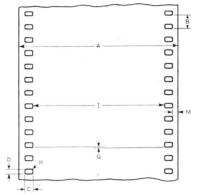

Dimensions and Tolerances

	Inches		Millimeters	
A	2.754	± 0.002	69.95	± 0.05
B	0.234	± 0.001	5.944	± 0.025
C	0.1300	± 0.0008	3.302	± 0.020
D	0.0800	± 0.0008	2.032	± 0.020
M	0.099	± 0.004	2.513	± 0.10
I	2.296	± 0.004	58.32	± 0.10
G	Not over	0.002	Not over	0.05
L*	23.400	± 0.030	594.36	± 0.76
R	0.016		0.406	
Thickness	0.006	± 0.001	0.1525	± 0.0254

* L = the length of any 100 consecutive perforation intervals.

NOTE 1: Unperforated 70-mm film shall have the same thickness and width ("A") dimensions as perforated film.

NOTE 2: These dimensions and tolerances apply to the material immediately after cutting and perforating.

Approved November 10, 1948, by the American Standards Association, Incorporated

Sponsor: Optical Society of America   *Universal Decimal Classification

American Standard for
Reels for Processed Microfilm

ASA
Reg. U.S. Pat. Off.
Z38.7.17-1946

UDC 778.14

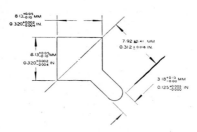

1. Spindle Holes

1.1 The spindle hole in one flange shall be square with a keyway at one corner as shown in the figure. The spindle hole in the other flange shall be either round, with a diameter of: $8.13 \, ^{+0.05}_{-0.10}$ mm ($0.320 \, ^{+0.002}_{-0.004}$ in.), or as shown in the figure.

2. Core

2.1 The diameter of the core shall be: 31.75 ± 0.38 mm (1.250 ± 0.015 in.).

3. Separation and Thickness of Flanges

3.1 For 16-mm reels, the space between the 2 flanges shall be: 16.76 ± 0.25 mm (0.660 ± 0.010 in.) at the core and $16.76 \, ^{+1.14}_{-0.64}$ mm ($0.660 \, ^{+0.045}_{-0.025}$ in.) at the periphery.

3.2 For 35-mm reels, the space between the 2 flanges shall be: 35.74 ± 0.25 mm (1.407 ± 0.010 in.) at the core and $35.74 \, ^{+1.14}_{-0.64}$ mm ($1.407 \, ^{+0.045}_{-0.025}$ in.) at the periphery.

3.3 The flange thickness, including embossings, shall not exceed 1.52 mm (0.060 in.).

4. Capacity and Outside Diameter

4.1 The normal capacities of microfilm reels and the standard outside diameters for reels of these sizes are:

(a) 16-mm reels
100-ft capacity: 93.42 ± 0.38 mm
(3.678 ± 0.015 in.)
50-ft capacity: 73.81 ± 0.38 mm
(2.906 ± 0.015 in.)

(b) 35-mm reels
100-ft capacity: 93.42 ± 0.38 mm
(3.678 ± 0.015 in.)

4.2 If reels of other capacities are required, the dimensions of the first three sections of this standard shall be met. In no case shall the outside diameter exceed that specified for 100-ft reels.

Universal Decimal Classification

Approved August 9, 1946, by the American Standards Association.
Sponsor: Optical Society of America

Authors' note: This standard is under revision at present.

APPENDIX C

American Standard Nomenclature for
Parts of a Photographic Objective Lens

Reg. U. S. Pat. Off.
Z38.4.19-1948
*UDC 771 35

1. Scope

1.1 This standard defines the terms "optical system," "member," "component," "element," "front," and "back" as applied to a photographic objective lens.

2. Nomenclature Applying to the Parts of a Photographic Objective Lens

2.1 Optical System. The optical system includes all the optical parts of a photographic lens which contribute to the formation of an image on the photographic emulsion.

2.2 Member. A member of an optical system is a group of parts considered as an entity because of the proximity of its parts or because it has a distinct but not always entirely separate function.

2.3 Component. A component is a subdivision of a member. It may consist of two or more parts cemented together or with near and approximately matching surfaces.

2.4 Element. An element is a single uncompounded lens; that is, a part constructed of a single piece.

2.5 Front of Photographic Lens. The front of a photographic lens, in general, is the end carrying the engraving, and usually facing the longer conjugate. A notable exception is certain lenses intended to be used in photomicrography in which the front of the lens faces the shorter conjugate.

2.6 Back of Photographic Lens. The back of a photographic lens, in general, is the end carrying the mounting thread or other attaching means, and usually facing the shorter conjugate.

Approved March 3, 1948, by the American Standards Association
Sponsor: Optical Society of America

*Universal Decimal Classification

American Standard Methods of
Designating and Measuring
Focal Lengths and Focal Distances
of Photographic Lenses

Reg. U. S. Pat. Off.
Z38.4.21-1948

SPONSOR
Optical Society of America

Approved March 3, 1948
American Standards Association

Foreword

(This Foreword is not a part of the American Standard Methods of Designating and Measuring Focal Lengths and Focal Distances of Photographic Lenses, Z38.4.21-1948.)

This American Standard defines the focal lengths of photographic objective lenses in terms of the size of the image of an infinitely distant object produced by the lens. Two types of focal length are defined —the equivalent focal length which, unless otherwise specified, is based upon the scale of the image near the axis of the lens in the plane of best axial definition, and the calibrated focal length which is based upon the average scale of the image over the entire used field measured in the plane of best average definition. This last named focal length is particularly useful in airplane mapping or for other photogrammetric purposes. Other terms in ordinary use, such as front focal length, back focal length, and flange focal length, are also defined. This specification also describes methods for measuring the focal lengths in accordance with the new definitions and suggests source of illumination, photographic emulsion, and development to be used in making the tests when not otherwise specified. Methods of measurement in which the focal plane is judged visually are not recommended because experience shows that such measurements, in general, will not agree with the results obtained by photographic methods.

Suggestions for improvement based upon experience gained in the use of these methods will always be welcome. They should be sent to the American Standards Association, 70 East Forty-fifth Street, New York 17, New York.

American Standard Methods of
Designating and Measuring Focal Lengths and Focal Distances of Photographic Lenses

1. Scope

1.1 This standard defines the equivalent focal length, the calibrated focal length, the front and back focal distances, and the flange focal distance; and gives methods for their measurement.

2. Distinguishing Characteristics of the Different Focal Lengths

2.1 Equivalent Focal Length. The equivalent focal length of a lens determines the scale of the image produced by the lens. When a given object is at an infinite distance, images produced by lenses of the same equivalent focal length will be equal in size, and images produced by lenses of different equivalent focal lengths will vary in size directly as the respective equivalent focal lengths. For the simpler types of photographic lenses (not including the telephoto lenses) the equivalent focal length is approximately equal to the distance of the lens from the image plane when the camera is focused for a distant object.

2.2 Calibrated Focal Length. The equivalent focal length as defined in this standard is a means for specifying the scale of the image in the immediate neighborhood of the axis. In the presence of distortion the scale of the image is different in different parts of the field of view. Even if a photographic objective is only moderately well corrected, for most photographic purposes this change of scale can be neglected and the equivalent focal length is a satisfactory measure of image size. When a lens is to be used for photogrammetric purposes, however, this change of scale over the picture is important. For such work the equivalent focal length should be replaced by the calibrated focal length. The calibrated focal length is a focal length adjusted to the average scale of the image over the entire field of view. The calibrated focal length is the value to be applied when a photograph is to be used for map making or other photogrammetric purposes. By its use the errors due to distortion are distributed more uniformly over the area mapped and the maximum errors are reduced. The use of the calibrated focal length does not require a refocusing of the lens and does not affect the ad-

justment of the lens with respect to the image plane in the camera.

2.3 Front, Back, and Flange Focal Distance. The equivalent focal length and the calibrated focal length relate only to the optical characteristics of the lens. Front and back focal distances and flange focal distance are terminated at one end by a part of the lens or lens mount and are useful when determining mechanical interferences or installing a lens in a camera. It is not safe to use any one of these three focal distances as a measure of image scale.

3. Definitions

3.1 Equivalent Focal Length. The equivalent focal length, often referred to more simply as the focal length, is defined by the equation

$$f = \lim_{\beta \doteq 0} \frac{\gamma'}{\tan \beta} \qquad \text{Eq 1}$$

where γ' is the transverse distance from the principal focus to the center of the image in the image-space focal plane of an infinitely distant object point which lies in a direction making an angle β with the axis of the objective.

3.2 Calibrated Focal Length. The calibrated focal length is an adjusted value of the equivalent focal length so chosen that the extreme positive and negative values of distortion over the useful field, as defined by Equation 3, are equal in magnitude.

3.3 Front Focal Distance. The front focal distance is the distance measured from the principal focus located in the front space to the vertex of the front surface.

3.4 Back Focal Distance. The back focal distance is the distance measured from the vertex of the back surface of a photographic lens to the principal focus located in the back space.

3.5 Flange Focal Distance. The flange focal distance is the distance measured from the locating surface of the lens mount to the principal focus located in the image space.

4. Methods of Measuring Focal Lengths

4.1 Equivalent Focal Length. To measure the equivalent focal length a photographic plate is placed in the focal plane of the image space. (Unless otherwise specified the focal plane is defined as the plane of best photographic imagery for an infinitely distant axial point.) A collimator and reticle may be conveniently used to provide an infinitely distant object point. Exposures are made with the beam of light from the collimator directed along the axis of the lens and at a series of angles β_1, β_2, etc. On the resultant negative, measurements are made of the distances (γ_1',γ_2', etc) of the images corresponding to the angles β_1, β_2, etc, from the axial image to the images corresponding to the angles β_1, β_2, etc, and the quotients $\dfrac{\gamma_1'}{\tan \beta_1}$, $\dfrac{\gamma_2'}{\tan \beta_2}$, etc, formed. The limiting value of this quotient as β approaches zero is the equivalent focal length.

4.1.1 If a photographic objective were free from distortion the quotient would be invariant with respect to the value of β. For many photographic purposes the distortion is negligible for points distant from the center of the useful field not more than one-fifth of its radius, and, consequently, it will very often be possible to obtain a satisfactorily accurate value of f by a single determination of β and γ' for a point lying near the axis.

4.1.2 The foregoing method is derived directly from the definition of equivalent focal length and has the merit of being based on a photographic method. For an objective free of aberration and diffraction effects, the focal length as thus defined would be exactly equal to the distance from the second nodal point of the objective to the principal focus. As a consequence of this equality the focal length may be measured on an optical bench equipped with a nodal slide. By means of the nodal slide the photographic objective is mounted to rotate about an axis through its second nodal point and the distance from this nodal point to position of best axial focus for an infinitely distant object point is measured. An important factor of uncertainty in using this method is the difference between the position of best focus as judged visually on the optical bench and the best focus as determined photographically by the first method of measurement.

4.2 Calibrated Focal Length

4.2.1 To compute the calibrated focal length let γ_1', γ_2', etc, represent the distances, in the focal plane, from the axial point to the images of infinitely distant object points lying in the directions making angles β_1, β_2, etc with the axis of the objective, and if f is the equivalent focal length,

in the absence of distortion, then

$$\gamma_1' = f \tan \beta_1$$
$$\gamma_2' = f \tan \beta_2$$
$$\text{Eq 2}$$

In the presence of distortion

$$\gamma_1' = f \tan \beta_1 + \triangle \gamma_1'$$
$$\gamma_2' = f \tan \beta_2 + \triangle \gamma_2'$$
$$\text{Eq 3}$$

4.2.2 The added terms are the values of the linear distortion for values β_1, β_2, etc, respectively. The values of γ' and β are measured directly. It is evident that the individual values of the distortion defined by the above group of equations can be changed by changing the value of f. If f is the equivalent focal length, as defined in this standard, in many instances values of the distortion in the neighborhood of the axial image point will be small, and near the edge of the field the values will be large and predominantly either negative or positive.

4.2.3 It is convenient to have targets at 5-degree intervals from the center of the field to the extreme corner. Infinitely distant targets are conveniently provided by a group of collimators or by one collimator which can be successively placed in the required angular positions. Exposures are made and the γ' corresponding to each angular distance from the axis is determined. In accordance with Equation 3 the calibrated focal length is determined as the value of f, which gives maximum positive and negative values of distortion equal in absolute value within the field to be covered. When determining the calibrated focal length it is customary to choose the plane of best average definition as the focal plane.

4.3 Front Focal Distance. To determine the front focal distance the focal plane in the object space is determined, preferably by a photographic method. The measured distance from this focal plane to the vertex of the front surface of the lens is the required focal distance.

4.4 Back Focal Distance. To determine the back focal distance, the focal plane in the image space is determined, preferably by a photographic method. The measured distance from the vertex of the back surface of the lens to the focal plane is the required focal distance.

4.5 Flange Focal Distance. To determine the flange focal distance the procedure is the same as for measuring the back focal distance, except that measurement of length is made from the plane of the locating surface of the flange to the focal plane.

5. Factors Affecting Precision of Measurement of Focal Length

5.1 A photographic lens always has residual aberrations which restrict the precision with which the equivalent focal length can be measured. Consequently, to determine a value of the equivalent focal length which can be reproduced with precision, it is necessary to specify the color of the source, the diaphragm opening, the spectral sensitivity of the photographic emulsion used, and the criterion for selecting the focal plane.

5.2 Distinguishing between Two Measured Values of Equivalent Focal Lengths. On the basis of first order imagery the focal length is independent of the direction in which the light passes through the lens, but measurements made on a photographic objective for the two orientations may yield values differing slightly because of the difference in extent to which the aberrations are corrected for the two sides of the lens. When it is necessary to distinguish between these two measured values of equivalent focal lengths, one is based upon a relation between an infinitely distant object and its image in the back focal plane is referred to as the back equivalent focal length. The other is referred to as the front equivalent focal length. Usually when the term "focal length" or "equivalent focal length," without additional modifiers is used, it is a less precise method of referring to the back equivalent focal length.

5.3 As a source it is customary to use an electric lamp operated at a specified color temperature either with or without a filter of known transmission, or a source spectrally homogeneous. The diaphragm opening selected for the test should be chosen to conform as closely as practicable with the use to be made of the lens. The photographic emulsion should correspond in spectral sensitivity with the intended use of the lens, but, in some instances, it is desirable to select a finer grained emulsion in order that the position of best definition may be judged more accurately. Except for lenses to be used for fixed focus cameras, it is customary to select the best definition at center of the field as the criterion for selecting the focal plane.

5.4 Absence of Specified Values for Variables. In the absence of specified values for the variables referred to in 5.1 and 5.3, for measurements of focal length and related lengths made on photographic lenses, conventions will apply as given in the following paragraphs.

5.4.1 A tungsten lamp operating at a color temperature of 2360 K, screened by a filter of such nature that the spectral distribution of the transmitted light very closely approximates that of noon sunlight, will serve as source.

NOTE 1. The Davis-Gibson liquid filter satisfies the requirements. See Transactions of the Society of Motion Picture Engineers, **33**, 225 (1928), and Miscellaneous Publications, National Bureau of Standards, No. 114 (1931).
NOTE 2. A filter that may be considered sufficiently close in characteristics to the Davis-Gibson filter is Wratten No. 78. See Macadam, Journal of the Optical Society of America, **35**, 670 (1945).

5.4.2 The diaphragm will be set at the aperture having an f number 1.4 times the f number of the maximum aperture.

Illustration: If the indicated values are 1.8, 2, 2.8, 4, 5.6, etc, the measurements will be made with the iris set at $1.8 \times 1.4 = 2.5$.

5.4.3 The focal plane of a photographic objective is defined as the plane, normal to the axis, of best photographic imagery for an infinitely distant axial object point under conditions as nearly as possible like those under which the objective is intended to be used.

5.4.4 For general purposes, panchromatic plates with a resolving power not less than 40 lines to the millimeter will be used.

5.4.5 The image point corresponding to any infinitely distant object point is defined as the point in the focal plane which best represents the position of the photographic image of the object point. In particular, the image point on the axis is called the principal focus, or the focal point.

6. Computed Value of Equivalent Focal Length

6.1 When one has complete constructional data (radii of curvature, indices of refraction, thicknesses, and separations) it is customary to compute the equivalent focal length as the distance from the second nodal point to the principal focus, this value being determined by application of the simplified equations referred to variously as "first" order, "paraxial," or "Gaussian." Effectively, this amounts to a computation of the focal length when both β and the diameter of the aperture approach zero as a limit. This double limiting process not only eliminates any influence of aberrations upon the focal length but also results in a considerable simplification of the computations. Because of this double limiting process the value obtained by such computation may be significantly different from that defined in 3.1.

American Standard Methods of Designating and Measuring
Apertures and Related Quantities
Pertaining to Photographic Lenses

ASA
Reg. U. S. Pat. Off
Z38.4.20-1948

*UDC 771·35

1. Scope

1.1 This standard defines the clear aperture, entrance pupil, aperture ratio, relative aperture, and *f*-number; and gives methods for their measurement.

2. Definitions

2.1 Clear Aperture. The clear aperture of a lens system, member, component, or element is the opening in the mount that limits the extent of the axial beam incident upon the front surface. It is usually circular and specified by its diameter. The clear aperture is sometimes referred to as the free aperture.

2.2 Effective Aperture. The effective aperture of a photographic objective, for a given setting of the diaphragm, is an opening equivalent to a right section of the largest beam of parallel light from an axial object point that is transmitted by the lens. It is usually circular, or approximately so, and is specified by its diameter.

2.3 Aperture Ratio. The aperture ratio is the ratio 1:N or the fraction $1/N$ (written in this manner with the first member of the ratio or the numerator of the fraction equal to 1) where N is defined by the equation,

$$N = \frac{1}{2\,n\,\sin a}$$

In this formula n is the index of refraction of the medium in which the image is formed (1 if the image is formed in air) and a is the angle, measured in the same medium, between the axis and an extreme ray of the circular conical bundle transmitted by the lens with a given diaphragm setting. (For any magnification the exposure time is proportional to the square of N.) If the aperture ratio is given without qualification its value is that corresponding to the largest indicated diaphragm opening and an infinitely distant object. If the object is at a finite distance, the value of the aperture ratio should be qualified by a statement of the corresponding magnification, thus:

1:4 *at m* = 0.5

indicating that $2\,n \sin a = 0.25$ when the conjugate planes are so selected that lengths in the image

plane are equal to one-half the conjugate lengths in the object plane.

2.4 Relative Aperture. The relative aperture is a measure of the diameter of the entrance pupil in terms of the equivalent focal length. It is written as a fraction, of which the numerator is *f*, referring to the equivalent focal length. To illustrate: the expression *f*/2 signifies that the diameter of the effective aperture is one-half the focal length. For an object at an infinite distance, the denominator of the relative aperture and the second member, N, of the aperture ratio are identical.

> NOTE: The relative aperture is applicable for determination of exposure time only when the object is at an infinite distance. On the other hand, the aperture ratio is applicable for determination of exposure time when the object is at an infinite or at a finite distance. In view of the more general application of the aperture ratio it is recommended that it be used instead of relative aperture whenever possible.

2.5 *f* Number. The *f* number is the denominator in the expression for the relative aperture. Thus, if the relative aperture is *f*/2, the *f* number is 2. More directly, the *f* number is obtained by dividing the equivalent focal length by the diameter of the effective aperture.

3. Methods of Measurement of the Apertures and Related Quantities Pertaining to a Photographic Lens

3.1 Determination of the Diameter of the Effective Aperture

3.1.1 A travelling compound microscope is required with means for translating the microscope in a direction at right angles to its axis through a measured distance not less than the diameter of the maximum effective aperture to be measured. The microscope must be of low power (10× to 20×). provided with a reticle, and with a working distance sufficiently long to permit the microscope to be focused on the limiting opening of the photographic objective through its front member.

3.1.2 The photographic objective, of which the effective aperture is to be measured, is mounted in a convenient position to permit the travelling microscope to be directed parallel to the axis of the

Approved March 3, 1948, by the American Standards Association

Sponsor: Optical Society of America

*Universal Decimal Classification

American Standard Methods of Designating and Measuring
Apertures and Related Quantities
Pertaining to Photographic Lenses

Z38.4.20-1948

objective and focused upon the edge of the opening having the smallest apparent diameter. (The photographic objective is not to be disassembled. This edge is viewed through the lens elements which are normally traversed by image-forming light before passing through the limiting opening. A microscope having a long working distance is required to avoid mechanical interference when looking through the lens elements.) The microscope is then traversed and measurements made to determine the apparent diameter of this opening which is the effective aperture.

3.1.3 When it is not practicable to use a microscope of sufficient working distance to permit the limiting opening to be observed through the lens elements, a source of light as small as practicable and emitting a cone sufficiently large to fill the lens may be placed at the second principal focus, directed toward the objective, and the diameter of the emergent beam measured to give the diameter of the effective aperture. The measurement of the beam should be made as near to the front surface of the objective as is practicable. This method of measurement is subject to a systematic error, the value obtained always being too large because of the angular subtense of the source.

3.2 Determination of the Aperture Ratio

3.2.1 For the special case in which the object is at an infinite distance (magnification $= 0$, N, the second member of the ratio may be determined as the quotient obtained when the equivalent focal length is divided by the effective aperture diameter.

3.2.2 For the general case in which the magnification may have any value, an axial luminous point emitting a cone of light sufficiently large to fill the objective is set up in the object plane corresponding to the prescribed magnification. A pinhole suitably illuminated by a light source and condensing system is a satisfactory source. (This method can be generalized to include zero magnification if the infinitely distant image of a luminous point, as formed by a collimator, is used as a source.) A photographic plate, normal to the axis of the objective, is exposed to record a section of the cone of light proceeding to or from the axial image point. A second section of the cone is similarly recorded at a known distance from the first, and on the same side of the image point. If r_1 and r_2 are the radii of the larger and smaller sections, respectively, as measured on the photographic recordings, and d is the distance separating the two sections, then:

$$a = \tan^{-1} \frac{r_1 - r_2}{d}$$

If n is the index of refraction of the medium in which the angle a is measured ($n = 1$ for air, used in the great majority of cases), the second member of the aperture ratio is $1/(2n \sin a)$. When measuring the aperture ratio by the method of this paragraph, the angular subtense of the object point as viewed from the first nodal point of the photographic objective must be small when compared with the value of the angle, a, between the axis of the objective and the extreme ray proceeding to the image point.

Approved March 3, 1948, by the American Standards Association
Sponsor: Optical Society of America

American Standard for
Distance Scales Marked in Feet for
Focusing Camera Lenses

ASA
Reg. U. S. Pat. Off.
Z38.4.3-1947
Revision of
Z38.4.3-1942
*UDC 771·35

1. General

1.1 Distance scales shall have their markings based on the plane of registration of the sensitized material in the camera to which the lens is fitted. If the lens is not interchangeable, the focusing scale may be computed from any other clearly marked reference plane.

2. Index Mark

2.1 The index mark for indicating the plane on which the distance scale is based shall consist of a circle crossed by a line having a length of between two and three times the diameter of the circle, as shown in the following figure. The line shall be in the plane of the sensitized material (or other plane from which the distance markings are computed).

3. Distance Scale Markings

3.1 Within the limits of the range or form of the camera and the lens fitted thereto, distance markings shall be indicated in terms of feet selected from the following: ∞, 100, 50, 25, 15, 10, 8, 6, 5, 4, etc.

4. Infinity Mark

4.1 Infinity shall be indicated by the mathematical mark for infinity, ∞.

Approved February 20, 1947, by the American Standards Association
Sponsor: Optical Society of America

*Universal Decimal Classification

American Standard for
Distance Scales Marked in Meters
for Focusing Camera Lenses

ASA
Reg. U. S. Pat. Off.
Z38.4.13-1948
Revision of
Z38.4.13-1944
•UDC 771 35

1. Distance Scales — General

1.1 Distance scales shall have their markings based on the plane of registration of the sensitized material in the camera to which the lens is fitted. If the lens is not interchangeable, the focusing scale may be computed from any other clearly marked reference plane.

2. Index Mark

2.1 The index mark for indicating the plane on which the distance scale is based shall consist of a circle crossed by a line having a length of between two and three times the diameter of the circle, as shown in the following figure. The line shall be in the plane of the sensitized material (or other plane from which the distance markings are computed).

3. Distance Scale Markings

3.1 Within the limits of the range or form of the camera and lens fitted thereto distance markings shall be indicated in terms of meters selected from the following: ∞, 30, 20, 15, 10, 7, 5, 4, 3, 2.5, 2, 1.75, 1.5, 1.25, 1.

4. Infinity Mark

4.1 Infinity shall be indicated by the mathematical mark for infinity "∞."

Approved March 3, 1948, by the American Standards Association
Sponsor: Optical Society of America

•Universal Decimal Classification

American Standard

Lens Aperture Markings

Reg. U. S. Pat. Off.
Z38.4.7-1950
(Revision of
Z38.4.7-1943)
*UDC 771.35

1. Symbol for Relative Aperture

1.1 The symbol for relative aperture of a lens shall be $f/$ followed by the numerical value of the quotient of the focal length divided by the effective aperture, as in the example $f/8$. Where preferable, the symbol $f:$ may be used.

2. Tolerance on Maximum Aperture

2.1 The diameter of the bundle of parallel entering rays which pass through the maximum aperture shall be at least 95 percent of the quotient obtained on dividing the marked focal length by the engraved f-number.

3. Standard Series of Diaphragm Markings

3.1 The standard series of diaphragm markings shall be $f/0.7$, 1.0, 1.4, 2.0, 2.8, 4.0, 5.6, 8, 11, 16, 22, 32, 45, 64, 90, 128.

4. Marking of Maximum Aperture

4.1 The maximum relative aperture marked on a lens need not be selected from the above series but should be followed by the above series of stop openings beginning with the next larger number whenever practical and progressing as far as required in the individual application. Example: An $f/1.9$ lens might be engraved $f/1.9$, 2.8, 4, 5.6, 8, etc, if it were believed that to mark it $f/1.9$, 2.0, 2.8, 4.0, 5.6, etc would confuse the markings at the $f/1.9$ end of the scale.

NOTE: See American Standard Methods of Designating and Measuring Apertures and Related Quantities Pertaining to Photographic Lenses, Z38.4.20-1948, or any subsequent revision thereof approved by the American Standards Association, Incorporated, for definitions and methods of measurement of apertures and related quantities of photographic lenses.

Approved March 1, 1950, by the American Standards Association, Incorporated

Sponsor: Optical Society of America

*Universal Decimal Classification

Authors' note: $T\text{-number} = f\text{-number} \div \sqrt{t}$, where $t = \text{transmittance}$ (MIL-STD 150).

American Standard

for

Focal Lengths of Lenses: Marking

Z38.4.4–1942
*UDC 771.35
REAFFIRMED 1947

Focal lengths of lenses marked on the lens mounts shall be in either mm (millimeters) or cm (centimeters). The actual equivalent focal length of a lens shall be within ±4 percent of the marked value. The symbol for focal length shall be lower case "*f*."

Sponsor: Optical Society of America   *Universal Decimal Classification

American Standard

Exposure-Time Markings for
Between-the-Lens Shutters
Used in Still Picture Cameras

Reg. U. S. Pat. Off.
PH3.5-1952
*UDC 771.36

General

This standard is intended to provide a uniform basis for determining and marking the exposure times on between-the-lens shutters used in still picture cameras, and to provide suitable definitions of the terms used. It is recognized that shutters now in use may not fall within the scope of these specifications. However, as implied through the existence of this standard, these specifications are to serve as a guide in subsequent design whenever conditions permit, in order that ultimately all shutters may be compared on a common basis.

1. Scope

1.1 This standard describes the exposure-time markings for between-the-lens shutters used in still picture cameras.

1.2 The quantities defined and selected as standard herein refer to the performance characteristics of between-the-lens shutters without the presence of optics.

2. Definitions

2.1 Total Open Time, t_o. The total open time for a particular exposure-time setting of a between-the-lens shutter is the time interval from the beginning of the opening period to the end of the closing period.

2.2 Efficiency, η. The efficiency of a between-the-lens shutter at a particular diaphragm opening and a particular exposure-time setting is the ratio of the quantity of light actually transmitted by the shutter at those settings to the quantity of light that would have been transmitted had the shutter been fully open at that diaphragm opening for that total open time.

2.3 Effective Exposure Time, t_e. The effective exposure time at a particular diaphragm opening and a particular exposure-time setting of a between-the-lens shutter is the product of the total open time and the efficiency at this particular diaphragm opening. This is the theoretical time which would be required for the quantity of light actually transmitted by the

shutter, at a particular speed setting and diaphragm opening, to pass through an "ideal shutter" with the same diaphragm opening. Such an "ideal shutter" would be one having infinitely small opening and closing periods, *i.e.*, having 100 percent efficiency.

2.4 Maximum Opening. For the purposes of this standard, the maximum opening of a between-the-lens shutter is the maximum diameter of the free opening of the shutter assembly.

2.5 Exposure-Time Marking. The exposure-time marking for a particular exposure-time setting of a between-the-lens shutter is the reciprocal of the effective exposure time at that particular setting when measured at the maximum opening as defined in 2.4.

3. Markings

3.1 Marking Series. The exposure-time markings on a between-the-lens shutter shall be selected from the following series: 800, 400, 200, 100, 50, 25, 10, 5, 2, 1. The highest marking, however, need not necessarily be selected from this series, but should be followed by numbers selected from the above series, beginning with the next lower number whenever practical and progressing as far as required in the particular application.

> EXAMPLE: A shutter with 1/500-second minimum effective exposure time (maximum shutter speed) could be marked 500, 200, 100, 50, etc, if including 400 would confuse the markings at this end of the scale.

4. Performance

4.1 Effective Exposure Time. The effective exposure times of a between-the-lens shutter, when measured at the maximum opening as defined in 2.4, shall not depart from their equivalent marked values by more than 20 percent for exposure-time markings of 1/100 second and longer and by not more than 30 percent for exposure-time markings shorter than 1/100 second at any temperature from $+32$ F (0 C) to $+104$ F ($+40$ C).

4.2 Operation at Low Temperature. A between-the-lens shutter, when cocked and tripped in the normal manner, shall open and completely close at any temperature down to 0 F (-18 C).

Approved December 23, 1952, by the American Standards Association, Incorporated

Sponsor: Photographic Standards (Correlating) Committee   *Universal Decimal Classification

American Standard

Exposure-Time Markings for Focal-Plane Shutters Used in Still Picture Cameras

Reg. U. S. Pat. Off.

PH3.3-1952

*UDC 771.36

Page 1 of 2 pages

General

This standard is intended to provide a uniform basis for determining and marking the exposure times on focal-plane shutters used in still picture cameras, and to provide suitable definitions of the terms used. It is recognized that shutters now in use may not fall within the scope of these specifications. However, as implied through the existence of this standard, these specifications are to serve as a guide in subsequent design whenever conditions permit, in order that ultimately all shutters may be compared on a common basis.

1. Scope

1.1 This standard describes the exposure-time markings for focal-plane shutters used in still picture cameras.

1.2 In this standard three quantities characteristic of the performance of focal-plane shutters have been defined and correlated. As defined in 2.2, 2.3, and 2.4, below, two of these quantities depend on the position of the shutter in the camera (more specifically, on the distance from the shutter slit to the camera focal plane) and on the f number of the lens. The third quantity, effective exposure time, is characteristic of the shutter alone and is used as a basis for the standard exposure-time markings.

2. Definitions

2.1 Symbols. The symbols used in this standard are as follows:

t_o = total open time
η = efficiency
t_e = effective exposure time
w = width of shutter slit
d_s = distance of shutter slit from camera focal (film) plane
v = linear velocity of shutter slit
f = the f number of lens

2.2 Total Open Time, t_o. The total open time of a focal-plane shutter, operating in a camera and with a lens, for a given point in the camera focal plane, is the total time of exposure in seconds at that point. This quantity indicates the motion-stopping ability of the shutter and is determined by the following equation:

$$t_o = \frac{w + d_s/f}{v} \qquad (1)$$

2.3 Efficiency, η. The efficiency of a focal-plane shutter, operating in a camera with a lens, for a given point in the camera focal plane, is the ratio of light transmitted to that point by the shutter-lens combination to the light that would be transmitted to the same point by the lens during the total open time if there were no shutter (or if the shutter were in the focal plane). The equation for determining the efficiency of the focal-plane shutter is:

$$\eta = \frac{w}{w + d_s/f} \qquad (2)$$

2.4 Effective Exposure Time, t_e. The effective exposure time of a focal-plane shutter is the time required for the shutter to move its own width:

$$t_e = \frac{w}{v} \qquad (3)$$

This is the time which would be required for the quantity of light actually transmitted by the shutter, operating at a given distance from the camera focal plane, to be transmitted by the shutter, had it been operating directly in the camera focal plane. By using obvious substitutions, equations 1 and 2 may be transposed into equation 4.

$$t_e = \eta t_o \qquad (4)$$

2.5 Exposure-Time Markings. Each exposure-time marking for a focal-plane shutter is the reciprocal of the arithmetic mean of the maximum and

Approved December 23, 1952, by the American Standards Association, Incorporated

Sponsor: Photographic Standards (Correlating) Committee   *Universal Decimal Classification

minimum effective exposure times over the entire picture aperture at that particular setting.

3. Markings

3.1 Marking Series. The exposure-time markings on a focal-plane shutter shall be selected from one of the following series: 1000, 500, 250, 125, 60, 30, 15, 8, 4, 2, 1, or 800, 400, 200, 100, 50, 25, 10, 5, 2, 1. The highest markings, however, need not necessarily be selected from either series, but should be followed by numbers selected from only one series, beginning with the next lower number whenever practicable and progressing as far as required in the particular application.

EXAMPLE: A shutter with 1/600-second minimum effective exposure time could be marked 600, 250, 125, 60, etc, if including 500 would confuse the markings at this end of the scale.

4. Performance

4.1 Effective Exposure Time. The effective exposure times of a focal-plane shutter, each taken as the reciprocal of the arithmetic mean of the maximum and minimum effective exposure times over the entire picture aperture at each particular setting, shall not depart from their equivalent marked values by more than 25 percent for exposures of 1/400 second and slower and by not more than 33 percent for exposures faster than 1/400 second at any temperature from +32 F (0 C) to +104 F (+40 C).

4.2 Ratio of the Maximum to the Minimum Effective Exposure Time. For effective exposure-time settings faster than 1/50 second, the ratio of the maximum to the minimum effective exposure time over the entire picture aperture shall not exceed 3 to 2 at any temperature from +32 F (0 C) to +104 F (+40 C).

4.3 Operation at Low Temperature. A focal-plane shutter, when wound and released in the normal manner, shall cause an exposure to be initiated and then terminated at any temperature down to 0 F (−18 C).

American Standard	ASA
	Reg. U.S. Pat. Off.
Dimensions of Front Lens Mounts for Cameras	Z38.4.10-1944
	R 1952 as
	PH3.14-1944
	•UDC 771.35

1. External Diameter* of Section of Lens Mount onto Which Lens Attachments Fit

Preferred Standard Diameters (Mm)	Secondary Standard Diameters (Mm)
16.5	13.5
19.5	15.0
21.0	18.0
24.0	22.5
25.5	27.0
28.5	30.0
32.0	33.0
37.0	34.5
42.0	36.0
	39.0
	40.5
	45.0
	48.0
	51.0
	54.0
	57.0
	60.0

Larger sizes by increments of 5.0 mm

Tolerances: + 0
　　　　　　 − 0.25 mm

* External diameter including plating, lacquer, or other finish.

2. Length of bearing surface provided for acceptance of slip-on attachments shall be at least 2 mm for lens mounts up to and including 33 mm in diameter and 3 mm for larger mounts.

Approved July 19, 1944, by the American Standards Association, Incorporated
Sponsor: Optical Society of America   •Universal Decimal Classification

American Standard Specifications for
Threads for Attaching Mounted Lenses to
Photographic Equipment

Reg. U.S. Pat. Of.
Z38.4.11-1944
*UDC 771.35

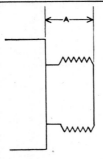

A=Maximum length to end of thread from shoulder,
given in third column

1. Dimensions

Standard Major Diameters for Lens Mounting Threads	Threads per Inch	Maximum Length (From Shoulder to End of Thread-A)
(Inch)		(Inch)
0.500	48	0.156
0.750	32	0.156
1.000	32	0.156
1.250	32	0.187
1.500	32	0.187
1.750	32	0.218
2.000	24	0.218
2.250	24	0.218
2.500	24	0.250
2.750	24	0.250
3.000	24	0.250
3.500	24	0.375
Larger sizes by increments of 0.500	24 for larger sizes	0.375

2. Thread Form

2.1 Thread form shall be American National Form.

3. Limiting Dimensions and Tolerances

3.1 Limiting dimensions and tolerances shall be Class 3, according to National Bureau of Standards Handbook H28, Screw Thread Standards for Federal Services (Section VI, Screw Threads of Special Diameters, Pitches, and Lengths of Engagement).

NOTE 1. The thread specified is that by which lens barrels, or between-the-lens shutters, for example, are attached to lens boards as in the case where flanges are used.
NOTE 2. The above series of dimensions is not intended to preclude the use of the threads specified by the Royal Microscopical Society.

Approved October 27, 1944, by the American Standards Association
Sponsor: Optical Society of America   *Universal Decimal Classification

American Standard Dimensions for

16-Millimeter 100-Foot Film Spool for
Recording Instruments and Still Picture Cameras

Reg. U. S. Pat. Off.

Z38.1.52-1951

*UDC 771.332

Page 1 of 2 Pages

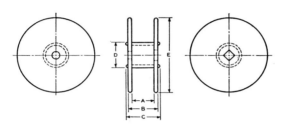

OPTIONAL DRIVE MEANS

| REAR FLANGE | FRONT FLANGE | REAR FLANGE | FRONT FLANGE |

STYLE 3

STYLE 4

STYLE 5

STYLE 6

Approved April 19, 1951, by the American Standards Association, Incorporated

Sponsor: Optical Society of America

*Universal Decimal Classification

American Standard Dimensions for 16-Millimeter 100-Foot Film Spool for Recording Instruments and Still Picture Cameras	ASA Reg. U. S. Pat. Off. Z38.1.52-1951

Page 2 of 2 Pages

16-Millimeter 100-Foot Spool		
Dimension	Inches	Millimeters
A*	0.640 ± 0.008	16.26 ± 0.20
B†	0.755 Max	19.18 Max
C‡	0.770 Max	19.51 Max
D§	1.250 ± 0.030	31.75 ± 0.76
E	3.630 ± 0.030	92.20 ± 0.76
F₁ Concentricity center hole and E‖	Tolerance 0.015	Tolerance 0.38
F₂ Concentricity center hole and D‖	Tolerance 0.015	Tolerance 0.38
I	0.320 ± 0.004	8.13 ± 0.10
O	0.320 ± 0.004	8.13 ± 0.10
P	0.437 ± 0.005	11.10 ± 0.13
Q	0.321 ± 0.005	8.15 ± 0.13
R	0.218 ± 0.003	5.54 ± 0.08
S	0.320 ± 0.004	8.13 ± 0.10

NOTES:

Lateral Runout = 0.050 inch (1.27 mm) = total indicator reading at periphery of flange when mounted on center line of center holes.

Clear Area of Flange: The periphery of the protruding rivets shall be governed by the driving means and shall be within a minimum diameter of 0.750 inch (19.05 mm) and a maximum diameter of 1.340 inches (34.04 mm).

Spool Assembly: When assembling a spool with a Style 4 drive means, the flanges should be oriented so that the center lines of the corresponding drive holes will coincide.

*Dimension A applies to spools with straight parallel flanges which are perpendicular to the core. A tolerance of 0.012 inch (0.30 mm) above maximum will be allowed for tilted or distorted flanges.

†Dimension B applies to straight flange spools or the clear area of the flange and the unembossed periphery of spools on which the flanges have an outward embossing.

‡Dimension C applies to the rivet head projection on straight flanged spool or the outside width of embossed flange spools.

§Dimension D is defined as the diameter of the core between the flanges.

‖One-half of the total indicator reading taken when spool is mounted on the center line of the center hole.

| American Standard Dimensions for

35-Millimeter 100-Foot Film Spool for
Recording Instruments and Still Picture Cameras | ASA
Reg. U. S. Pat. Off.
Z38.1.54-1951
*UDC 771.332 |

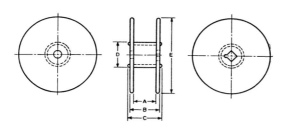

OPTIONAL DRIVE MEANS

| REAR FLANGE | FRONT FLANGE | REAR FLANGE | FRONT FLANGE |

STYLE 1

STYLE 2

STYLE 3

STYLE 4

Approved April 19, 1951, by the American Standards Association, Incorporated

Sponsor: Optical Society of America

*Universal Decimal Classification

American Standard Dimensions for

35-Millimeter 100-Foot Film Spool for
Recording Instruments and Still Picture Cameras

Reg. U. S. Pat. Off.

Z38.1.54-1951

Page 2 of 2 Pages

35-Millimeter 100-Foot Spool		
Dimension	Inches	Millimeters
A*	1.387 ± 0.008	35.22 ± 0.20
B†	1.490 Max	37.85 Max
C‡	1.520 Max	38.61 Max
D§	0.987 ± 0.037	25.12 ± 0.89
E	3.632 ± 0.032	92.25 ± 0.81
F_1 Concentricity center hole and E‖	Tolerance 0.015	Tolerance 0.38
F_2 Concentricity center hole and D‖	Tolerance 0.015	Tolerance 0.38
G	0.125 ± 0.005	3.17 ± 0.13
H	0.310 ± 0.010	7.87 ± 0.25
I	0.320 ± 0.004	8.13 ± 0.10
O	0.320 ± 0.004	8.13 ± 0.10
P	0.437 ± 0.005	11.10 ± 0.13
Q	0.321 ± 0.005	8.15 ± 0.13
R	0.218 ± 0.003	5.54 ± 0.08
S	0.320 ± 0.004	8.13 ± 0.10

NOTES:

Lateral Runout = 0.050 inch (1.27 mm) = total indicator reading at periphery of flange when mounted on center line of center holes.

Clear Area of Flange: The periphery of the protruding rivets shall be governed by the type of driving means and shall lie within a minimum diameter of 0.750 inch (19.05 mm) and a maximum diameter of 1.084 inches (27.53 mm) with the Style 1 and Style 2 drive means or 1.340 inches (34.04 mm) with the Style 3 and Style 4 drive means.

Spool Assembly: When assembling a spool with a rear flange the same as a front flange, the flanges should be oriented so that the center lines of the corresponding drive holes will coincide.

*Dimension A applies to spools with straight parallel flanges which are perpendicular to the core. A tolerance of 0.015 inch (0.38 mm) above the maximum will be allowed for tilted or distorted flanges.

†Dimension B applies to straight flange spools or the clear area of the flange and the unembossed periphery of spools on which the flanges have an outward embossing.

‡Dimension C applies to the rivet head projection on straight flanged spool or the outside width of embossed flange spools.

§Dimension D=1.250 inches ±0.030 inch (31.75 mm ±0.76 mm) for spool with Style 3 and Style 4 drive means. D is defined as the diameter of the core between the flanges.

‖One-half of the total indicator reading taken when spool is mounted on the center line of the center hole.

American Standard Dimensions for

70-Millimeter 100-Foot Film Spool for
Recording Instruments and Still Picture Cameras

Reg. U. S. Pat. Off.
Z38.1.55-1951
*UDC 771.332

Page 1 of 2 Pages

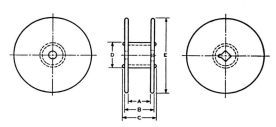

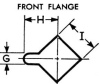

REAR FLANGE   FRONT FLANGE

70-Millimeter 100-Foot Spool		
Dimension	Inches	Millimeters
A*	2.763 ± 0.006	70.18 ± 0.15
B†	2.872 Max	72.95 **Max**
C‡	2.900 Max	73.66 **Max**
D§	0.987 ± 0.037	25.12 ± 0.89
E	3.632 ± 0.032	92.25 ± 0.81
F₁ Concentricity center hole and E‖	Tolerance 0.015	Tolerance 0.38
F₂ Concentricity center hole and D‖	Tolerance 0.015	Tolerance 0.38
G	0.125 ± 0.005	3.17 ± 0.13
H	0.310 ± 0.010	7.87 ± 0.25
I	0.320 ± 0.004	8.13 ± 0.10
S	0.320 ± 0.004	8.13 ± 0.10

Approved April 19, 1951, by the American Standards Association, Incorporated

Sponsor: Optical Society of America

*Universal Decimal Classification

American Standard Dimensions for
70-Millimeter 100-Foot Film Spool for
Recording Instruments and Still Picture Cameras

ⒶⓈⒶ
Reg. U. S. Pat. Off.
Z38.1.55-1951

Page 2 of 2 Pages

NOTES:

Lateral Runout = 0.050 inch (1.27 mm) = total indicator reading at periphery of flange when mounted on center line of center holes.

Clear Area of Flange: The periphery of the protruding rivets shall be governed by the type driving means and shall be within a minimum diameter of 0.750 inch (19.05 mm) and a maximum diameter of 1.084 inches (27.53 mm).

Spool Assembly: When assembling a spool with a rear flange the same as a front flange, the flanges should be oriented so that the center lines of the corresponding drive holes will coincide.

*Dimension A applies to spools with straight parallel flanges which are perpendicular to the core. A tolerance of 0.040 inch (1.02 mm) above maximum will be allowed for tilted or distorted flanges.

†Dimension B applies to straight flange spools or the clear area of the flange and the unembossed periphery of spools on which the flanges have an outward embossing.

‡Dimension C applies to the rivet head projection on straight flanged spool or the outside width of embossed flange spools.

§Dimension D is the diameter of the core between the flanges.

‖One-half of the total indicator reading taken when spool is mounted on the center line of the center hole.

APPENDIX D

American Standard Specifications for

Contact Printers

Reg. U. S. Pat. Off.
PH3.8-1953
Revision of
Z38.7.10-1944

*UDC 771.4

1. Scope and Purpose

1.1 These specifications cover photographic contact printers for amateur and professional uses except in the graphic arts and for other special purposes.

2. Size Accommodation

2.1 Printing equipment for a given nominal size shall accommodate all negative and positive materials within the standard dimensions for that nominal size,* and the exposure opening shall cover the full picture area for that nominal size.

3. Aperture Angles

3.1 All angles of the mask aperture should be 90 degrees ±0 degrees 10 minutes.

4. Illumination

4.1 The ratio of corner-to-center illumination should be 65 percent or greater, and the field should be free

---

*REFERENCES: American Standard Dimensions for Film Packs, Z38.1.1-1951; American Standard Dimensions for Amateur Roll Film, Backing Paper, and Film Spools, Z38.1.7-1950; American Standard Dimensions for Professional Portrait and Commercial Sheet Film (Inch Sizes), Z38.1.28-1947; American Standard Dimensions for Photographic Dry Plates (Inch Sizes), Z38.1.30-1951; American Standard Dimensions for Photographic Dry Plates (Centimeter Sizes), Z38.1.31-1944 (Reaffirmed 1949); American Standard Dimensions for Photographic Paper Sheets, PH1.12-1953; or any subsequent revisions thereof approved by the American Standards Association, Incorporated.

from local irregularities having intensity differences of more than 15 percent per 1.0 inch (2.5 cm).

4.2 Corner illumination should be measured as close to the extreme corners of the field as possible. If the measuring instrument integrates the illumination over an appreciable area, the maximum dimension of that area should not exceed one-fifth of the width of the field. The extreme corners of the field should be as bright, visually, as the areas actually measured with such an instrument.

5. Contact

5.1 Contact between negative and positive materials, when tested by the method described in 1.1 of American Standard Methods of Testing Printing and Projection Equipment, Z38.7.5-1948, usually is satisfactory if in the body of the print no region with a maximum dimension of more than ⅜ inch (9.5 mm) departs from a uniform gray tone. The zone of poor contact at the border may be continuous, but preferably should not exceed ⅛ inch (3.2 mm) in width.

6. Temperature

6.1 The temperature rise in one hour from intermittent exposures of 10 seconds on and 10 seconds off should not exceed 40 C (72 F) when measured according to the method given in 2.1 of American Standard Methods of Testing Printing and Projection Equipment, Z38.7.5-1948. The actual temperature should not exceed +65 C (+149 F).

Approved July 6, 1953, by the American Standards Association, Incorporated

Sponsor: Photographic Standards Board

*Universal Decimal Classification

American Standard

Specifications for Printing Frames

ASA
Reg. U.S. Pat. Off.
Z38.7.11-1944
R 1952 as
PH3.15-1944

*UDC 771.4

1. Size Accommodation

1.1 Printing frames for a given nominal size shall accommodate all negative and positive materials within the standard dimensions for that nominal size,* and the exposure opening shall cover the full picture area for that nominal size.

2. Aperture Angles

2.1 All angles of the masking aperture should be 90 degrees ±0 degrees 10 minutes.

3. Contact

3.1 Contact between negative and positive materials, when tested by the method described in 1.1 of American Standard Methods of Testing Printing and Projection Equipment Z38.7.5-1943, or latest revision thereof, usually is satisfactory if in the body of the print no region with a maximum dimension of more than 3/8 inch (9.5 mm) departs from a uniform gray tone. The zone of poor contact at the border may be continuous but preferably should not exceed 1/8 inch (3.2 mm) in width.

*References: American Standard Dimensions for Film Pack Tabs and Films, Z38.1.1-1941; American Standard Dimensions for Amateur Roll Film, Backing Paper, and Film Spools, Z38.1.7 through Z38.1.15-1943, or latest revisions thereof. Proposed American Standard Dimensions for Professional Portrait and Commercial Sheet Film (Inch Sizes), Z38.1.28; Proposed American Standard Dimensions for Photographic Dry Plates (Inch Sizes), Z38.1.30; Proposed American Standard Dimensions for Photographic Dry Plates (Centimeter Sizes), Z38.1.31; Proposed American Standard Dimensions of Inch-Size Photographic Papers, Z38.1.43.

Approved July 19, 1944, by the American Standards Association, Incorporated
Sponsor: Optical Society of America

*Universal Decimal Classification

American Standard Methods of Testing Printing and Projection Equipment	ASA *Reg. U. S. Pat. Off.* **Z38.7.5-1948** Revision of **Z38.7.5-1943** UDC 778.11:778.2

1. Test for Uniformity of Contact Between Negative and Positive in Printing Equipment

1.1 A test negative shall be made from an engraver's 120-line-per-inch screen in such a manner as to have alternating clear and opaque regions of equal area. The base material of the test negative shall be the same (*i.e.*, film or glass) as the base material of the negative to be used in the equipment being tested. A contact print of the test negative shall be made on photographic paper. Any departure from a uniform gray tone in the print indicates poor contact.

2. Measurement of Film or Slide Temperature

2.1 A thermocouple of No. 38 or 39 Brown and Sharpe gage wire shall be held in contact with the test film at the center of the maximum aperture standard for the given nominal size being tested, and the rise in degrees Centigrade above room temperature determined with an instrument accurate to ± 2 C. The test film shall be of a uniform density of 2.0 or greater. The thermocouple should be cemented to or held in good contact (as in a bound lantern slide) with the emulsion side of the test film. This should be the side away from the light source during the test.

Film strip, lantern slide projectors, microfilm readers, and similar instruments shall be continuously operated for one hour with the test film in place, and the temperature rise measured at the end of this one-hour period, unless another time period is specified for the instrument measured.

3. Measurement of the Uniformity of Illumination of the Screen

3.1 A clear, glass slide shall be focused on the screen, masked to the maximum aperture given in the standards for the nominal size being tested, and magnified to the arbitrary height (h) and width (b). The width shall be not less than 40 inches (1 meter). The slide shall be removed during measurement, but the other adjustments shall remain unchanged. The lamp of the projector shall be operated at its rated voltage.

3.2 The measuring equipment used shall have a precision of ± 5 percent. If a photoelectric cell is used, it shall have an attached filter to correct its sensitivity to that of human visibility for the different wave lengths of light.

3.3 Corner-to-Center Ratio. Measurement shall be made at the center and at the four points in the corners, located 1/20 of the screen width from the top or bottom edge and the same distance from the side edges of the screen. The average illumination of the four corner points, divided by that of the center, and multiplied by 100, shall be the percentage of corner-to-center illumination.

3.4 Lumen Output. The screen image (3.1) is divided into nine equal areas as shown in the figure. The illumination I_n is measured at the center of each area in foot-candles and h and b in feet.

$$\text{Screen Lumens} = \frac{hb}{9} \sum_{n=1}^{n=9} I_n$$

Approved August 3, 1948, by the American Standards Association, Incorporated
Sponsor: Optical Society of America

American Standard Specifications for
Masks (Separate) for Use in Photographic Contact Printing of Roll Film Negatives

ASA
Reg. U. S. Pat. Off.
PH3.9-1953
Revision of
Z38.7.12-1944
*UDC 77P II

1. Aperture Angles

1.1 All angles of rectangular or square mask apertures should be 90 degrees ± 0 degrees 10 minutes.

2. Light Control

2.1 Any light transmitted by the mask should not fog the sensitized material under normal handling.

3. Size

3.1 Mask Sizes for Use with Roll Film Negatives

3.1.1 For sizes smaller than 2¼ by 2¼ inches, the mask opening should be between ⅟₃₂ inch (0.8 mm) and ⅟₁₆ inch (1.6 mm) smaller in both directions than the nominal size.

3.1.2 For sizes of 2¼ by 2¼ inches and larger, the mask opening should be between ⅟₁₆ inch (1.6 mm) and ⅛ inch (3.2 mm) smaller in both directions than the nominal size.

4. Thickness

4.1 Masks should not exceed 0.010 inch (0.25 mm) in thickness.

Approved July 6, 1953, by the American Standards Association, Incorporated

Sponsor: Photographic Standards Board   *Universal Decimal Classification

American Standard
Methods for Testing
Photographic Enlargers

ASA

Reg. U. S. Pat. Off.
Z38.7.6-1950
UDC 771.3:620.084

SPONSOR

Optical Society of America

Approved October 6, 1950

American Standards Association
Incorporated

Foreword

(This Foreword is not a part of the American Standard Methods for Testing Photographic Enlargers, Z38.7.6-1950.)

This American Standard describes methods for testing photographic enlargers for amateur and professional use in ordinary photographic practice. For special uses, as in photogrammetry and photoengraving, more critical tests may be required. The basic tests include uniformity of illumination, light tightness, effectiveness of safety filter, resolving power of lens, color correction of lens, alignment of optical axis, negative and easel, temperature and scratching of negatives. Tentative values were tried when this standard was published for a year's test and criticism in 1941, but owing to the wide variation in quality and requirements for enlargers, such values appeared to be premature. Standard methods can now be used and it is expected that their use will lead ultimately to a standard which will include numerical limits. Other characteristics of enlargers, such as convenience of operation, nicety of finish, and sturdiness are important and should not be overlooked although they are not subject to specific testing methods in this standard.

Suggestions for improvement of this standard, based upon experience gained by its use, are welcome and should be addressed to the American Standards Association, Incorporated, 70 East Forty-fifth Street, New York 17, N. Y.

The ASA Committee on Standardization in the Field of Photography, Z38, was initiated in September, 1938, on the recommendation of a general conference of the American photographic industry following a request by the International Standards Association, that the ASA accept the Secretariat for ISA Committee 42 on Photography. Before international action could be taken the war intervened and the work was suspended. A new international standardization organization, known as the International Organization for Standardization (ISO), has been set up and in October, 1946, the American Standards Association was designated as Secretariat for international standardization work in the field of still photography.

The Optical Society of America was designated as sponsor for the ASA project. The scope for the ASA project is as follows:

The formulation of definitions, dimensional standards, and recommended practices in the field of photography, and the establishment of methods for testing, rating, and classifying the performance characteristics of materials and devices used in photography, including its industrial applications, but excluding cinematography.

American Standard Methods for Testing
Photographic Enlargers

1. Scope

1.1 The methods outlined in this standard are intended primarily for testing enlargers for amateur and professional use; more critical tests may be required for at least some functions of enlargers for photogrammetry, photoengraving, and other special purposes. Some characteristics of enlargers, for example, convenience of operation, nicety of finish, and sturdiness, are not readily subject to specific testing. Nevertheless, it is recognized that they are important and should not be overlooked.

2. Uniformity of Illumination

2.1 **Adjustments of Equipment.** Before checking the uniformity of the illumination falling on the easel, make the following adjustments.

2.1.1 Set the enlarger for maximum magnification.

2.1.2 Install the negative carrier with the largest (longest diagonal) aperture. The carrier should be empty.

2.1.3 If a specific lens is not supplied or recommended by the manufacturer, fit the enlarger with a lens having a focal length approximately equal to the diagonal of the negative aperture. Focus the lens to give a sharp image of the edges of the negative aperture.

2.1.4 Make any adjustments, such as centering the lamp, which may be recommended by the manufacturer.

2.1.5 Inspect the enlarger for possible interference of the safety-filter bracket or other parts with the light beam.

2.1.6 If it is desired to determine the maximum uniformity obtainable with the enlarger, and if the lens has an adjustable diaphragm, reduce the lens opening until maximum uniformity of illumination is obtained; that is, until there is no vignetting of the corner rays by the lens barrel. If it is desired to test the lens and enlarger in combination, set the lens diaphragm at its largest opening.

2.2 **Uniformity Test.** With a foot-candle meter or other photometer, measure the illumination at the brightest point (usually the center) and at the darkest point (usually the corners) on the easel.

2.2.1 For purposes of comparison, compute the darkest point as a percentage of the brightest point.

2.2.2 If any local irregularity is apparent and if the measuring area of the photometer permits, the gradient of illumination across the irregularity should be measured.

2.2.3 Some common and convenient photometers integrate the light over an appreciable area. In no case should the diameter of this area exceed one-fifth of the width of the field.

2.3 **Alternate Test.** An alternative test that may be used to determine the comparative uniformity of two or more enlargers is to expose sheets of photographic paper, with no negatives in the carriers, and develop these in the normal manner. The exposure should be chosen to give a reflection density between 0.8 and 1.0 at the center of the prints. High-contrast paper will give the most critical test.

2.3.1 The prints may be examined visually or measured with a densitometer for both general and local uniformity.

2.3.2 It is essential that all prints be made with uniform paper and conditions of exposure and processing.

3. Light Tightness

3.1 To test an enlarger for light tightness the procedure outlined below should be followed.

3.1.1 Place it in a darkroom with light-colored walls. (The smaller the room, the more critical the test.)

3.1.2 Insert a negative with average over-all density of about 1.0 in the carrier and place an opaque cap on the lens.

3.1.3 Determine the length of time the enlarger lamp must be lighted at normal voltage to produce the maximum acceptable fogging of sheets of the sensitized material on the easel and adjacent to the easel at the same level. The manufacturer's recommendations for development of the material should be followed, carrying the development to the greatest specified amount. Darkroom safelight illumination should be turned off during this test. This can be done most conveniently by covering portions of the sensitized sheets for various lengths of time. For example, in making a test for safety with ordinary enlarging paper, the lamp might be on for 16 minutes, and parts of the paper could be covered with opaque cards to give exposure times of

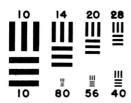

NOTE: Figures indicate number of black lines per millimeter.

Figure 1
Resolution Test Patterns

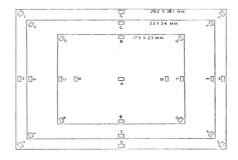

Figure 2
Resolving Power Test Chart

0, 2, 4, 8, and 16 minutes. When this test is made, it is desirable to have an unexposed area of the sensitized material adjacent to each of the exposed areas. This can be accomplished, for example, by making the exposures through holes in an opaque mask covering the sensitized sheet.

3.1.4 This test should be made with the most light-sensitive material to be used on the enlarger, *i.e.*, if separation negatives or matrices are to be made, panchromatic film should be used for the test.

3.2 With the enlarger in a darkroom, inspect it for direct light leaks.

4. Effectiveness of Safety Filter

4.1 Determine the time required, with the safety filter in its operating position, to result in detrimental fogging of the sensitized material on the easel. The procedure outlined in 3.1.3 can be adapted to this test. The test will be most critical if the enlarger is set for minimum magnification and the diaphragm is at its largest opening.

4.2 Determine, by inspection, if the safety-filter mount is interfering with the image beam.

5. Vibration

5.1 If the support for the enlarger or any part of the enlarger is suspected of causing detrimental vibration, the vibration should be eliminated before making the resolving-power test.

6. Resolving Power of Lens

6.1 Any slight movement or vibration of the enlarger or enlarging easel must be eliminated before making this test. Tests should be made at the extremes of the magnification range provided by the enlarger, with the diaphragm at its largest opening, and with a test negative of the maximum size recommended for the lens under test. For some purposes, it will be desirable to make additional tests at other diaphragm stops.

NOTE: It is assumed that a high-contrast resolving-power chart negative will be used. For the paper on which the resolving-power chart is printed, the use of glossy paper in "normal" grade is recommended (American Standard log exposure scale of about 1.1 as given in the American Standard Sensitometry of Photographic Papers, Z38.2.3-1947, and the paper manufacturer's recommended development).

6.2 For simple comparative purposes, it often is adequate to make the sharpest possible prints at maximum lens aperture from a negative carrying an image with fine, sharp detail.

6.3 For purposes requiring quantitative or numerical ratings, test prints should be made from a special test negative carrying resolution test patterns at its center, corners, and several intermediate points as shown in Figure 1.

The test pattern should have groups of lines in both radial and tangential directions. For most enlarging lenses a range of 10 to 80 lines per mm is satisfactory. In the test pattern the width of the line and the space between lines are equal, and the width of one line plus one space is equal to the reciprocal of the number of lines per mm.

The test negative should be a glass plate, to insure flatness.

7. Color Correction of Lens

7.1 If a lens has lateral color it will give images of slightly different magnifications for different colors of light. This can be checked conveniently by making a print from a negative that has a number of lines crossing and perpendicular to a diagonal of the negative and with strips of filters laid side by side across these lines. After the print is developed any discontinuity in the lines provides a measure of the lateral color.

If the lens is to be used for some process involving specific filters, the check should be made with those filters. For a more general test, it usually is satisfactory to use commercially available filters having dominant wavelengths of 650 mμ (transmission of wavelengths shorter than 590 mμ should be negligible) and 440 mμ (370 to 510 mμ).

8. Alignment of Optical Axis, Negative, and Easel

8.1 Lack of symmetry in the resolving-power test prints may indicate that the negative, or easel, or both, are not perpendicular to the optical axis.

8.1.1 If the dissymmetry is reversed when the lens and lens board are rotated 90 degrees, that indicates the lens is not properly mounted in the lens board (or possibly that the lens is defective).

8.1.2 If the dissymmetry is not affected by rotating the lens, the negative, easel, or frame that holds the lens board may be out of square. Dependent on the facilities available, the member at fault may be detected by trial and error methods, careful mechanical measurements, or measurement and analysis of image magnification in various parts of the field.

8.2 If the negative and easel are parallel, alignment of the optical axis can be determined by making a print

(or simply projecting an image on the easel) from a negative having pairs of widely-spaced parallel lines in several directions. Each pair of lines should be symmetrical with respect to the center of the negative. If, in any pair, the lines in the image are not parallel, nonperpendicularity of the optical axis is indicated.

9. Temperature

9.1 If the temperature rise of the negative is to be measured, the following conditions of measurement are recommended.

9.1.1 The ambient temperature should be about 21 C.

9.1.2 The negative should have a uniform density of 2.0 ± 0.1, and the emulsion side should be away from the lamp.

9.1.3 The lamp should be operated at its rated voltage.

9.1.4 To simulate operating conditions, the enlarger light source should be turned on for 10 seconds, off for 10 seconds, etc. The measurement may be to determine the maximum temperature or to determine the time required to reach some specified temperature.

9.1.5 The temperature should be measured by means of a thermocouple of small wire (No. 38 or 40 BS gage) cemented to the emulsion side of the film, usually at the center of the negative area.

9.2 The temperature rise of the exterior of the lamphouse can be determined by using an insulator to press a thermocouple against the points to be measured and operating the enlarger as in 9.1.

10. Scratching of Negative

10.1 Although it is difficult to prescribe a test that will give a quantitative measurement of negative scratching, it is a simple matter to insert, manipulate, and remove a fresh negative several times and then examine it for scratches. The handling should be in accordance with the manufacturer's instructions.

APPENDIX E

Proposed
American Standard Specifications
For Microfilm Readers
For 16- and 35-mm Film on Reels

ASA
PH5.1/12
Revision of
Z38.7.9-1946
Third Draft
April 8, 1954

1. Definitions

1.1 A microfilm reader is defined as a projection device for showing a readable image of a micro-transparency (see American Standard Practice for Microfilms Z38.7.8-1947 or latest revision thereof approved by the American Standards Association), usually on a self-contained screen.

1.2 Magnification is defined as the ratio of a linear dimension of the screen image to the corresponding dimension of the object on the film and is expressed as enlargement X.

2. Dimensions

2.1 Readers for processed microfilm shall accommodate film of dimensions specified on American Standard Practice for Microfilms Z38.7.8-1947 or latest revision thereof approved by American Standards Association.

2.2 In readers without provision for film scanning, the width of the aperture of the film gate shall accommodate an image width at least as great as those specified on American Standard Practice for Microfilm Z38.7.8-1947 for unperforated films. The length should be at least as great as the width.

2.3 In readers without provision for scanning the screen shall be of sufficient size to accommodate the projected aperture.

2.4 In readers which do not project the image widths specified in American Standard Practice for Microfilm Z38.7.8-1947, provision should be made to scan those image widths.

3. Optics

3.1 The image should not require refocusing as a line of print is read from one side across the center to the opposite side.

3.2 Color or distortion, or both, should not be obvious in the projected image of black and white printed matter.

Author's note: Withdrawn from Letter Ballot Action by PH5.1—for a revision of Sect. 4.1.

4. Illumination

4.1 So far as is compatible with other required features, the ratio of any corner-to-center brightness of the screen, as measured at normal viewing position, should be not less than 65 to 100, and any two adjacent areas shall vary from each other by not more than a 4 to 5 ratio. Brightness shall be measured at the center and at four points in the corners located 1/10 of the screen dimension from the adjacent edges of the screen.

4.2 It is desirable that means be provided to vary the brightness of the screen.

4.3 The leakage of stray light shall be restricted so that neither direct or reflected rays distract the operator.

5. Temperature

5.1 The temperature of the film should not exceed 75° C. (167° F.) when measured by the testing method specified in American Standard Methods of Testing Printing and Projection Equipment Z38.7.5-1948 or the latest revision thereof.

6. Reels

6.1 Provision shall be made for projecting film on standard reels, as defined in American Standard for Reels for Processed Microfilm, Z38.7.17-1946 or the latest revision thereof.

6.2 It is desirable that provision should be made for the insertion and manual transport of film strips not shorter than 10 inches or 25 cm. in length.

7. General

7.1 Readers should have provision either for rotating the projected image 360°, or for showing the images right side up on the screen when they have been taken as described in American Standard Practice for Microfilms, Z38.7.8-1947 or any subsequent revision thereof.

7.2 The image shall be properly oriented on the screen when the film is wound on the reel as specified in the American Standard Practice for Microfilm, Z38.7.8-1947 or any subsequent revision thereof.

7.3 Means shall be provided to release pressure or minimize abrasion on the image area during movement of the film. Means shall also be provided to hold the film image in focus for viewing for extended periods of time.

APPENDIX F

Proposed
American Standard for Microcards

ASA PH5/7
November 18, 1953

The Microcard Code
As revised August 15, 1953

I. All Microcards for library use shall be of the standard international card size. 75 by 125 mm.

II. On all Microcards for library use the catalog entry, classification numbers, collation, etc., shall be placed at the top of the face card, the micro-text below, or one side may be entirely text, and the other side cataloging entry, etc.

III. All Microcards for library use shall be made of white stock, of 100 percent rag, or equivalent quality, 1/100 of an inch thick.

IV. Microcards may, or may not, be punched with holes at the option of each publisher.

XVII. The language used upon the Microcards themselves shall follow these rules:

    a. The micro-text will, of course, always be entirely in the language of the original publisher.

    b. The classification symbols will be automatically international in their form for all countries which use Arabic numerals and the Roman alphabet.

    c. The subject heading shall, on cards for materials in the English language, be in English only; on cards for material in other languages it may, at the option of the publisher, be either in English only or bilingual. If bilingual, it shall be given in two lines, the upper line in the language of issuance (if the language be one in non-Roman type transliterated or not, at the option of the publisher); the lower line in an English translation of the upper line.

    d. The author's name shall be given in accordance with the cataloging practice of the Library of Congress.

    e. The language used in the main cataloging entry (i.e., the transcript of the title page) shall follow L.C. Practice. This will mean, in most cases, that it will be in the language of issuance.

      f.   On the cards for material in other than the English language the abstract (if there is one) may, at the option of the publisher, be bilingual, first in the language of issuance (transliterated or not at the option of the publisher) followed by a translation in English; or it may be in English only.

XVIII.   The cataloging practice of the Library of Congress shall be adopted as Microcard cataloging practice, with the following exceptions and modifications:

      a.   Where, in an imprint, more than one place and/or publisher are given, the first one only is to be cited, followed by ''etc.'' in brackets.

      b.   The repetition of the author's name in the title page transcript is to be omitted where it is identical, or substantially identical, with the author heading, but it is to be retained in the case of joint authors, or where grammatical construction requires it.

      c.   All notes typographically descriptive of the item cataloged, such as ''reproduced from typewritten copy,'' ''mimeographed,'' ''lithographed,'' etc., are to be omitted.

      d.   All ''contents'' notes are to be omitted except as the abstract may be in contents form.

      e.   All notes regarding an item's previous history are to be omitted, except as these may be given in the abstract.

      f.   Such descriptive notes as ''illustrated title page,'' ''title enclosed in ornamental border,'' ''limited edition in twenty numbered copies,'' are to be omitted.

      g.   In the case of long titles, all matter not directly pertinent is to be omitted.

      h.   In the author entry, death rates are to be omitted.

      i.   In the case of books with more than one title page only the main title page is to be quoted (or the first if they seem to be of equal importance).

XIX.   The printing format of the catalog entry of all Microcards shall be in accordance with the following rules:

      a.   All type matter is to be set 120 mm. (28 picas) wide. The top margin and the side margins are to be the same, 2½ mm.

      b.   The two subject classification symbols are to be set on the first line in ten point bold face, slightly letter-spaced, each one being flush with its respective margin, the Decimal Classification symbols on the left and the Library of Congress classification on the right.

      c.   The subject heading is to be set in ten point bold face indented one inch, and placed between the two classification symbols, and on the first line with them.

         d.   The author entry is to be set flush with the left hand edge of the second line in ten point bold-face.

XIX.   e.   The contents indicia phrase (i.e. "card 1—P. 1-86") etc., is to be set in ten point bold face, set solid and flush with the right hand edge of the second line.

         f.   The title page transcript is to begin on the third line flush with the left hand margin. It is to be set in ten point Roman lower case. The remaining lines of the title page transcript are to be set in six point Roman lower case, set solid.

         g.   Collation, size, series notes (if any) and similar data are to be set in six point italic lower case, set solid and run in immediately after the title page transcript. They are to be enclosed in parentheses.

         h.   The Microcard imprint and card serial number (which will also be the manufacturing job number) shall consist of (a) a two letter symbol of the publisher's name, (b) the (abbreviated) year of manufacture, (c) a serial number of that year, and the whole printed in two lines thus:

Fo—48
3296

Below this serial number shall be placed the trademark notice. These four lines shall all be photographed on each card in eye-readable size.

         i.   The trade-mark notice shall consist of the word "MICRO-CARD" in block type and below it, in smaller italic type, the word "Trade-Mark."

         j.   Abstracts, or similar explanatory material, may be included in the catalog entry at the option of the publisher. It is suggested that, if abstracts are given, they be very short; in most cases only a line or two. In some cases explanatory material can more easily be included as a part of the title entry. Often here a single word, or two or three words, has greater informative value; and such material can be so included in the title, at the option of the publisher, provided that it be bracketed.

XX.   The format of Microcard micro-text shall be in accordance with the following rules:

         a.   The basic, and always controlling, first rule shall be: that no more text shall ever be placed on any card than can be placed there at a reduction which can surely be easily and *clearly* read on available Microcard reading machines.

         b.   Pages shall be imposed for photographing in such a way that, on the completed card, they begin at the top, and run in lines of pages from left to right across the card. Exceptions to this

      arrangement may occasionally occur to take care of folded
inserts and other special material.

c.   All pages shall be photographed: except that advertising pages
may, or may not, be included, at the option of the publisher:
(If they are omitted, a statement to that effect should be given
in the cataloging entry notes).

d.   Where the material photographed for a given card is going to
cover only a small portion of the card (as in the case of single
maps and prints) it should be centered on the card.

APPENDIX G

Reg. U. S. Pat. Off.
PH4.12-1954
Revision of
Z38.8.17-1948

UDC 772.1:620.193

American Standard Method for Indicating

The Stability of the Images of
Processed Black-and-White Films, Plates, and Papers

1. Scope

1.1 This standard specifies test methods for indicating the relative stability of the images of processed films, plates, and papers as conditioned by the internal factors resulting from processing. It applies only to processed photographic materials containing silver particles in an organic colloid layer and not to dye images, tinted, toned, or intensified photographs.

1.2 The purposes of the three test methods given are as follows:

Section	Test	Effect
3.1	Test for Effect of Thiosulfate	Fading or darkening due to chemical reaction of residues of thiosulfate or other treating agents.
3.2	Test for Light Stability	Darkening due to action of light on residual silver compounds.
3.3	Test for Silver Compounds	Discoloration due to chemical action on residual silver compounds.

Appropriate criteria are given for archival and non-archival cases, respectively. All three tests are necessary to characterize image stability, but any one test may be useful for a particular purpose.

2. General

2.1 Factors Affecting Stability. Deterioration of the image of processed photographic materials is controlled by factors which may be classified as internal and external.

2.1.1 *Internal Factors.* The internal factors determine the stability and are the subject of the test methods. They include the state of division of the silver, the form of the image (for example, narrow lines or small spots of low density in a field of high density, or the converse), and a group of factors governed by the processing treatment, the presence of protective substances, the content of uncombined fixing or "stabilizing" agents, such as the thiosulfates, the acidity and the residual silver compounds in the material. Instability of the base or other layers may be an internal factor in so far as decomposition in any of them may yield products which stain or attack any part of the image.

2.1.2 *External Factors.* Some of the most common external factors are the conditions of temperature and humidity, the intensity and quality of light, or other radiation to which the material is exposed, the presence of active gases in the atmosphere, and the time of exposure to any of these.

The durability of the photographic record when subjected to weathering, biological attack, or mechanical wear is not within the scope of this standard.

2.2 Purpose of Test. The test methods are intended to evaluate the internal factors by subjecting representative samples of the processed materials to some of the external factors in a severe but controlled degree.

2.3 Effect of Type of Fixing or "Stabilizing" Process. Following completion of photographic development, the photographic material is subjected either to fixing and washing or to a so-called "stabilizing" treatment to impart the required resistance to darkening, discoloration, and fading during subsequent use or storage.

2.3.1 When the fixing and washing procedure is employed, the object is to convert the unused silver salt to a soluble complex which, along with the fixing chemicals, will then be removed by thorough washing so as to assure a relatively high degree of stability.

2.3.2 In contrast, the "stabilization" processes usually consist of bathing the developed material in a solution containing, for example, thiosulfate, thiourea, or thiocyanate to convert the unused silver salt to a comparatively stable chemical complex. In some of these processes half or more of the silver compounds are removed from the photographic material. Drying follows either without any washing or, at the most, with a superficial rinse. Generally speaking, the degree of stability attainable by "stabilization" is less in one respect or another than that attainable with the more usually employed fixing and washing processes.

2.4 Effect of Excess Thiosulfate. The possible extent of fading which results from reactions involving thiosulfate and image silver, with the consequent conversion of the latter to silver sulfide, is dependent, among other things, upon the relative quantities of metallic silver and excess thiosulfate and the state of subdivision of the silver. Conversion to silver sulfide

423

does not necessarily render the image useless, unless legibility, image detail, or esthetic quality is too much impaired. The amount of such fading or discoloration allowable in a negative or print will depend somewhat upon the use for which the material is intended. Thus a slight discoloration may be seriously objectionable in pictorial matter, especially if it is uneven, while extensive sulfiding of a line image may be inconsequential if legibility is not lost.

The rate at which the actual chemical conversion takes place varies widely, not only with the factors mentioned above, the form of the image, the presence of protective material, the acidity or alkalinity, and the relative quantities of free thiosulfate and sulfite, but also with temperature and humidity. It is impossible to assign a definite figure for the expected life of a given sample of processed material on the basis of any one factor, such as free thiosulfate content. However, the relative stability of the image can be indicated from the results of empirical accelerated tests on samples of typical image matter.

2.5 Effect of Other Fixing or "Stabilizing" Agents. Fading effects may be produced when the silver grains are attacked by a residual excess of other fixing or "stabilizing" agents. Depending on the agent employed, the silver compound formed in the fading process may be the sulfide as previously discussed or some other compound which effects a change in color or loss in density. The influence of the other internal and external factors is of similar significance with the above-mentioned agents. Considerations governing the choice of test material and the criteria for evaluating image impairment are as mentioned in 2.4.

2.6 Effect of Residual Silver Compounds. The residual silver compounds are primarily responsible for the over-all staining of processed photographic materials often encountered under conditions of high temperature and humidity or on exposure to actinic light or to other radiation which causes the light-sensitive substance to darken or "print-out." The presence of labile sulfur (active with respect to silver) either in the atmosphere or as the product of decomposition of sulfur compounds in the material will also cause the conversion of these silver compounds to silver sulfide, even when the temperature and humidity are not extreme.

3. Test Methods

3.1 Test for Effect of Thiosulfate and Other Residual Chemicals. Representative samples* of the

*While a single specimen may be tested, the selection of truly representative samples will entail the use of an adequate sampling procedure.

processed photographic materials to be tested, chosen to include typical image matter (see 2.1), are perforated at one end and suspended from a glass rod support in a closed (but not sealed) all-glass container low in form. Contact of the samples with each other or the container walls shall be avoided. The atmosphere within the container shall be maintained at 37.8 C $\pm$ 0.3 C (100 F $\pm$ 0.5 F) and 94 percent $\pm$ 4.0 percent relative humidity. A relative humidity of approximately 96 percent can be attained by keeping in the bottom of the container a generous amount of a saturated water solution of potassium sulfate in contact with an excess of the solid salt (K_2SO_4). Grades designated as Technical or Purified may be used. Alternatively, exposure to these conditions of temperature and humidity may be provided by means of air conditioning cabinets or rooms in which the samples are similarly suspended to keep them separated from each other and shielded from contamination.

If no noticeable change of image color or density or staining of the clear areas has occurred after 30 days' incubation under these conditions, the material shall be reported as satisfactorily stable for archival purposes with respect to the internal factors resulting from processing. Comparison shall be made with an adjacent portion of the sample which has been given the following special processing treatment and incubated with the test sample.

3.1.1 *Treatment of Sample for Comparison.* Treat the comparison sample for the time customarily used in good practice for the class of material in a fresh fixing bath consisting of 250 grams $Na_2S_2O_3 \cdot 5H_2O$ (sodium thiosulfate) in one liter of distilled water. Continue the fixation for a similar time in another fresh portion of this fixing bath and then wash for 1 hour in running water which is flowing at a rate equivalent to that needed to fill the vessel (tray or tank) once every 5 minutes. Air-dry the sample.

For images on paper supports, terminate the washing after 30 minutes and then bathe them for 5 minutes in the following hypo eliminator:

Hypo Eliminator

Water	300 ml
Hydrogen peroxide (3 percent solution)	500 ml
Ammonia solution*	100 ml
Potassium bromide	1 gram
Water to make	1 liter

*Prepared by adding 1 part of concentrated ammonia (28 percent) to 9 parts of water.
CAUTION: Prepare the solution immediately before use and keep in an open container during use. Do not store the mixed solution in a stoppered bottle, or the gas evolved may break the bottle.

Remove the prints directly to a 1-percent solution of sodium sulfite and treat them for 2 minutes. Finally, wash in fresh running water for 10 minutes before drying.

In the preparation of comparison samples, the temperature of all baths including the wash water shall be 20 C $\pm$ 1.7 C (68 F $\pm$ 3 F).

3.1.2 For nonarchival purposes, exposure to the prescribed conditions of incubation for 10 days will suffice and the results shall be reported in terms of nonarchival use.

The 10-day exposure also may be used when judgment is based on the nonarchival criterion of retention of legibility instead of the absence of noticeable change, and the legibility criterion shall be mentioned if it is used. In this case comparison may be made with an adjacent portion of the sample which has been retained at no higher than 75 F and 40 percent relative humidity.*

3.2 Test for Light Stability. A representative sample† of the processed photographic material to be tested, together with a comparison sample, shall be exposed to actinic (with respect to silver compounds) radiation such as provided in a Color Fade-Ometer or other exposure apparatus of similar ultraviolet distribution. Any instability of the unknown sample for archival use with respect to the internal factors resulting from processing will be evident if it shows any change of density or hue before the comparison sample.

---

*Indoor conditions during winter will usually be found adequate. Suitable storage can also be provided by sealing the sample with an ample quantity of activated silica gel in a fruit jar which is kept in a household refrigerator.

†While a single specimen may be tested, the selection of truly representative samples will entail the use of an adequate sampling procedure.

3.2.1 Treatment of Sample for Comparison. Prepare a comparison sample in accordance with 3.1.1.

3.2.2 If retention of legibility only is required with nonarchival material, exposure shall be continued for twice the time required to produce the first perceptible change of density or hue of the comparison sample or at least for 24 hours in the exposure apparatus. Then the judgment of legibility shall be made by visual examination of typical image matter (see 2.1) and the legibility criterion shall be mentioned in reporting.

3.3 Test for Silver Compounds. Choose a portion of a sheet or strip which has received representative* processing treatment, blot dry, if necessary, and spot a clear area of the image side using an 0.2-percent freshly prepared solution of pure fused sodium sulfide [see American Standard Specification for Photographic Grade Sodium Sulfide, Fused (Na_2S), Z38.8.182-1949, or the latest revision thereof approved by the American Standards Association, Incorporated]. In the case of papers, spot both sides. Wash away or blot up the reagent after 3 minutes. If the spot-treated areas show no more than a just perceptible tint, the photographic material may be considered stable in respect to susceptibility to staining arising from the action of sulfide (internal or external) on residual silver compounds. In case of doubt, a control sample should be prepared by similarly spot-treating a portion of the material from the same lot which has been processed as described for the comparison sample under 3.1.1.

3.3.1 In the case of nonarchival material, legibility in a spot-treated area of typical image matter (see 2.1) may be used as a criterion instead of nondarkening. This criterion shall then be included in a statement of the test results.

---

*While a single specimen may be tested, the selection of truly representative samples will entail the use of an adequate sampling procedure.

American Standard
Registered United States Patent Office

An American Standard implies a consensus of those substantially concerned with its scope and provisions. The consensus principle extends to the initiation of work under the procedure of the Association, to the method of work to be followed, and to the final approval of the standard.

An American Standard is intended as a guide to aid the manufacturer, the consumer, and the general public. The existence of an American Standard does not in any respect preclude any party who has approved of the standard from manufacturing, selling, or using products, processes, or procedures not conforming to the standard.

An American Standard defines a product, process, or procedure with reference to one or more of the following: nomenclature, composition, construction, dimensions, tolerances, safety, operating characteristics, performance, quality, rating, certification, testing, and the service for which designed.

American Standards are subject to periodic review. They are reaffirmed or revised to meet changing economic conditions and technological progress. Users of American Standards are cautioned to secure the latest editions.

Producers of goods made in conformity with an American Standard are encouraged to state on their own responsibility, in advertising, promotion material, or on tags or labels, that the goods are produced in conformity with particular American Standards. The inclusion in such advertising and promotion media, or on tags or labels, of information concerning the characteristics covered by the standard to define its scope is also encouraged.

Bibliography

(This Bibliography is not a part of American Standard Method for Indicating the Stability of the Images of Processed Black-and-White Films, Plates, and Papers, PH4.12-1954.)

1. CRABTREE, J. I., EATON, G. T., and MUEHLER, L. E.: The removal of hypo and silver salts from photographic materials as affected by the composition of the processing solutions. *Journal of the Society of Motion Picture Engineers*, **41**, 9-63 (1943)

2. JAMES, T. H., and HIGGINS, G. C.: *Fundamentals of Photographic Theory*. John Wiley and Sons, Inc, New York (1948)

3. LEVINOS, STEVEN, and BURNER, W. C.: Stabilization processing. *Photographic Engineering*, **2**, No. 3, 148-160 (1951)

4. RUSSELL, H. D., YACKEL, E. C., and BRUCE, J. S.: Stabilization processing of films and papers. *PSA Journal (Photographic Science and Technique)*, **16B**, 59-62 (1950)

Sponsor

PHOTOGRAPHIC STANDARDS BOARD

Approved May 19, 1954

AMERICAN STANDARDS ASSOCIATION
INCORPORATED

American Standard Requirements for

Photographic Filing Envelopes for Storing
Processed Photographic Films, Plates, and Papers

Reg. U. S. Pat. Off.
Z38.8.21-1950
*UDC 77.025/.026

Page 1 of 2 Pages

Foreword

When filing processed films, plates, or papers, it is customary and good practice to enclose them in a paper or glassine envelope in order to exclude dirt, avoid finger marks and scratches, and to facilitate titling and handling. If the photographic material is not thoroughly fixed and washed during processing so that traces of thiosulfates or unreduced silver salts remain in the photographic layer, there will always be a tendency for the image to fade and a general brown stain to be produced, somewhat in proportion to the degree of faulty processing. These effects are accelerated by high temperature, or humidity, or both, and by the action of acidic substances such as may be present in certain envelope papers and adhesives.

Many filing envelopes employ a pasted seam located at or near the center, and experience has shown that in the case of processed materials stored in such envelopes, especially under conditions of high relative humidity, very serious staining may occur in the vicinity of the seam. Usually, such a streak is impossible to remove. The stain may be considered to be due to one or some combination of the following causes:

(a) The combined effect of residual processing chemicals and adhesive;

(b) Unsuitable adhesive—which may stain by itself or promote fungus growth;

(c) Poor paper—a low-grade paper will affect an otherwise satisfactory adhesive.

The danger of local image fading and the production of stain in the region of the seam may be minimized by the use of a high-grade paper, acceptable adhesive, and the avoidance of high relative humidities. However, the positive control of these elements is a difficult problem. Even a well-processed photographic material may be stained by contact with an unsatisfactory adhesive.

Any general over-all stain is due to high relative humidity, together with imperfect processing, or low-grade paper, or both. Storage at a prevailing relative humidity between 25 and 60 percent is considered essential. The films, plates, or papers should be filed in such a manner that they are not subjected to excessive pressure which might cause "pressure markings."

1. Scope

This standard gives the principal physical and chemical requirements for paper filing envelopes for storing processed photographic films, plates, and papers under conditions such that a relative humidity exceeding 60 percent does not prevail. It is not intended to cover the requirements of transparent sleeves or sheaths commonly used for protecting and viewing color transparencies.

2. Requirements

2.1 Materials

2.1.1 Paper. Envelopes shall be constructed of regular or glassine paper made from high-grade, bleached or unbleached rag, sulfite or sulfate pulp. No ground wood pulp shall be present in the finished paper. The paper should be free from surface fibers which might offset onto the emulsion surface. The paper shall not contain waxes or plasticizers or other ingredients which transfer to the photographic material in the test given in 2.4, Accelerated Aging Test. The paper shall be essentially free of particles of metal or metallic compounds.

Such papers shall be chemically stable to the extent that when heated in dry air for 72 hours at 105 C ±2 C the decrease in folding endurance* shall be not more than 30 percent.

2.1.2 Adhesive. If an adhesive is used, it shall be nondeliquescent and have no harmful effect on the photographic image or envelope paper when tested according to the method given in 2.4, Accelerated Aging Test.

2.2 Size of Envelope. The length and width of envelopes shall be at least 5 percent or not less than ⅛ inch greater than the maximum dimensions specified in the various American Standards covering dimensions for sheet films, plates, or papers.

2.3 Construction of Envelope

2.3.1 Seamless Type. A single sheet of paper

*Effect of Heating on Folding Endurance of Paper, Technical Association of the Pulp and Paper Industry 453M-44 (American Society for Testing Materials D776-46)

Approved June 28, 1950, by the American Standards Association, Incorporated

Sponsor: Optical Society of America   *Universal Decimal Classification

folded down the center may be used as a folder without cemented seams.

2.3.2 Cemented Seam Type. The seams of the envelope shall be at the extreme edges only and as narrow as possible and shall not exceed 3/8-inch width for the 5 × 7-inch size or smaller, or 1/2 inch for the larger sizes.

2.4 Accelerated Aging Test

2.4.1 Physical Conditions. An accelerated aging is achieved by incubating the test material at 50 C and 74 ±0.5-percent relative humidity for 10 days.*

2.4.2 Residual Processing Chemicals. The photographic material to be used for test purposes

---

*Such a condition can be readily obtained by storing the material in a closed container over a saturated sodium chloride solution. The chief precaution to be taken in this method of attaining a given relative humidity is that good circulation of the air in the closed container must be accomplished. This is most easily done by building in a driven fan. More complete information is given in the U. S. Department of Commerce Letter Circular LC 752, May, 1944, and in Physical and Chemical Examination of Paints, Varnishes, Lacquers, and Colors by Henry A. Gardner, ninth edition, pp 92-97, or tenth edition, pp 126-132.

should have the hypo and silver contents of poorly washed negatives. A medium speed (American Standard Exposure Index of about 50) film negative shall be chosen and exposed and processed to give a medium density (0.5 to 1.5), fixed in a used fixing bath (silver content 2 to 4 grams per liter), and washed for about 15 minutes or to give a hypo content between 0.2 and 0.4 mg per square inch.

2.4.3 Procedure. The photographic test film shall be placed in the test envelope and a piece of smooth, surfaced filter paper not exceeding one-half the size of the envelope shall be placed therein against the emulsion surface as a control. The test package shall then be bent back upon itself to form a cylinder with the emulsion facing outward and secured by tying with string. After the incubation described in 2.4.1, Physical Conditions, there should be no noticeable pattern on the photographic material.

2.5 Printed Matter. Any printing on the envelope shall not produce any visible effect on the processed photographic materials under the conditions of the test described in 2.4, Accelerated Aging Test.

APPENDIX H

Microfilm Services †

International

Directory of Photocopying and Microcopying Services, Int. Fed. for Documentation (F.I.D.) Publ. No. 248, November 1955, 2nd rev. ed. The Hague, 6 Willern Wilsenplein, The Netherlands.

U. S. Service Companies

The following have offices in principal cities:
Burroughs Corp.
Diebold, Inc.
Eastman Kodak Co.
Recordak Corp.
Remington-Rand Division of Sperry-Rand Corp.

The following provides service in principal cities:
Microdealers Inc., 711 14th St., N.W., Washington, D. C.

U. S. service companies geographically arranged:

* Mark Larwood Co., P. O. Box 1, Redwood City, Calif.

* Bay Microfilm Service, 852 Laurel St., San Carlos, Calif.

* American Microfilming Service Co., 412 Temple St., New Haven, Conn.

* Records Engineering, Inc., 815 15th St., N.W., Washington, D. C.

* Dakota Southern Microfilm Service, 115½ West Rich St., P. O. Box 60, Deland, Fla.

* Watland Inc., 4756 No. Clark St., Chicago, Illinois.

* Frederic Luther Co., 405 East 34th St., Indianapolis 5, Ind.

* Kentuckiana Microfilm Service, Seventh & Spring Sts., New Albany, Ind.

* Microfilm Foto-File Co.. 1306 Minnesota Ave., Kansas City, Kans.

* Micro-Master Inc., Suite 303, 915 Grand Ave., Kansas City 6, Mo.

* Louisville Microfilms Inc., 1318 Bardstown Rd., Louisville, Ky.

* Southern Microfilm Corp., 2301 Perido St., New Orleans 19, La.

* General Microfilm Co., 100 Inman St., Cambridge 39, Mass.

* Graphic Microfilm of N.E., Inc., 806 Massachusetts Ave., Cambridge 39, Mass.

* Micro-Photography Co., 97 Oliver St., Boston 15, Mass.

* Industrial Microfilm Co., 2970 W. Gd. Blvd., Detroit, Mich.

* Lowden Accounting Microfilming Service, 607 Garfield St., Jackson, Mich.

* Precision Microfilm Corp., 6615 Tireman Ave., Detroit 4, Mich.

* University Microfilms, 313 North First St., Ann Arbor, Mich.

---

* National Microfilm Association Members.
† Companies that either photograph and process or perform both operations.

* Weger Microfilm Service, 117 West Shiawassee St., Lansing, Mich.
* Swank Microfilm Service, 614 North Skinker Blvd., St. Louis, Mo.
* Certified Microfilm Inc., 430 Bergen Blvd., Palisades Park, N. J.
* Microfilm Co. of New Jersey, 36 West Front St., Red Bank, N. J.
* The Microlog Corp., 25 Broad Ave., Palisades Park, N. J.
* Microfilming Corp. of America, 11 East Pleasant Ave., Maywood, N. J.
* Paul E. Killion, Inc., 78-80 Maiden Lane, Albany, N. Y.
* Biel's Photocopy & Microfilm Service, 1037 Ellicott Square Bldg.,
    Buffalo 3, N. Y.
* Atlantic Microfilm Corp., 41 Union Square West, New York 3, N. Y.
* Griscombe Products Inc., 132 West 21st St., New York 11, N. Y.
* Graphic Microfilm Corp., 112 Liberty St., New York 6, N. Y.
* Micro Facsimile Corp., 56-27 184th St., Flushing, N. Y.
* Hall & McChesney Inc., 1233 Oswego Blvd., Syracuse, N. Y.
* Allied Microfilm Co., 892 South Arlington St., Akron 6, Ohio
* Columbus Microfilm Inc., 383 East Broad St., Columbus 15, Ohio
* John A. Cox & Associates, 816 Renkert Bldg., Canton, Ohio
* Micro Photo Inc., 4614 Prospect Ave., Cleveland 3, Ohio
* Microfilm Corp. of Ohio, 1051 Power Ave., Cleveland 14, Ohio
* Ohio Micro Co., 213 Euclid Ave., Akron, Ohio
* Security Microfilming Corp., 2903 Detroit Ave., Toledo, Ohio
* Microfilming, Flower Road, R.D. No. 3, Erie 7, Pa.
* Microsurance Inc., 1228 Locust St., Philadelphia 7, Pa.
* Microfilm Service, 1228 Locust St., Philadelphia 7, Pa.
* Dakota Microfilm Service, Graphic Arts Bldg., Vermillion, So. Dak.
* Jim Vance Custom Microfilming, P. O. Box 185, El Paso, Tex.
* Southern Microfilm Corp., 1122 Jackson St., Dallas, Tex.
* Southern Microfilm Corp., 2110 Chartres St., Houston, Tex.
* Microcard Corp., 365 South Oak St., West Salem, Wis.

Canadian Service Companies
    Dougherty-Garand Registered, 1165 Bleury St., Montreal 2, Quebec,
        Canada
    Kendon Microfilm Ltd., Bell Bldg., Regina, Saskatchewan, Canada
    Microfilming Services, 2215 Queen Street East, Toronto, Ontario,
        Canada
    * West Canadian Microfilm Ltd., 351 Eleventh Avenue West, Calgary,
        Alberta, Canada

-----

* National Microfilm Association members.

University and Research Libraries Microfilm Rates *

Library	Rates in effect since	Bound vols. per exposure (first 100)	Bound vols. per exposure (over 1000)	Manuscripts per exposure	Minimum per item handled	Volume charge, size change	Minimum per order
California (Berkeley)	1952	.035		.05		.15	1.00
California (Los Angeles)	1951	.035		.05		.15	1.00
Chicago		.03		.05		.25	1.00
Columbia	1954	.04		.05		.25	1.00
Duke	1952	.04		.05		.25	1.00
Harvard	1946	.035					1.00
Huntington Library	1954	.07					1.50
Illinois	1949	.03				.25	1.00
John Crerar Library	1951	.056					1.40
Johns Hopkins [a]	1953	.04					1.00
Linda Hall Library	1948	.03	.01(500+)			.50	1.25
Michigan [b]	1948	.035			.50		1.00

431

* From "Microfilming Services of Large University and Research Libraries in the United States," by Robert H. Muller, *College and Research Libraries*, July 1955, p. 264.

[a] Microfilming rates established by non-library campus laboratory.

[b] Microfilming rates established by commercial laboratory.

University and Research Libraries Microfilm Rates (*Continued*)

Library	Rates in effect since	Bound vols. per exposure (first 100)	Bound vols. per exposure (over 1000)	Manuscripts per exposure	Minimum per item handled	Volume charge, size change	Minimum per order
Minnesota	1954	.03	.02 (500+)				1.50
New York Public Library	1950	.04	.03 (1000+)	.05	1.00	.25	1.00
New York Library [a]	1948	.05			.75		.75
Newberry Library [b]	1954	.03			.50	.25	.50
Ohio State	1949	.03				.25	1.00
Pennsylvania	1947	.04					1.00
Princeton	1936	.03					
Stanford [a]	1952	.035		.05		.15	
U. S. Dept. of Agriculture	1945	.04 [c]					1.00
U. S. Armed Forces Medical	1943	.02			.50		.50
U. S. Library of Congress	1952	.04	.03 (1000+)	.05	1.00		1.00
Wisconsin [b]	1954	.08 [d]	.03 (125+)		2.00		2.00
Yale	1952	.04			1.00	.10	1.00

[a] Microfilming rates established by non-library campus laboratory.
[b] Microfilming rates established by commercial laboratory.
[c] $1.00 for each 50 pages or fraction thereof.
[d] $.04 per page.

432

APPENDIX I

Selected References and Resources for Microrecords

1. Microfilms and Microcards: Their Use in Research. A Selected List of References. June 1950. Library of Congress, Washington 25, D. C. 81 pp. 55c. A bibliography of books, monographs and journals and articles in periodicals from 1946 to 1950.

2. Union List of Microfilms. Revised, enlarged, and cumulated ed., J. W. Edwards, Ann Arbor, Mich., 1951. 1961 cols. $17.50. Lists approximately 25,000 titles through June 1949.

3. Union List of Microfilms. Revised, enlarged, and cumulated ed., 1949-1952. J. W. Edwards, Ann Arbor, Mich., 1953. 995 cols. $10.00. Supplement includes 14,080 entries from July 1, 1949 through July 31, 1952.

4. Newspapers on Microfilm. 2nd ed. 1953. 126 pp. Library of Congress, Washington 25, D. C. $2.25.

5. Negro Newspapers on Microfilm—A Selected List. 8 pp. 1953, Photoduplication Service, Library of Congress, Washington 25, D. C. 15c.

6. Dissertation Abstracts: A Guide to Dissertations and Monographs Available in Microfilm. University Microfilms, Ann Arbor, Mich., 1952–. $6 annually.

7. List of National Archives Microfilm Publications. *Natl. Archives Publ.* 54-5, 1953, 98 pp. (Free.) Lists basic documentation history, genealogy, etc.

8. Microfilm Clearing House Supplements. Occasional appendix to the *Information Bulletin* of the Library of Congress. Lists of new microfilm projects.

9. Consolidated Catalog of Microcard Publications. Microcard Foundation, Middletown, Conn. Listings of American Microcard publishers.

10. *The Microcard Bulletin.* Microcard Foundation, Box 2145, Madison 5, Wisc. News regarding the field and new publications.

11. ASTIA (AD) Documents Available in Microcard Form. Armed Services Tech. Inf. Agency, Documents Service Center, Knott Building, Dayton 2, Ohio. A listing of ''unclassified'' material distributed to military agencies and those engaged in activities on behalf of the Department of Defense.

12. ''Microprint Publications.'' Readex Microprint Co., 100 5th Ave., New York 11, N. Y.

13. The Microlex Corp., 1 Graves St., Rochester 14, N. Y. Lists publications.

14. ''Centres et Services de Documentation.'' 1951, 288 pp. UNESCO, Fr. 450. Documentation centers and their services in France.

15. ''International Repertory of Social Science Documentation Centers.'' 1952, 42 pp. UNESCO, 50c.

16. ''A Register of Legal Documentation in the World.'' 1953, 362 pp. UNESCO, $4.00.

17. ''Protection of Business Records—Supplemental Data.'' Commerce and Industry Association of New York, 99 Church St., New York 7, N. Y.